The ARRL
General Class
License Manual

For Ham Radio

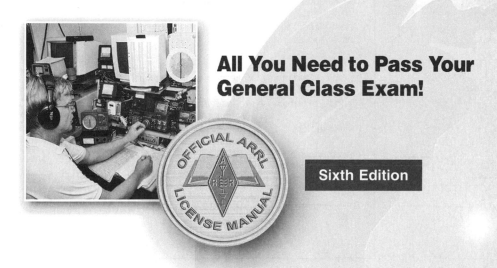

All You Need to Pass Your General Class Exam!

Sixth Edition

By **Ward Silver NØAX**

Contributing Editors: Mark Wilson, K1RO

Larry Wolfgang, WR1B

Production Staff: Maty Weinberg, KB1EIB, Editorial Assistant

Michelle Bloom, WB1ENT, Production Supervisor, Layout

Jodi Morin, KA1JPA, Assistant Production Supervisor, Layout

David Pingree, N1NAS, Senior Technical Illustrator

Kathy Ford, Proofreader

Sue Fagan, KB1OKW, Graphic Design Supervisor, Cover Design

ARRL *The national association for* *AMATEUR RADIO*

225 Main Street, Newington, CT 06111-1494

This book may be used for General license exams given beginning July 1, 2007. *QST* and the ARRL Web site (**www.arrl.org**) will have news about any rules changes affecting the General class license or any of the material in this book.

We strive to produce books without errors. Sometimes mistakes do occur, however. When we become aware of problems in our books (other than obvious typographical errors), we post corrections on the ARRL Web site. If you think you have found an error, please check **www.arrl.org/gclm** for corrections. If you don't find a correction there, please let us know, either using the Feedback Form at the back of this book or by sending e-mail to **pubsfdbk@arrl.org**.

The ARRL General Class License Manual ON THE WEB

WWW.ARRL.ORG/GCLM

Visit *The ARRL General Class License Manual* home on the Web for additional resources as you prepare for your first Amateur Radio license.

Contents

Foreword

Welcome to the sixth edition of *The ARRL General Class License Manual*, your guide to passing the General class Amateur Radio examination. Making the decision to upgrade from Technician to General is something you won't regret as it opens up whole new realms of ham radio enjoyment and service. You will get a lot more out of using your new license than the amount of study required to pass the test.

You will have a lot of company as you join in the fun, adding the traditional shortwave or HF bands to your tool kit. Have you used *EchoLink* or IRLP to converse with someone on the other side of the world? As a General you can communicate with those same amateurs directly without any network technology required! You can put your computer to work with one of the many new digital modes of communication. Your value to a local emergency communications team just increased dramatically with your increased operating privileges, too!

The ARRL General Class License Manual does more than just help you memorize the answers in the question pool. Each topic is addressed in sufficient detail to help you learn the "why" behind the rules, the "what" of basic electronic, and the "how" of amateur operating practices. There are drawings, photographs and tables to guide you in your studies. If you would like a more concise study guide, *ARRL's General Q&A* is a companion to this book, presenting each question and a short explanation of the correct answer. The pair is a powerful one-two punch to help you pass the exam.

Even the best study material can't address all of the things you'll encounter as a General, so the book's companion Web site — **www.arrl.org/gclm** — provides supplemental references and links to resources you can use to go beyond the exam questions. This book and the Web site also list a number of other useful references that you'll find especially helpful in translating your new privileges into real radio action.

If you have been holding back from upgrading to General because of the Morse code requirement, that barrier has been removed. Don't give up on Morse code just yet, though! CW operation has always been part of Amateur Radio and will be for a long time to come. Its simplicity, efficiency and elegance have made life-long "brass pounders" out of many hams. This book contains a chapter on learning the Morse code if you care to try now or at any time in the future. The ARRL provides other resources to help you learn, as well as on-the-air code practice transmitted by W1AW every day.

Whatever your journey through Amateur Radio, there are books and supplies in the ARRL's "Radio Amateurs Library" to support almost any amateur operating practice today. Check out the full line at **www.arrl.org** (follow the links to the catalog).

Now that you'll be upgrading to General, you can participate in the largest of all amateur volunteer examiner (VE) programs coordinated by the ARRL/VEC. General licensees can "give back" by volunteering as a VE for Technician license exams. You can learn more about providing this valuable and appreciated service by visiting the ARRL Web site.

Thanks for making the decision to upgrade. We hope to hear you on the air soon, using your new General class privileges and enjoying more of Amateur Radio. Good luck!

David Sumner, K1ZZ
Chief Executive Officer
Newington, Connecticut
March 2007

When to Expect New Books

A Question Pool Committee (QPC) consisting of representatives from the various Volunteer Examiner Coordinators (VECs) prepares the license question pools. The QPC establishes a schedule for revising and implementing new Question Pools. The current Question Pool revision schedule is as follows:

Question Pool	Current Study Guides	Valid Through
Technician (Element 2)	*The ARRL Ham Radio License Manual* ARRL's Tech Q&A, 4th Edition	June 30, 2010
General (Element 3)	*The ARRL General Class License Manual*, 6th edition *ARRL's General Q&A*, 3rd Edition	June 30, 2011
Amateur Extra (Element 4)	*The ARRL Extra Class License Manual*, 8th Edition *ARRL's Extra Q&A*, 1st Edition	June 30, 2008

As new question pools are released, ARRL will produce new study materials before the effective date of the new Pools. Until then, the current Question Pools will remain in use, and current ARRL study materials, including this book, will help you prepare for your exam.

As the new Question Pool schedules are confirmed, the information will be published in *QST* and on the ARRL Web site at **www.arrl.org**.

"Join ARRL and experience the BEST of Ham Radio!"

ARRL Membership Benefits and Services:

- *QST* magazine — your monthly source of news, easy-to-read product reviews, and features for new hams!
- Technical Information Service — access to problem-solving experts!
- Members-only Web services — find information fast, anytime!
- ARRL clubs, mentors and volunteers — ready to welcome YOU!

FREE Book Offer!

I want to join ARRL.
Send me the FREE book I have selected (choose one)

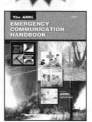

- ☐ **The ARRL Repeater Directory**
- ☐ **Getting Started with Ham Radio**
- ☐ **The ARRL Emergency Communication Handbook**

Name _____ Call Sign _____

Street _____

City _____ State _____ ZIP _____

Please check the appropriate one-year[1] rate:
- ☐ **$39 in US.**
- ☐ **Age 21 or younger rate, $20 in US** (see note*).
- ☐ **Canada $49.**
- ☐ **Elsewhere $62.**
- **Please indicate date of birth** _____ •

[1] 1-year membership dues include $15 for a 1-year subscription to QST. International 1-year rates include a $10 surcharge for surface delivery to Canada and a $23 surcharge for air delivery to other countries. Other US membership options available: Blind, Life, and QST by First Class postage. Contact ARRL for details.
*Age 21 or younger rate applies only if you are the oldest licensed amateur in your household.
International membership is available with an annual CD-ROM option (no monthly receipt of QST). Contact ARRL for details.
Dues subject to change without notice.

Sign up my family members, residing at the same address, as ARRL members too! They'll each pay only $8 for a year's membership, have access to ARRL benefits and services (except QST) and also receive a membership card.

☐ Sign up _____ family members @ $8 each = $ _____. Attach their names & call signs (if any).

☐ Total amount enclosed, payable to ARRL $ _____ . (US funds drawn on a bank in the US).

☐ Enclosed is $ _____ ($1.00 minimum) as a donation to the Legal Research and Resource Fund.

☐ Charge to: ☐ VISA ☐ MasterCard ☐ Amex ☐ Discover

Card Number _____ Expiration Date _____

Cardholder's Signature _____

Call Toll-Free (US) **1-888-277-5289**
Join Online **www.arrl.org/join** or
Clip and send to:

☐ If you do not want your name and address made available for non-ARRL related mailings, please check here.

ARRL *The national association for* **AMATEUR RADIO**
225 Main Street
Newington, CT 06111-1494 USA

GCLM-09

The Adventure Continues!

Congratulations! You've taken the next step in your journey through Amateur Radio. As a General licensee, you'll experience a whole new dimension of operating enjoyment — new frequencies, new modes and new activities. To help you make the most of Amateur Radio, your national association — the ARRL — offers a wide range of services. Here are some that may be interesting and useful to you.

ARRL The national association for Amateur Radio: What's in it for You?

♦ **Help for New Hams:** Are you a beginning ham looking for help in getting started in your new hobby? The hams at ARRL HQ in Newington, Connecticut, will be glad to assist you. Call 800-32-NEWHAM. ARRL maintains a computer database of ham clubs and ham radio "helpers" from across the country who've told us they're interested in helping beginning hams. There are probably several clubs in your area! Contact us for more information.

♦ **Licensing Classes:** If you're going to become a ham, you'll need to find a local license exam opportunity sooner or later. ARRL Registered Instructors teach licensing classes all around the country, and ARRL-sponsored Volunteer Examiners are right there to administer your exams. To find the locations and dates of Amateur Radio licensing classes and test sessions in your area, visit **www.arrl.org** or call the New Ham Desk at 800-32-NEWHAM.

♦ **Clubs:** As a beginning ham, one of the best moves you can make is to join a local ham club. Whether you join an all-around group or a special-interest club (repeaters, DXing, and so on), you'll make new friends, have a lot of fun, and you can tap into a ready reserve of ham radio knowledge and experience. To find the ham clubs in your area, visit **www.arrl.org** or call HQ's New Ham Desk at 800-32-NEWHAM.

♦ **Technical Information Service:** Do you have a question of a technical nature? (What new ham doesn't?) Contact the Technical Information Service (TIS) at HQ. Our resident technical experts will help you over the phone, send you specific information on your question (antennas, interference and so on) or refer you to your local ARRL Technical Coordinator or Technical Specialist. It's expert information — and it doesn't cost Members an extra cent!

♦ **Regulatory Information:** Need help with a thorny antenna zoning problem? Having trouble understanding an FCC regulation? Vacationing in a faraway place and want to know how to get permission to operate your ham radio there? HQ's Regulatory Information Specialist has the answers you need!

♦ **Operating Awards:** Like to collect "wallpaper"? The ARRL sponsors a wide variety of certificates and Amateur Radio achievement awards. For information on awards you can qualify for, visit **www.arrl.org** or contact the Membership and Volunteer Programs Department at HQ.

♦ **QSL Service and Logbook of the World (LoTW):** With your expanded HF privileges, you're likely to try your hand at working DX stations in other countries. You can confirm these exciting contacts by exchanging paper QSL cards through ARRL's QSL service. Many hams also collect confirmations through ARRL's secure on-line Logbook of the World. Visit **www.arrl.org** to learn more about these services.

♦ **Equipment Insurance:** When it comes to protecting their Amateur Radio equipment investments, ARRL Members travel First Class. ARRL's "all-risk" equipment insurance plan protects you from loss or damage to your station. (It can protect your ham radio computer, too.) It's comprehensive and cost effective, and it's available only to ARRL Members. Why worry about losing your valuable radio equipment when you can protect it for only a few dollars a year?

♦ **Amateur Radio Emergency Service:** If you're interested in providing public service and emergency communications for your community, you can join more than 25,000 other hams who have registered their communications capabilities with local Emergency Coordinators. Your EC will call on you and other ARES members for vital assistance if disaster should strike your community. Visit **www.arrl.org** or contact the Membership and Volunteer Programs Department at HQ for information.

♦ **Audio-Visual Programs:** Need a program for your next ham club meeting, informal get-together or public display? ARRL offers many programs to choose from, ranging from VHS videotapes to video CDs and DVDs, to PowerPoint and other computer-based presentations. Visit **www.arrl.org/FandES/ead/materials/videos. html** for a complete list.

♦ **Blind, Disabled Ham Help:** For a list of available resources and information on the Courage HANDI-HAM System, contact the ARRL Program for the Disabled at HQ.

With your membership you also receive the monthly journal *QST*. Each colorful issue is packed with valuable information you can use. You'll find technical information, weekend projects, operating tips, news, ads for the latest equipment and much more. *QST* Product Reviews are the most respected source of information to help you get the most for your Amateur Radio equipment dollar. (For many hams, *QST* alone is worth far more than the cost of ARRL membership.)

The ARRL also publishes newsletters and dozens of books covering all aspects of Amateur Radio. Our Headquarters station, W1AW, transmits bulletins of interest to radio amateurs and Morse code practice sessions.

When it comes to representing Amateur Radio's best interests in our nation's capital, ARRL's team in Washington, DC, is constantly working with the FCC, Congress and industry to protect and foster your privileges as a ham operator.

Regardless of your Amateur Radio interests, ARRL Membership is relevant and important. We will be happy to welcome you as a Member. Use the *Invitation to Membership* on the next page to **join today**. And don't hesitate to contact us if you have any questions!

What is Amateur Radio?

Perhaps you've just picked up this book in the library or from a bookstore shelf and are wondering what this Amateur Radio business is all about. Maybe you have a friend or relative who is a "ham" and you're interested in becoming one, as well. In that case, a short explanation is in order.

Amateur Radio or "ham radio" is one of the longest-lived wireless activities. Amateur experimenters were operating right along with Marconi in the early part of the 20th century. They have helped advance the state-of-the-art in radio, television and dozens of other communications services since then, right up to the present day. There are more than half a million amateur radio operators or "hams" in the United States alone and several million more around the world!

Amateur Radio in the United States is a formal *communications service*, administered by the Federal Communications Commission or FCC. Created officially in its present form in 1934, the Amateur Service is intended to foster electronics and radio experimentation, provide emergency backup communications, encourage private citizens to train and practice operating, and even spread the goodwill of person-to-person contact over the airwaves.

WHO IS A HAM AND WHAT DO HAMS DO?

Anyone can be a ham — there are no age limits or physical requirements that prevent anyone from passing their license exam and getting on the air. Kids as young as 6 years old have passed the basic exam, and there are many hams out there over the age of 100. You probably fall somewhere in the middle of that range.

Once you get on the air and start meeting other hams, you'll find a wide range of capabilities and interests. Of course, there are many technically skilled hams who work as engineers, scientists or technicians. But just as many don't

Amateurs are often one of the first groups to respond to disasters, providing communications until normal systems are working again. They set up temporary, portable stations and help emergency preparedness agencies and relief organizations.

Sophisticated earth stations with giant antennas are not necessary to contact amateur satellites, or "OSCARs." The simple handheld transceiver and antenna shown here will do the job on a "bird" in low earth orbit.

have a deep technical background. You're just as likely to encounter writers, public safety personnel, students, farmers, truck drivers — anyone with an interest in personal communications over the radio.

The activities of Amateur Radio are incredibly varied. Amateurs who hold the Technician class license — the usual first license for hams in the US — communicate primarily with local and regional amateurs using relay stations called *repeaters*. Known as "Techs," they sharpen their skills of operating while portable and mobile, often joining emergency communications teams. They may instead focus on the burgeoning wireless data networks assembled and used by hams around the world. Techs can make use of the growing number of Amateur Radio satellites, built and launched by hams along with the commercial "birds." Technicians transmit their own television signals, push the limits of signal propagation through the atmosphere and experiment with microwaves. Hams hold most of the world records for long-distance communication on microwave frequencies, in fact!

Hams who advance or *upgrade* to General class are granted additional privileges to use the frequencies usually associated with shortwave operation. This is the traditional Amateur Radio you probably encountered in movies or books. On these frequencies, signals can travel worldwide and so General and Amateur Extra amateurs can make direct contact with foreign hams. No Internet, phone systems, or data networks are required. It's just you, your radio, and the ionosphere — the upper layers of the Earth's atmosphere!

Many hams use voice, Morse code, computer data modes and even image transmissions to communicate. All of these signals are mixed together on the frequencies where hams operate, making the experience of tuning a radio receiver through the crowded bands an interesting experience.

One thing common to all hams is

that all of their operation is noncommercial, especially the volunteers who provide emergency communications. Hams pursue their hobby purely for personal enjoyment and to advance their skills, taking satisfaction from providing services to their fellow citizens. This is especially valuable after natural disasters such as hurricanes and earthquakes when commercial systems are knocked out for a while. Amateur operators rush in to provide backup communication for hours, days, weeks or even months until the regular systems are restored. All this from a little study and a simple exam!

WANT TO FIND OUT MORE?

If you'd like to find out more about Amateur Radio in general, there is lots of information available on the Internet. A good place to start is on the American Radio Relay League's (ARRL) ham radio introduction page, **www.hello-radio.org**. Books like *Ham Radio*

More technically inclined hams build radios and accessory equipment – either from scratch or from kits. There's a certain satisfaction gained from using a radio you built to contact other hams.

Digital communications are popular with hams. Barb Elliott, KE7AJ, was active in a recent competition for radioteletype operators.

for Dummies and *Getting Started With Ham Radio* will help you "fill in the blanks" as you learn more.

Along with books and Internet pages, there is no better way to learn about ham radio than to meet your local amateur operators. It is quite likely that no matter where you live in the United States, there is a ham radio club in your area — perhaps several! The ARRL provides a club lookup Web page at **www.arrl.org/FandES/ field/club/clubsearch. phtml** where you can find a club just by entering your ZIP code or state. Carrying on the tradition of mutual assistance, many clubs make helping newcomers to ham radio a part of their charter.

If it sounds like hams are confident that you'll find their activities interesting, you're right! Amateur Radio is much more than just talking on a radio, as you'll find out. It's an opportunity to dive into the fascinating world of radio communications, electronics and computers as deeply as you wish to go. **Welcome!**

About the ARRL

The seed for Amateur Radio was planted in the 1890s, when Guglielmo Marconi began his experiments in wireless telegraphy. Soon he was joined by dozens, then hundreds, of others who were enthusiastic about sending and receiving messages through the air—some with a commercial interest, but others solely out of a love for this new communications medium. The United States government began licensing Amateur Radio operators in 1912.

By 1914, there were thousands of Amateur Radio operators—hams—in the United States. Hiram Percy Maxim, a leading Hartford, Connecticut inventor and industrialist, saw the need for an organization to band together this fledgling group of radio experimenters. In May 1914 he founded the American Radio Relay League (ARRL) to meet that need.

Today ARRL, with approximately 150,000 members, is the largest organization of radio amateurs in the United States. The ARRL is a not-for-profit organization that:
• promotes interest in Amateur Radio communications and experimentation
• represents US radio amateurs in legislative matters, and
• maintains fraternalism and a high standard of conduct among Amateur Radio operators.

At ARRL headquarters in the Hartford suburb of Newington, the staff helps serve the needs of members. ARRL is also International Secretariat for the International Amateur Radio Union, which is made up of similar societies in 150 countries around the world.

ARRL publishes the monthly journal *QST*, as well as newsletters and many publications covering all aspects of Amateur Radio. Its headquarters station, W1AW, transmits bulletins of interest to radio amateurs and Morse code practice sessions. The ARRL also coordinates an extensive field organization, which includes volunteers who provide technical information and other support services for radio amateurs as well as communications for public-service activities. In addition, ARRL represents US amateurs with the Federal Communications Commission and other government agencies in the US and abroad.

Membership in ARRL means much more than receiving *QST* each month. In addition to the services already described, ARRL offers membership services on a personal level, such as the ARRL Volunteer Examiner Coordinator Program and a QSL bureau.

Full ARRL membership (available only to licensed radio amateurs) gives you a voice in how the affairs of the organization are governed. ARRL policy is set by a Board of Directors (one from each of 15 Divisions). Each year, one-third of the ARRL Board of Directors stands for election by the full members they represent. The day-to-day operation of ARRL HQ is managed by an Executive Vice President and his staff.

No matter what aspect of Amateur Radio attracts you, ARRL membership is relevant and important. There would be no Amateur Radio as we know it today were it not for the ARRL. We would be happy to welcome you as a member! (An Amateur Radio license is not required for Associate Membership.) For more information about ARRL and answers to any questions you may have about Amateur Radio, write or call:

ARRL—The national association for Amateur Radio
225 Main Street
Newington CT   06111-1494
Voice: 860-594-0200
   Fax: 860-594-0259
   E-mail: **hq@arrl.org**
   Internet: **www.arrl.org/**

Prospective new amateurs call (toll-free):
800-32-NEW HAM (800-326-3942)
You can also contact us via e-mail at **newham@arrl.org**
or check out *ARRLWeb* at **www.arrl.org/**

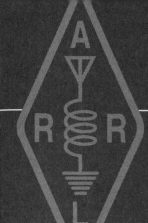

Chapter 1

Introduction

In this chapter, you'll learn about:
- **Excitement enjoyed by General licensees**
- **New frequencies available to Generals**
- **Reasons to upgrade from Technician**
- **Requirements and study materials for the General exam**
- **How to prepare for your exam**
- **How to find an exam session**
- **Where to find more resources**

Welcome to *The ARRL General Class License Manual*! Earning your General class license opens up the full Amateur Radio experience — the excitement and challenge of traditional shortwave operation along with the VHF+ and limited HF privileges enjoyed by Technician class licensees. You'll gain access to the broadest and most capable set of communication privileges available to private citizens. Only Amateur Extra licensees have more.

This study guide will not only teach you the answers to the General class exam questions, but will also provide explanations and supporting information. That way, you'll find it easier to learn the basic principles involved, which helps you remember what you've learned. The book is full of useful facts and figures, so you'll want to keep it handy after you pass the test and are using your new privileges.

1.1 The General Class License and Amateur Radio

Most of this book's readers will have already earned their Technician class license. Some may have been a ham for quite a while, and others may be new to the hobby. In either case, you're to be commended for making the effort to upgrade. We'll try to make it easy to pass your exam by teaching you the fundamentals and rationale behind each question and answer.

REASONS TO UPGRADE

If you're browsing through this book, trying to decide whether to upgrade, here are a few good reasons:

● *More frequencies.* The General class licensee has access to more bands. That's a lot more space in which to enjoy Amateur Radio! See **Figure 1-1** for details of all of the frequencies available to General licensees.

● *More communications options.* Those new frequencies give you many more ways to make contacts on new modes and with new groups of hams. Your new skills are also valuable to your emergency team or club.

● *New technical opportunities.* With your new privileges come new ways of assembling and operating a station. The effects of the ionosphere and solar conditions will

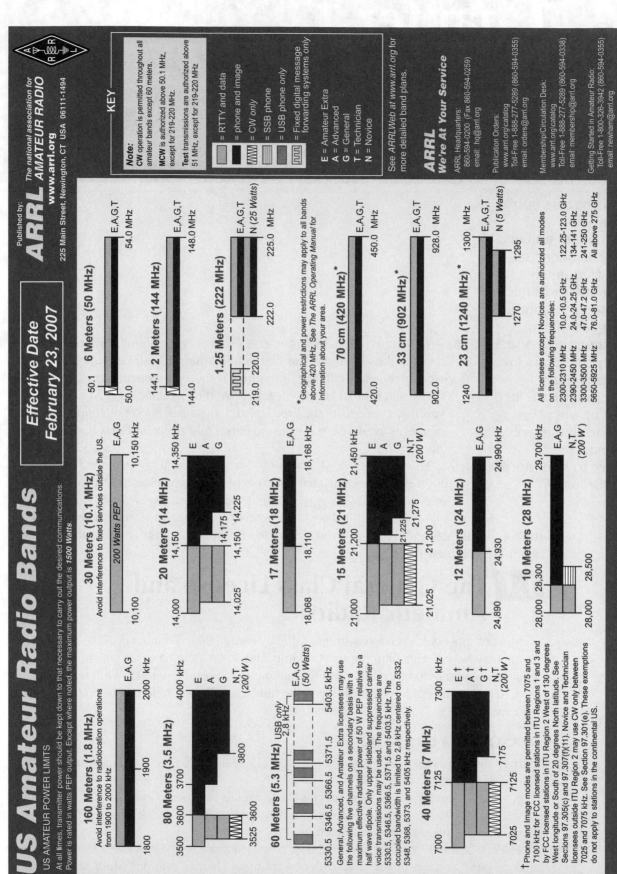

Figure 1-1 — Amateur operating privileges.

become second nature to you. Your improved technical understanding of how radio works will make you a more knowledgeable and skilled operator.

• *More fun*. The traditional activities of ragchewing, DXing and contesting continue to attract hams as they have for decades. You'll find that even familiar activities take on new and interesting aspects on the HF bands!

Not only does upgrading grant you more privileges, but your experiences will be much broader. You'll enjoy the hobby in ways that hams have pioneered and fostered for generations. The extra privileges are well worth your effort!

Roger Hayward, KA7EXM, enjoys operating a portable VHF and UHF station from remote mountaintops and campsites.

GENERAL CLASS OVERVIEW

There are three classes of license being granted today: Technician, General and Amateur Extra. Each grants the licensee more and more privileges, meaning access to frequencies and modes. **Table 1-1** shows the elements for each of the amateur licenses as of early 2007.

As shown in **Table 1-2**, to qualify for a General class license, you must have passed Elements 2 (Technician) and 3 (General). If you hold a Technician license, you are credited with Element 2, so you don't have to take it again. If you have a Technician license issued before March 21, 1987, you can upgrade to General simply by going to a test session with proof of being licensed before that date.

The 35 question multiple-choice test for Element 3 is more comprehensive than the Element 2 Technician exam because you'll be granted wider privileges. As we mentioned before, the General class licensee gains access to nearly all amateur frequencies. There are no bands on which a General class ham can't transmit! As a more experienced ham, your wider knowledge will allow you to experiment with, modify and build equipment and antennas to improve your communications abilities.

Table 1-1
Amateur License Class Examinations

License Class	Element Required	Number of Questions
Technician	2 (Written)	35 (passing is 26 correct)
General	3 (Written)	35 (passing is 26 correct)
Amateur Extra	4 (Written)	50 (passing is 38 correct)

Table 1-2
Exam Elements Needed to Qualify for a General Class License

Current License	Exam Requirements	Study Materials
None or Novice	Technician (Element 2)	*The ARRL Ham Radio License Manual* or *ARRL's Tech Q&A*
	General (Element 3)	*The ARRL General Class License Manual* or *ARRL's General Q&A*
Technician (issued on or after March 21, 1987)*	General (Element 3)	*The ARRL General Class License Manual* or *ARRL's General Q&A*

*Individuals who qualified for the Technician license before March 21, 1987, will be able to upgrade to General class by providing documentary proof to a Volunteer Examiner Coordinator, paying an application fee and completing NCVEC Quick Form 605. No additional exam is required.

Elaine Larson, KD6DUT, takes a turn at logging as Fred Martin, KI6YN, works the paddles during an ARRL Field Day. This annual event, held in June, is part emergency preparedness exercise, part competition, and part excuse to get together and have some fun with local hams.

Alan Eshelman, K6SRZ, participated in a ham radio expedition to Kure Atoll in the Pacific, making hundreds of Morse code contacts over the K7C team's two week stay on the island. Your new General license is the key to chasing DX stations throughout the HF bands.

MORSE CODE

Although you no longer need to learn Morse code for any license exam, Morse code or "CW" has been part of the rich amateur tradition for 100 years and many hams still use it extensively. There are solid reasons for it to be used, too! It's easy to build Morse code transmitters and receivers. There is no more power-efficient mode of communications that is copied by the human ear. The extensive set of prosigns and signals allow amateurs to communicate a great deal of information even if they don't share a common language. Morse is likely to remain part of the amateur experience for a long time to come.

If you are interested in learning Morse code, the ARRL has a complete set of resources listed on its Web page at **www.arrl. org/FandES/ead/learncw**. Computer software and on-the-air *code practice* sessions are available for personal training and practice. Organizations such as FISTS (**www.fists.org**) — an operator's style of sending is referred to as his or her "fist" — help hams learn Morse code and will even help you find a "code buddy" to share the learning with you.

1.2 How to Use this Book

To earn a General class Amateur Radio license, you must pass (or receive credit for) FCC Elements 2 (Technician class) and 3 (General class). This book is designed to help you prepare for and pass the Element 3 written exam. If you do not already have a Technician Amateur Radio license, you will need some additional study materials for the Element 2 (Technician) exam.

The Element 3 exam consists of 35 questions about Amateur Radio rules, theory and practice, as well as some basic electronics. A passing grade is 74%, so you must answer 26 of the 35 questions correctly.

The General Class License Manual begins with sections on the operating practices you'll encounter on the HF bands and the applicable rules and regulations. The following sections delve into radio technology — Circuits and Components, Radio Signals and Equipment, Antennas and Propagation. Radio and electrical safety is covered in its own section, and the final section is all about Morse code.

Each section may begin with a short review of material from the Technician exam and has practical examples and information you can use for reference later. As you learn about each topic, the set of related questions from the license exam are listed in a shaded box. Turn to the Question Pool and confirm that you can answer those questions before moving on.

The ARRL also maintains a special Web page for General class students at **www.arrl. org/gclm**. Organized in the same manner as this text, you can go to the Web page to find helpful supplements and clarifications to the material in the book. The useful and interesting on-line references listed there put you one click away from related and useful information.

If you are taking a licensing class, help your instructors by letting them know about areas in which you need help. They want you to learn as thoroughly and quickly as possible, so don't hold back with your questions. Similarly, if you find the material particularly clear or helpful, tell them that, too, so it can be used in the next class!

Stu Cohen, N1SC, enjoys restoring and operating vintage radio equipment. Many fans of older gear hang out on 80 and 40 meters.

At the back of the book you'll find a large Glossary of radio terminology. It is followed by the Question Pool, which includes the complete set of exam questions and answers.

WHAT WE ASSUME ABOUT YOU

You don't have to be a technical guru or an expert operator to upgrade to General class! As you progress through the material, you'll build on the basic science of radio and electricity that you mastered for Technician. No advanced mathematics is introduced, and if math gives you trouble, tutorials are listed at **www.arrl.org/gclm**. As with the Technician license, mastering rules and regulations will require learning some new words and remembering a few numbers. You should have a simple calculator, which you'll also be allowed to use during the license exam.

Advanced Students

If you have some background in radio, perhaps as a technician or trained operator, you may be able to short-circuit some of the sections. To find out, find the shaded boxes in the text that list the exam questions for each topic. Turn to the Question Pool, and if you can answer the questions correctly, move to the next topic in the text. It's common for technically minded students to focus on the rules and regulations while students with an operating background tend to need the technical material more. Whichever you may be, be sure that you can answer the questions because they will certainly be on the test!

Self-Study or Classroom Students

The ARRL General Class License Manual can be used either by an individual student, studying on his or her own, or as part of a licensing class taught by an instructor. If you're part of a class, the instructor will guide you through the book, section by section. The solo student can move at any pace and in any convenient order. You'll find that having a buddy to study with makes learning the material more fun as you help each other over the rough spots.

Don't hesitate to ask for help! Your instructor can provide information on anything you find difficult. Classroom students may find asking their fellow students to be helpful. If you're studying on your own, there are resources for you, too! If you can't find the answer in the book or at the Web site, email your question to the ARRL's New Ham Desk, **newham@arrl.org**. The ARRL's experts will answer directly or connect you with another ham that can answer your questions.

Want More Information?

Looking for more information about General class instruction in your area? Are you ready to take the General class exam? Do you need a list of ham radio clubs, instructors or examiners in your local area? The following Web pages are very helpful in finding the local resources you need to successfully pass your General exam:

www.arrl.org — the ARRL's home page, it features news and links to other ARRL resources

www.arrl.org/gclm — the Web site that supports this book

www.arrl.org/FandES/field/club/clubsearch.phtml — a search page to find ARRL-Affiliated clubs

www.arrl.org/arrlvec/examsearch.phtml — the ARRL/VEC exam session search page

www.arrl.org/tis — the ARRL's Technical Information Service is an excellent resource

www.ac6v.com — a Web site that compiles links to hundreds of ham radio Web pages

USING THE QUESTION POOL

As you complete each topic, be sure to review each of the exam questions highlighted in the shaded text boxes. This will tell you which areas need a little more study time. When you understand the answer to each of the questions, move on. Resist the temptation to just memorize the answers. Doing so leaves you without the real understanding that will make your new General class privileges enjoyable and useful. *The General Class License Manual* covers every one of the exam questions, so you can be sure you're ready at exam time.

When using the Question Pool, cover or fold over the answers at the edge of the page to be sure you really do understand the question. Each question also includes a cross-reference back to the section of the book that covers that topic. If you don't completely understand the question or answer, please go back and review that section. The ARRL's condensed guide, *ARRL's General Q&A*, also provides short explanations for each one of the exam questions.

ON-LINE EXAMS

While you're studying and when you feel like you're ready for the actual exam you can get some good practice by taking one of the on-line Amateur Radio exams. These Web sites use the same Question Pool to construct an exam with the same number and variety of questions that you'll encounter on exam day. The exams are free and you can take them over and over again in complete privacy. Links to on-line exams can be found on the ARRL's *General Class License Manual* Web page.

These exams are quite realistic and you get quick feedback about the questions you missed. When you find yourself passing the on-line exams by a comfortable margin, you'll be ready for the real thing! A note of caution, be sure that the questions used are current — the General question pool is completely rewritten every three years. The set of questions put in place in July of 2007 will be replaced in 2010. (The Amateur Extra license question pool expires in 2008.)

FOR INSTRUCTORS

If you're an instructor, the structure of this version of the book may be unfamiliar. Previous license manuals were organized with the sections in the same sequence as found in the Question Pool. This edition rearranges the topics in a sequence that is intended to be easier for the student to learn. For example, the section on rules and regulations comes after the presentation of the procedures and technical topics. By providing context and background for the rules and regulations the student is more likely to understand (and remember) them.

The ARRL has also created supporting material for instructors such as graphics files, handouts and a detailed topics list. Check **www.arrl.org/FandES/ead/instructor** for support materials.

CONVENTIONS AND RESOURCES

Throughout your studies keep a sharp eye out for words in *italics*. These words are important so be sure you understand them. Many are included in the extensive Glossary in the back of the book. Another thing to look for are the addresses or URLs for Web resources in **bold**, such as **www.arrl.org/gclm**. By browsing these Web pages while you're studying, you will accelerate and broaden your understanding.

Throughout the book, there are many short sidebars that present topics related to the subject you're studying. These sidebars may just tell an interesting story or they might tackle a subject that needs its own space in the book. The information in sidebars helps you understand how the information you're studying relates to ham radio in general.

Books to Help You Learn

As you study the material on the licensing exam, you will have lots of other questions about the hows and whys of Amateur Radio. The following references, available from your local bookstore or the ARRL (**www.arrl.org/catalog**) will help "fill in the blanks" and give you a broader picture of the hobby:

✔ *Ham Radio for Dummies* by Ward Silver, NØAX. Written for new Technician and General class licensees, this book supplements the information in study guides with an informal, friendly approach to the hobby.

✔ *ARRL Operating Manual*. With in-depth chapters on the most popular ham radio activities, this is your guide to nets, award programs, DXing and more. It even includes a healthy set of reference tables and maps.

✔ *Understanding Basic Electronics* by Larry Wolfgang, WR1B. Students who want more technical background about electronics should take a look at this book. It covers the fundamentals of electricity and electronics that are the foundation of all radio.

✔ *Basic Radio* by Joel Hallas, W1ZR. Students who want more technical background about radio theory should take a look at this book. It covers the key building blocks of receivers, transmitters, antennas and propagation.

✔ *ARRL Handbook*. This is the grandfather of all Amateur Radio references and belongs on the shelf of hams. Almost any topic you can think of in Amateur Radio technology is represented here.

✔ *ARRL Antenna Book*. After the radio itself, all radio depends on antennas. This book provides information on every common type of amateur antenna, feed lines and related topics, and construction tips and techniques.

1.3 The Upgrade Trail

As you begin your studies remember that you've already overcome the biggest hurdle of all — taking and passing your first license exam! The questions may be more challenging for the General class exam, but you already know all about the testing procedure and the basics of ham radio. You can approach the process of upgrading with confidence!

FOCUS ON HF AND ADVANCED MODES

The General class exam mostly deals with the new types of operating you'll encounter on the HF bands. You'll also be expected to understand more about the modes you're already familiar with from Technician class operating. We'll cover more advanced modes and signals, too. The goal is to help you "fill in the blanks" in your ham radio knowledge. Here are some examples of topics that you'll be studying:

- HF power amplifier use and adjustment
- New digital modes such as PSK31
- Solar effects on HF propagation
- Test instruments such as the oscilloscope
- Practical electronic circuits
- More types of antennas

Not every ham uses every mode and frequency, of course. By learning about this wider range of ideas, it helps hams to make better choices for regular operating. You will become aware of just how wide and deep ham radio really is. Better yet, the introduction of these new ideas may just get you interested in giving them a try!

The ARRL November Sweepstakes contest is a long-time favorite activity of HF operators. One weekend is devoted to CW, another to phone, and the objective is to contact as many stations as possible, in as many ARRL Sections as possible. Some operators, like Randy Thompson, K5ZD, have been entering Sweepstakes annually for many years.

TESTING PROCESS

When you're ready, you'll need to find a test session. If you're in a licensing class, the instructor will help you find and register for a session. Otherwise, you can find a test session by using the ARRL's Web page for finding exams, **www.arrl.org/arrlvec/examsearch. phtml**. If you can register for the test session in advance, do so. Other sessions, such as those at hamfests or conventions, are available to anyone that shows up or *walk-ins*. You may have to wait for an available space though, so go early!

As for all amateur exams, the General class exam is administered by Volunteer Examiners (VEs). All VEs are certified by a Volunteer Examiner Coordinator (VEC) such as the ARRL/VEC. This organization trains and certifies VEs and processes the FCC paperwork for their test sessions.

Bring your current license *original* and a photocopy (to send with the application). You'll need two forms of identification including at least one photo ID, such as a driver's license, passport or employer's identity card. Know your Social Security Number (SSN). You can bring pencils or pens, blank scratch paper and a calculator, but any kind of computer or on-line device is prohibited.

Once you're signed in, you'll need to fill out a copy of the National Conference of Volunteer Examiner Coordinator's (NCVEC) Quick Form 605 (see **Figure 1-2**). This is an application for a new or upgraded license. It is used only at test sessions and for a VEC to process a license renewal or a license change. *Do not* use an NCVEC Quick Form 605 for any kind of application directly to the FCC — it will be rejected. Use a regular FCC Form 605 (**Figure 1-3**). After filling out the form, pay the current test fee and get ready.

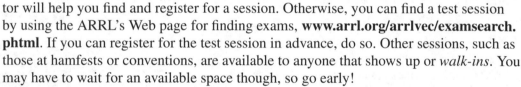

Special Testing Procedures

The FCC allows Volunteer Examiners (VEs) to use a range of procedures to accommodate applicants with various disabilities. If this applies to you, you'll still have to pass the test, but special exam procedures can be applied. Contact your local VE or the Volunteer Examiner Coordinator (VEC) responsible for the test session you'll be attending. Contact the ARRL/VEC Office at 225 Main St, Newington CT 06111, by phone at 860-594-0200, or via e-mail to **vec@arrl.org**. Ask for more information about special examination procedures.

NCVEC QUICK-FORM 605 APPLICATION FOR
AMATEUR OPERATOR/PRIMARY STATION LICENSE

SECTION 1 - TO BE COMPLETED BY APPLICANT

PRINT LAST NAME	SUFFIX (Jr., Sr.)	FIRST NAME	INITIAL	STATION CALL SIGN (IF ANY)
MORIN		Joanne	B	KA1JPA

MAILING ADDRESS (Number and Street or P.O. Box)
225 Main St.

SOCIAL SECURITY NUMBER (SSN) or (FRN) FCC FEDERAL REGISTRATION NUMBER
987-654-321

CITY	STATE CODE	ZIP CODE (5 or 9 Numbers)	E-MAIL ADDRESS (OPTIONAL)
Newington	CT	06067	

DAYTIME TELEPHONE NUMBER (Include Area Code) OPTIONAL	FAX NUMBER (Include Area Code) OPTIONAL	ENTITY NAME (IF CLUB, MILITARY RECREATION, RACES)

Type of Applicant: ☒ Individual ☐ Amateur Club ☐ Military Recreation ☐ RACES (Modify Only)

CLUB, MILITARY RECREATION, OR RACES CALL SIGN

SIGNATURE OF RESPONSIBLE CLUB OFFICIAL (not trustee)

I HEREBY APPLY FOR (Make an X in the appropriate box(es))

☐ **EXAMINATION** for a **new** license grant

☒ **EXAMINATION** for **upgrade** of my license class

☐ **CHANGE** my **name** on my license to my new name

Former Name: _____
(Last name) (Suffix) (First name) (MI)

☐ **CHANGE** my mailing address to **above** address

☐ **CHANGE** my station **call sign** systematically

Applicant's Initials: _____

☐ **RENEWAL** of my license grant.

Do you have another license application on file with the FCC which has not been acted upon?	PURPOSE OF OTHER APPLICATION	PENDING FILE NUMBER (FOR VEC USE ONLY)

I certify that:
* I waive any claim to the use of any particular frequency regardless of prior use by license or otherwise;
* All statements and attachments are true, complete and correct to the best of my knowledge and belief and are made in good faith;
* I am not a representative of a foreign government;
* I am not subject to a denial of Federal benefits pursuant to Section 5301of the Anti-Drug Abuse Act of 1988, 21 U.S.C. § 862;
* The construction of my station will NOT be an action which is likely to have a significant environmental effect (See 47 CFR Sections 1.1301-1.1319 and Section 97.13(a));
* I have read and WILL COMPLY with Section 97.13(c) of the Commission's Rules regarding RADIOFREQUENCY (RF) RADIATION SAFETY and the amateur service section of OST/OET Bulletin Number 65.

Signature of applicant (Do not print, type, or stamp. Must match applicant's name above.) (Clubs: 2 different individuals must sign)

X _Joanne B Morin_   Date Signed: 2/23/07

SECTION 2 - TO BE COMPLETED BY ALL ADMINISTERING VEs

Applicant is qualified for operator license class:

☐ **NO NEW LICENSE OR UPGRADE WAS EARNED**

☐ **TECHNICIAN**   Element 2

☒ **GENERAL**   Elements 2 and 3

☐ **AMATEUR EXTRA**   Elements 2, 3 and 4

DATE OF EXAMINATION SESSION
EXAMINATION SESSION LOCATION
VEC ORGANIZATION
VEC RECEIPT DATE

I CERTIFY THAT I HAVE COMPLIED WITH THE ADMINISTERING VE REQUIRMENTS IN PART 97 OF THE COMMISSION'S RULES AND WITH THE INSTRUCTIONS PROVIDED BY THE COORDINATING VEC AND THE FCC.

1st VEs NAME (Print First, MI, Last, Suffix)	VEs STATION CALL SIGN	VEs SIGNATURE (Must match name)	DATE SIGNED
Steven R. Ewald	WV1X	Steven R. Ewald	2/23-07
2nd VEs NAME (Print First, MI, Last, Suffix)	VEs STATION CALL SIGN	VEs SIGNATURE (Must match name)	DATE SIGNED
Rose-Anne Lawrence	KB1DMW	Rose-Anne Lawrence	2-23-07
3rd VEs NAME (Print First, MI, Last, Suffix)	VEs STATION CALL SIGN	VEs SIGNATURE (Must match name)	DATE SIGNED
Penny E Harts	N1NAC	Penny E Harts	2·23·07

DO NOT SEND THIS FORM TO FCC — THIS IS NOT AN FCC FORM.
IF THIS FORM IS SENT TO FCC, FCC WILL RETURN IT TO YOU WITHOUT ACTION.

NCVEC FORM 605 · February 2007
FOR VE/VEC USE ONLY · Page 1

ARRL0138

Figure 1-2 — This sample NCVEC Quick Form 605 shows how your form will look after you have completed your upgrade to General.

FCC 605 Main Form

Quick-Form Application for Authorization in the Ship, Aircraft, Amateur, Restricted and Commercial Operator, and General Mobile Radio Services

Approved by OMB
3060 - 0850

See instructions for public burden estimate

---

1) Radio Service Code: **HA**

Application Purpose (Select only one) (**MD**)

2) **NE** – New   **RO** – Renewal Only   **WD** – Withdrawal of Application
    MD – Modification   **RM** – Renewal / Modification   **DU** – Duplicate License
    AM – Amendment   **CA** – Cancellation of License   **AU** – Administrative Update

3) If this request if for Developmental License or STA (Special Temporary Authorization) enter the appropriate code and attach the required exhibit as described in the instructions. Otherwise enter 'N' (Not Applicable).	(**N**) **D** **S** N/A
4) If this request is for an Amendment or Withdrawal of Application, enter the file number of the pending application currently on file with the FCC.	File Number
5) If this request is for a Modification, Renewal Only, Renewal / Modification, Cancellation of License, Duplicate License, or Administrative Update, enter the call sign (serial number for Commercial Operator) of the existing FCC license. If this is a request for consolidation of DO & DM Operator Licenses, enter serial number of DO. Also, if filing for a ship exemption, you must provide call sign.	Call Sign/Serial # **AB1FM**
6) If this request is for a New, Amendment, Renewal Only, or Renewal Modification, enter the requested expiration date of the authorization (this item is optional).	MM DD
7) Does this filing request a Waiver of the Commission's Rules? If 'Y', attach the required showing as described in the instructions.	(**N**) **Y**es **N**o
8) Are attachments (other than associated schedules) being filed with this application?	(**N**) **Y**es No

Applicant/Licensee Information

9) FCC Registration Number (FRN): **0012345678**

10) Applicant/Licensee legal entity type: (Select One)
[X] Individual   ☐ Corporation   ☐ Unincorporated Association   ☐ Trust   ☐ Government Entity
☐ Consortium   ☐ General Partnership   ☐ Limited Liability Company   ☐ Limited Liability Partnership
☐ Limited Partnership   ☐ Other (Description of Legal Entity) _____

11) First Name (if individual): **MARIA**	MI: **A**	Last Name: **SOMMA**	Suffix:

12) Entity Name (if other than individual):

13) If the licensee name is being updated, is the update a result from the sale (or transfer of control) of the license(s) to another party and for which proper Commission approval has not been received or proper notification not provided?   (   ) **Y**es   **N**o

14) Attention To:

15) P.O. Box:	And/Or	16) Street Address: **225 MAIN ST.**

17) City: **NEWINGTON**	18) State: **CT**	19) Zip Code/Postal Code: **06111**	20) Country:

21) Telephone Number: **860-594-0200**	22) FAX Number:

23) E-Mail Address:

Ship Applicants/Licensees Only

24) Enter new name of vessel: _____

Aircraft Applicants/Licensees Only

25) Enter the new FAA Registration Number (the N-number): _____
     NOTE: Do not enter the leading "N".

FCC 605 – Main Form
February 2007 - Page 1

Figure 1-3 — Portions of FCC Form 605 showing the sections you would complete for a modification of your license, such as a change of address.

Fee Status

26) Is the applicant/licensee exempt from FCC application fees?	(N)	Yes No
27) Is the applicant/licensee exempt from FCC regulatory fees?	(N)	Yes No

General Certification Statements

1)	The applicant/licensee waives any claim to the use of any particular frequency or of the electromagnetic spectrum as against the regulatory power of the United States because of the previous use of the same, whether by license or otherwise, and requests an authorization in accordance with this application.
2)	The applicant/licensee certifies that all statements made in this application and in the exhibits, attachments, or documents incorporated by reference are material, are part of this application, and are true, complete, correct, and made in good faith.
3)	Neither the applicant/licensee nor any member thereof is a foreign government or a representative thereof.
4)	The applicant/licensee certifies that neither the applicant/licensee nor any other party to the application is subject to a denial of Federal benefits pursuant to Section 5301 of the Anti-Drug Abuse Act of 1988, 21 U.S.C. § 862, because of a conviction for possession or distribution of a controlled substance. **This certification does not apply to applications filed in services exempted under Section 1.2002(c) of the rules, 47 CFR § 1.2002(c).** See Section 1.2002(b) of the rules, 47 CFR § 1.2002(b), for the definition of "party to the application" as used in this certification.
5)	Amateur or GMRS applicant/licensee certifies that the construction of the station would NOT be an action which is likely to have a significant environmental effect (see the Commission's Rules 47 CFR Sections 1.1301-1.1319 and Section 97.13(a) rules (available at web site http://wireless.fcc.gov/rules.html).
6)	Amateur applicant/licensee certifies that they have READ and WILL COMPLY WITH Section 97.13(c) of the Commission's Rules (available at web site http://wireless.fcc.gov/rules.html) regarding RADIOFREQUENCY (RF) RADIATION SAFETY and the amateur service section of OST/OET Bulletin Number 65 (available at web site http://www.fcc.gov/oet/info/documents/bulletins/).

Certification Statements For GMRS Applicants/Licensees

1)	Applicant/Licensee certifies that he or she is claiming eligibility under Rule Section 95.5 of the Commission's Rules.
2)	Applicant/Licensee certifies that he or she is at least 18 years of age.
3)	Applicant/Licensee certifies that he or she will comply with the requirement that use of frequencies 462.650, 467.650, 462.700 and 467.700 MHz is not permitted near the Canadian border North of Line A and East of Line C. These frequencies are used throughout Canada and harmful interference is anticipated.
4)	Non-Individual applicants/licensees certify that they have NOT changed frequency or channel pairs, type of emission, antenna height, location of fixed transmitters, number of mobile units, area of mobile operation, or increase in power.

Certification Statements for Ship Applicants/Licensees (Including Ship Exemptions)

1)	Applicant/Licensee certifies that they are the owner or operator of the vessel, a subsidiary communications corporation of the owner or operator of the vessel, a state or local government subdivision, or an agency of the US Government subject to Section 301 of the Communications Act.
2)	This application is filed with the understanding that any action by the Commission thereon shall be limited to the voyage(s) described herein, and that apart from the provisions of the specific law from which the applicant/licensee requests an exemption, the vessel is in full compliance with all applicable statues, international agreements and regulations.

Signature

28) Typed or Printed Name of Party Authorized to Sign

First Name: MARIA	MI: A	Last Name: SOMMA	Suffix:

29) Title:

Signature: _Maria Somma_	30) Date: 02-23-07

Failure to Sign This Application May Result in Dismissal Of The Application And Forfeiture Of Any Fees Paid

WILLFUL FALSE STATEMENTS MADE ON THIS FORM OR ANY ATTACHMENTS ARE PUNISHABLE BY FINE AND/OR IMPRISONMENT (U.S. Code, Title 18, Section 1001) AND / OR REVOCATION OF ANY STATION LICENSE OR CONSTRUCTION PERMIT (U.S. Code, Title 47, Section 312(a)(1)), AND / OR FORFEITURE (U.S. Code, Title 47, Section 503).

FCC 605 – Main Form
February 2007 - Page 2

THE EXAM

The General test takes from 30 minutes to an hour. You will be given a question booklet and an answer sheet. Be sure to read the instructions, fill in all the necessary information and sign your name wherever its required. Check to be sure your booklet has all the questions and be sure to mark the answer in the correct space for each question.

You don't have to answer the questions in order — skip the hard ones and go back to them. If you read the answers carefully, you'll probably find that you can eliminate one or more "distracters." Of the remaining answers, only one will be the best. If you can't decide which is the correct answer, go ahead and guess. There is no penalty for an incorrect guess. When you're done, go back and check your answers and double-check your arithmetic — there's no rush!

Once you've answered all 35 questions, the Volunteer Examiners (VEs) will grade and verify your test results. Assuming you've passed (congratulations!) you'll fill out a *Certificate of Successful Completion of Examination* (CSCE). The exam organizers will submit your results to the FCC while you keep the CSCE as evidence that you've passed your General test.

Volunteer examiners will try to make Exam Day as painless as possible. They grade the tests at the end of the exam session, so you'll know right away how you did. After you pass the exam, you will be issued a Certificate of Successful Completion (CSCE) and can start using your General privileges right away. Just use the identifier "temporary AG" after your call sign until your upgrade appears in the FCC online database, or your new license shows up in the mail.

If you are licensed and already have a call sign, you can begin using your new privileges immediately. When you give your call sign, append "/AG" (on CW or digital modes) or "temporary AG" (on phone). As soon as your name and call sign appear in the FCC's database of licensees, typically a week to 10 days later, you can stop adding the suffix. The CSCE is good for 365 days in case there's a delay or problem with license processing or you decide to upgrade to Amateur Extra before receiving your paper license.

If you don't pass, don't be discouraged! You might be able to take another version of the test right then and there if the session organizers can accommodate you. Even if you decide to try again later, you now know just how the test session feels — you'll be more relaxed and ready next time. The bands are full of hams who took their General test more than once before passing. You'll be in good company!

Hams enjoy exchanging colorful and informative QSL cards to confirm contacts. QSL cards are often used to apply for operating achievement awards.

FCC AND ARRL/VEC LICENSING RESOURCES

After you pass your exam, the examiners will file all of the necessary paperwork so that your license will be granted by the Federal Communications Commission (FCC). Soon, you will be able see your new call sign in the FCC's database via the ARRL's Web site and later, you'll receive a paper license by mail.

When you passed your Technician exam, you may have applied for

In the aftermath of Hurricane Katrina in 2005, hams provided countless hours of service. Outside the American Red Cross marshaling center in Montgomery, Alabama, Section Manager Greg Sarratt, W4OZK (center) assists David Wilcox, K1DJW (left), and David Hyatt, K1DAV, headed into the hurricane stricken zone.

your FCC Federal Registration Number (FRN). This allows you to access the information for any FCC licenses you may have and to request modifications to them. These functions are available via the FCC's Universal Licensing System Web site (**wireless.fcc.gov/uls**) and complete instructions for using the site are available at **www.arrl.org/fcc/uls-qa.html**.

The ARRL/VEC can also process license renewals and modifications for you as described at **www.arrl.org/arrlvec/renewals.html**.

TIME TO GET STARTED

By following these instructions and carefully studying the material in this book, soon you'll be joining the rest of the General and Amateur Extra licensees on the HF bands! Each of us at the ARRL Headquarters and every ARRL member looks forward to the day when you join the fun. 73 (best regards) and good luck!

Table 1-3

General Class (Element 3) Syllabus

SUBELEMENT G1 — COMMISSION'S RULES
[5 exam questions — 5 groups]

G1A — General class control operator frequency privileges; primary and secondary allocations

G1B — Antenna structure limitations; good engineering and good amateur practice; beacon operation; restricted operation; retransmitting radio signals

G1C — Transmitter power regulations; HF data emission standards

G1D — Volunteer Examiners and Volunteer Examiner Coordinators; temporary identification

G1E — Control categories; repeater regulations; harmful interference; third party rules; ITU regions

SUBELEMENT G2 — OPERATING PROCEDURES
[6 exam questions — 6 groups]

G2A — Phone operating procedures; USB/LSB utilization conventions; procedural signals; breaking into a QSO in progress; VOX operation

G2B — Operating courtesy; band plans

G2C — Emergencies, including drills and emergency communications

G2D — Amateur auxiliary; minimizing Interference; HF operations

G2E — Digital operating: procedures, procedural signals and common abbreviations

G2F — CW operating procedures and procedural signals, Q signals and common abbreviations; full break in

SUBELEMENT G3 — RADIO WAVE PROPAGATION
[3 exam questions — 3 groups]

G3A — Sunspots and solar radiation; ionospheric disturbances; propagation forecasting and indices

G3B — Maximum Usable Frequency; Lowest Usable Frequency; propagation "hops"

G3C — Ionospheric layers; critical angle and frequency; HF scatter; Near Vertical Incidence Sky waves

SUBELEMENT G4 — AMATEUR RADIO PRACTICES
[5 exam questions — 5 groups]

G4A — Two-tone Test; amplifier tuning and neutralization; DSP

G4B — Test and monitoring equipment

G4C — Interference with consumer electronics; grounding

G4D — Speech processors; S meters; common connectors

G4E — HF mobile radio installations; emergency and battery powered operation

SUBELEMENT G5 — ELECTRICAL PRINCIPLES
[3 exam questions — 3 groups]

G5A — Resistance; reactance; inductance; capacitance; impedance; impedance matching

G5B — The Decibel; current and voltage dividers; electrical power calculations; sine wave root-mean-square (RMS) values; PEP calculations

G5C – Resistors, capacitors, and inductors in series and parallel; transformers

SUBELEMENT G6 — CIRCUIT COMPONENTS
[3 exam question — 3 groups]

G6A — Resistors; capacitors; inductors

G6B — Rectifiers; solid state diodes and transistors; solar cells; vacuum tubes; batteries

G6C — Analog and digital integrated circuits (IC's); microprocessors; memory; I/O devices; microwave IC's (MMIC's); display devices

SUBELEMENT G7 — PRACTICAL CIRCUITS
[2 exam question — 2 groups]

G7A — Power supplies; transmitters and receivers; filters; schematic symbols

G7B — Digital circuits (gates, flip-flops, shift registers); amplifiers and oscillators

SUBELEMENT G8 — SIGNALS AND EMISSIONS
[2 exam questions — 2 groups]

G8A — Carriers and modulation: AM; FM; single and double sideband ; modulation envelope; deviation; overmodulation

G8B — Frequency mixing; multiplication; HF data communications; bandwidths of various modes

SUBELEMENT G9 — ANTENNAS
[4 exam questions — 4 groups]

G9A — Antenna feedlines: characteristic impedance, and attenuation; SWR calculation, measurement and effects; matching networks

G9B — Basic antennas

G9C — Directional antennas

G9D — Specialized antennas

SUBELEMENT G0 — ELECTRICAL AND RF SAFETY
[2 exam questions — 2 groups]

G0A — RF safety principles, rules and guidelines; routine station evaluation

G0B — Safety in the ham shack: electrical shock and treatment, grounding, fusing, interlocks, wiring, antenna and tower safety

The Considerate Operator's Frequency Guide

A guide to where on the HF bands various modes and activities are generally found. All frequencies are in MHz.

The following frequencies are generally recognized for certain modes or activities (all frequencies are in MHz).

Nothing in the rules recognizes a net's, group's or any individual's special privilege to any specific frequency. Section 97.101(b) of the Rules states that "Each station licensee and each control operator must cooperate in selecting transmitting channels and in making the most effective use of the amateur service frequencies. No frequency will be assigned for the exclusive use of any station." No one "owns" a frequency.

It's good practice — and plain old common sense — for any operator, regardless of mode, to check to see if the frequency is in use prior to engaging operating. If you are there first, other operators should make an effort to protect you from interference to the extent possible, given that 100% interference-free operation is an unrealistic expectation in today's congested bands.

Frequencies	Modes/Activities	Frequencies	Modes/Activities
1.800-2.000	CW	14.100	IBP/NCDXF beacons
1.800-1.810	Digital	14.1005-14.112	Automatically controlled data stations
1.810	QRP CW calling frequency	14.230	SSTV
1.843-2.000	SSB, SSTV and other wideband modes	14.285	QRP SSB calling frequency
1.910	SSB QRP	14.286	AM calling frequency
1.995-2.000	Experimental		
1.999-2.000	Beacons	18.100-18.105	RTTY /Data
		18.105-18.110	Automatically controlled data stations
3.500-3.510	CW DX window	18.110	IBP/NCDXF beacons
3.560	QRP CW calling frequency		
3.570-3.600	RTTY/Data	21.060	QRP CW calling frequency
3.585-3.600	Automatically controlled data stations	21.070-21.110	RTTY/Data
3.590	RTTY/Data DX	21.090-21.100	Automatically controlled data stations
3.790-3.800	DX window	21.150	IBP/NCDXF beacons
3.845	SSTV	21.340	SSTV
3.885	AM calling frequency	21.385	QRP SSB calling frequency
3.985	QRP SSB calling frequency		
		24.920-24.925	RTTY/Data
7.030	QRP CW calling frequency	24.925-24.930	Automatically controlled data stations
7.040	RTTY/Data DX	24.930	IBP/NCDXF beacons
7.080-7.125	RTTY/Data		
7.100-7.105	Automatically controlled data stations	28.060	QRP CW calling frequency
7.171	SSTV	28.070-28.120	RTTY/Data
7.285	QRP SSB calling frequency	28.120-28.189	Automatically controlled data stations
7.290	AM calling frequency	28.190-28.225	Beacons
		28.200	IBP/NCDXF beacons
10.106	QRP CW calling frequency	28.385	QRP SSB calling frequency
10.130-10.140	RTTY/Data	28.680	SSTV
10.140-10.150	Automatically controlled data stations	29.000-29.200	AM
		29.300-29.510	Satellite downlinks
14.060	QRP CW calling frequency	29.520-29.580	Repeater inputs
14.070-14.095	RTTY/Data	29.600	FM simplex
14.095-14.0995	Automatically controlled data stations	29.620-29.680	Repeater outputs

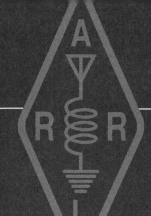

Chapter 2

Procedures and Practices

In this chapter, you'll learn about:
- **Basic HF operating procedures**
- **Common HF practices and modes**
- **Receiving and transmitting on HF**
- **Digital operating**
- **Net structure and procedures**
- **Emergency communications**
- **ARES and RACES organizations**

Technician licensees focus their studies and develop operating skills for techniques used on the VHF and higher bands. The most popular mode of operation on these bands is FM voice repeaters with evenly spaced channels and local or regional contacts. On HF, however, operating is similar to that of the so-called "weak signal" modes on the lower portions of the VHF and UHF bands. Simplex SSB, CW and digital modes are by far the most commonly used. As a Technician, you may have some HF experience on 10 meters or the 80, 40 and 15 meter CW bands. The General license opens up many more frequencies, modes and activities.

2.1 HF Operating Techniques

BASIC OPERATING

To begin with, HF operation is not channelized at all, except for the small 60-meter band that consists of five specific channels for USB operation only. Channel designations are not used, although *calling frequencies* are common along with regular meeting frequencies for nets and special operations. On the HF amateur bands, "channel" only means "current frequency," not "assigned frequency."

Figure 2-1 — The VFO control is usually front-and-center on a transceiver. It allows continuous frequency adjustments in tiny steps.

As a result, HF equipment is designed for continuous tuning. The control used for continuous frequency adjustment is called a *VFO* for *variable frequency oscillator*. This is usually the largest knob on an HF transceiver (**Figure 2-1**), replacing the channel select control on a VHF/UHF FM rig. The VFO tunes the radio (both receiver and transmitter) in steps of 100 Hz or less. The minimum frequency change is called *step size* or *step rate*. (Memory channels are also used on HF, but they are not the primary way frequencies are selected.)

Aside from nets and schedules, random contacts are the norm on HF as hams tune across the bands looking for someone calling CQ or an ongoing QSO that sounds interesting. While calling CQ is rare on VHF/UHF FM channels, it's how most contacts are initiated on HF. When calling CQ, a station from literally anywhere could respond to your call.

To call CQ on phone, you would say "CQ CQ CQ, this is [your call repeated three times using phonetics]" and then repeat that sequence two or three times. On CW, "this is" is replaced by "DE" and of course no phonetics. Many stations say "from" rather than "this is" on phone. On digital modes you usually see "DE," although some stations may use "from." You may have to repeat your CQ several times before you get an answer. Calling variations include:

- CQ DX (to attract faraway stations — DX meaning "distant stations")
- CQ for stations operating in a contest or from a special event
- CQ for stations from a certain area

Joining an ongoing QSO or *breaking in* is also common. On phone the customary procedure is to say just your call sign during a pause in the conversation. On CW or digital modes, send "BK" (break). Your transmission must be short to be received as stations switch from receive to transmit, called "turning it over." If you are heard and the stations in the ongoing QSO want to accept stations breaking in, they will stand by and ask "the breaking station" to go ahead or some similar remark. Identify yourself with your call sign and ask if you may join the contact.

You'll find that HF contacts can be made over extremely long distances, even with modest equipment and antennas. The ionosphere reflects HF signals back to earth quite readily under the right conditions and time of day or season. This is called *skip* propagation. For contacts with nearby stations, you may want to use a band with stronger *ground wave* propagation along the surface of the Earth. Some bands also support *NVIS* or *Near Vertical Incidence Sky-wave* propagation that travels straight up to be reflected back to Earth over a wide area around the transmitter — very useful for emergency communications.

At first you'll find HF practices somewhat different from what you're used to as a Technician licensee. Nevertheless, you'll quickly learn the basics!

> **Before you go on, study test questions G2A12 and G2A13. Review this section if you have difficulty.**

GOOD PRACTICES

Almost everything you know about operating courtesy and good practices from VHF and UHF operating can be applied to HF operating. There are some differences in terminology, of course, but the main difference comes from the new environment of VFO-based operating.

Selecting a Frequency

Choosing a frequency to use is the most important step. After all, you only get one chance to make a good first impression! The process is greatly simplified by tuning around the band and finding some other station calling CQ or engaged in a QSO. You can answer or break in as described above. If you're unsure of yourself, listen for other stations answering or calling and emulate successful and friendly practices.

If you want to call CQ yourself — and why shouldn't you? — start by selecting an appropriate band. If you're interested in short-range, regional contacts, maybe 80 or 40 meters would be a good choice. Longer range contacts are easiest on the higher-frequency bands of 30 through 10 meters, depending on solar conditions. Don't use a long-distance band for short-range contacts since your signal will be heard over a much wider range than you are using. This needlessly occupies precious radio spectrum space.

What if a nearby ham calls you on a long-distance band? The best thing to do is to change bands and move to a frequency more suitable for short distance contacts — even to a VHF or UHF repeater! (There is an extensive discussion of signal propagation in Chapter 7 where you can find out more about the properties of the different bands.)

Now that you've decided on which band to use, what's next? As a General, you should check the FCC Part 97 frequency and mode restrictions to be sure you're within the privileges allocated to Generals. A colorful chart showing frequency privileges for the various license classes can be downloaded from **www.arrl.org/FandES/field/regulations/bands.html**. Once that's done, check to be sure your QSO will follow the recommendations of the *band plan*, which we'll discuss later in this chapter.

Table 2-1
Recommended Signal Separation

CW	150-500 Hz
SSB	Approximately 3 kHz
RTTY	250-500 Hz
PSK31	150-500 Hz

Within the appropriate frequency limits, tune around looking for a clear frequency. On a repeater, you simply have to wait until any ongoing QSOs are over before making your call. On HF, however, a perfectly clear channel is a rarity. There will always be some noise present and the signals of adjacent stations may occasionally be heard. Your goal is to find a frequency on which your transmissions minimize interference to adjacent stations. **Table 2-1** shows the recommended station-to-station spacings for different modes under normal conditions.

If the band is very busy, such as on the weekends when many more hams may be active in contests, chasing DX or just making QSOs, you will find fewer open frequencies and experience more incidental interference. Learning how to make contacts under such circumstances is what makes a good operator!

After selecting your frequency, check for any other station that might be using it. Just as with a VHF simplex contact, you might not be able to hear both stations taking part in a QSO. On phone, the customary technique is to ask "Is the frequency in use? This is [your call]" once or twice before starting your CQ. On CW and the digital modes, "QRL? DE [your call]" does the trick. If a station is listening, they'll usually say, "Yes, it is" or send "C" or make some other transmission that lets you know the frequency is occupied. Move to a new frequency and try again.

Nets and Schedules

Many on-the-air activities are scheduled in advance, such as person-to-person contacts between friends or family members ("skeds") and regularly scheduled nets. For scheduled contacts and events to go smoothly, courtesy is required from two sides.

If you're the one scheduling the activity, avoid calling frequencies and popular band areas. Use the ARRL Net Search and Contest Corral to avoid congestion (see the sidebar, "Radio Calendars"). Always have a Plan B, such as an alternate time or frequency for your contact.

If you're engaged in a QSO and a station calls to request the use of a frequency for a scheduled activity, try to accommodate their need and move your contact to a new frequency. After all, we are a variable frequency service!

Both parties must remember that no group or amateur has a priority on any frequency except in the case of emergency

Radio Calendars

If you need to arrange a scheduled contact or "sked" with another station, you can avoid conflicts by referring to the many online calendars of activities. The HF bands can be pretty crowded at times, so why not plan ahead?

✓ ARRL Net Search — **www.arrl.org/FandES/field/nets/client/index.html**
✓ ARRL Contest Corral — **www.arrl.org/contests**
✓ ARRL Special Events list — **www.arrl.org/contests/spev.html**
✓ SM3CER Contest Service — **www.sk3bg.se/contest**

communications. Be flexible and take advantage of Amateur Radio's unique ability to use any frequency within its allocations! For example, if you are a net control station and find the net's chosen frequency to be occupied, find a clear frequency nearby and run the net there or change to your backup frequency.

Band Plans

The FCC's regulations dividing the amateur bands help stations using compatible modes stay together. There are additional divisions of the band, however, that are created by amateurs themselves and are strictly voluntary. These are called *band plans*. You are probably familiar with them from the VHF and UHF bands where repeaters are grouped together in one section of the band. Other modes and activities, such as satellites or amateur television, have their own segments. The ARRL maintains a set of band plans for 160 meters through the microwaves at **www.arrl.org/FandES/field/regulations/bandplan.html**

Band plans go beyond what the FCC requires and were created in the interests of efficient spectrum use. Many features of band plans evolved over the years while others were created deliberately in response to a particular need. In either case, the FCC considers the band plans "good practice" and expects amateurs to follow them voluntarily when possible and practical.

HF bands have band plans, too. A typical band plan for the 20 meter band is shown in **Table 2-2**. This set of recommendations does not overrule the FCC license class and mode rules — not at all! Instead, it works *within* the FCC rules to reduce interference and frustration. There are three specific frequencies identified: one for a worldwide system of propagation beacons, one for SSTV signals and another for AM enthusiasts. Notice how the packet signals are sandwiched around the beacons. Without the band plan, most users of packet signals wouldn't even know the beacons existed! That's what band plans are for — education and guidance.

When choosing a frequency for a mode such as SSTV, RTTY or PSK31, check the band plans for recommended frequencies. Sometimes a range of frequencies is available; in other cases a spot frequency is shown. Other stations using that mode are much more likely to be operating there or nearby than on other frequencies.

Band plans are voluntary, but they are also flexible. A band plan is not a regulation, it is a guideline. There will be circumstances in which conditions or the number of stations on the band overwhelm the usual customs. For example, a major contest or DX-pedition can result in thousands of stations on a band at once, making it very difficult to adhere to a plan written for normal conditions. These situations are just temporary, however, and things return to normal in a short time.

Housekeeping and Operating Support

Part of keeping an orderly and efficient station is maintaining a *log*, a record of your station's activities. A typical log contains the time, date and frequency or band of each contact; the contacted station's call

Table 2-2
Typical HF Band Plan (20 Meters)

Frequency (MHz)	Mode or Use
14.070-14.095	RTTY
14.07015	PSK31 calling frequency
14.095-14.0995	Packet
14.100	NCDXF/IARU Beacons
14.1005-14.112	Packet
14.230	SSTV
14.286	AM calling frequency

Windows on the World

Outside the United States, particularly in ITU Regions 1 and 3, amateurs share the 160 and 80 meter bands with government and commercial stations. They may have very limited allocations, as well. Under such circumstances, it's useful to have an area of the band set aside for contacts with these amateurs. *DX windows* are a section of the band where these stations may be contacted without their having to compete with stronger domestic signals. DX windows are also generally used only for contacts with stations outside the contiguous United States and Canada.

sign; and information about the contact such as signal reports, names and equipment used. The FCC does not require amateurs to keep a formal log, but most do because it helps them verify contacts in the future. (Requirements for written record keeping are discussed in Chapter 3.) Many amateurs collect awards, and these awards often require data about certain contacts you have made. Your log is the most convenient way to keep track. A log also establishes the identity of the control operator at any date and time in case it is questioned. **Figure 2-2** shows a typical paper log entry. Many amateurs prefer to keep their logs on a computer, making it easy to find and sort QSO information.

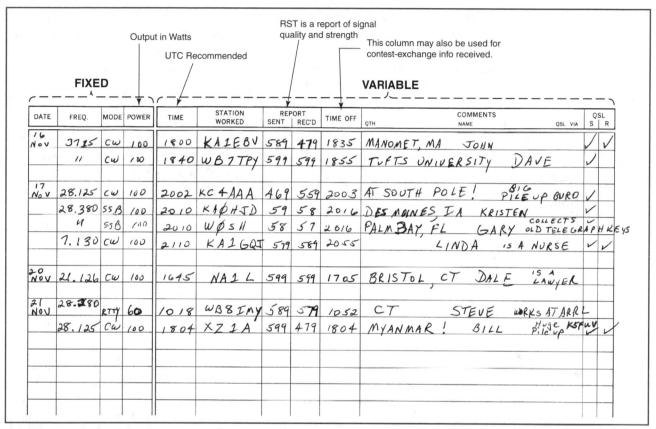

Figure 2-2 — This example of a paper log shows the information usually kept in a log, whether computer or paper. It is a record of your contacts and time spent on the air.

A log is also needed to support *QSLing*, the practice of exchanging cards to confirm a contact. (QSL stands for "received and understood.") Although exchanging cards is relatively infrequent among VHF/UHF FM operators, QSLs have a rich history and tradition on the HF bands. They stem from the early days of radio when every contact was a triumph. Now they are an interesting and often beautiful signature of the station, providing information on equipment, antennas and operator. Collecting these cards from around the world is very popular among HF operators.

Before you go on, study test questions G2B01, G2B02, G2B04, G2B05, G2B06, G2B07, G2B08, G2B09, G2B10, G2B11, G2B12, G2B13, G2D08 and G2D09. Review this section if you have difficulty.

MANAGING INTERFERENCE

Amateur Radio's HF frequencies are not channelized and there are very many amateurs. *Voila!* Interference! Interference occurs not only from crowding, but also from propagation and personal choice. Regardless of its source, every amateur needs to be skilled at dealing with interference. This section talks about dealing with interference from other amateur signals (also called "QRM"), but not interference from signals generated by consumer electronics or atmospheric noise ("QRN").

Types of Interference

Most interference caused by signals from other hams is incidental and not terribly disruptive. Once you've gained some experience, it's easy to copy a desired signal through a little bit of QRM from a nearby signal. You may experience (or even cause!) accidental interference when another station begins transmitting on or very near a frequency that you're using. Like collisions between grocery carts at the store, these incidents are easily managed.

There are two types of interference, however, that are not so easily managed. The first is *harmful interference*, defined by the FCC in §97.3(a)(23) as "Interference which…seriously degrades, obstructs or repeatedly interrupts a radiocommunication service operating in accordance with the Radio Regulations." Harmful interference is not always illegal, but needs to be resolved for all parties to be able to continue to use the amateur bands. The second and more pernicious type of interference is *malicious, deliberate* or *willful interference* and it is specifically forbidden by the FCC rules [§97.101(d)]. Sad to say that it does happen on the amateur bands, but it is uncommon.

Avoiding Interference

The best way to avoid interference is to be smart and use your knowledge of the Amateur Service to your advantage, starting with reasonable expectations. Learn what bands are crowded and when. Learn the characteristics of each band with respect to propagation and noise. Know how to use your station and understand its weaknesses and strengths. Check published operating calendars so that you are not surprised by major operating events. Armed with this information, you'll have a much better idea of what to expect and a much higher chance of having a good experience on the air.

Next, hone your frequency selection skills. There are many sources of good propagation prediction information to help you choose an optimum band or time for operating. Band plans and calling frequencies are widely published on the Web and in print. Net frequencies are available online and in directories. With a few minutes of research, you can avoid many sources of interference and operate on a frequency well-suited for your intended purpose.

While on the air, operate so as to maximize the enjoyment of other operators. Use an appropriate power level to the job at hand. Avoid long-distance bands for short-distance contacts. And make sure your transmitted signal is clean and free of interference-causing spurious signals.

Reacting to Interference

Sooner or later, you will experience interference. What is the appropriate way to react? Start by keeping your options open and being flexible. No one has a claim to any frequency — it's often easy to change frequency to avoid an interfering signal. Know how to operate your receiver to reject interference from adjacent frequencies.

During a contact, you should expect signal propagation to change as the Earth rotates, changing the way sunlight illuminates the ionosphere. Propagation may improve or degrade to your target area and you may begin to hear other stations on the same frequency.

And they may begin to hear you! Changing the heading of a directional antenna or switching to a different antenna may reduce signals to and from the newly heard region. Be prepared to move to a new frequency if both your signal and the interfering signal are strong.

Plan ahead by always having a backup or alternate operating plan in place. This is particularly important for scheduled contacts and nets. Everyone involved should know what to do in case the primary frequency is occupied or propagation is poor. The time to create these procedures is in advance, not at contact time!

Above all, keep a cool head! Sometimes harmful interference leads to deliberate interference when emotions get the better of us. Don't let a sorehead get into your head! Even though it may be vexing, don't react to a jammer or someone creating deliberate interference as that just encourages them. Sometimes it's just best to turn the power switch OFF and find something else to do. Encourage your fellow amateurs to follow these simple guidelines and everyone will benefit.

Before you go on, study test question G2B03. Review this section if you have difficulty.

MODES

Amateurs use many different modes of communication — more than any other service, licensed or unlicensed. The invention, use and management of different modes is a good example of Amateur Radio fulfilling its mission to advance the state of the radio art! (That's a key part of the "basis and purpose" of Amateur Radio as set forth in Part 97 of the FCC regulations.) This section presents some of the conventions associated with each mode and compares them.

CW

Morse code is found at the bottom of each HF band because FCC rules prohibit phone signals there. It's often forgotten that CW can be transmitted anywhere on the HF bands, including the portion allocated to phone operation (except on 60 meters, which is USB only)! Nevertheless, most operators prefer to operate toward the lowest frequency they're licensed to use.

Morse speed for on-air contacts ranges from 5 to 10 WPM to as high as 50 WPM between experts. You'll hear even higher speeds sent by keyboards! The majority of day-to-day contacts are made at speeds between 15 and 30 WPM with a mix of straight keys and keyers or computer-generated code. Contest signals will be heard up to 40 WPM, but contesters will slow down if asked to "QRS" and there isn't a pileup of faster operators calling. Higher speed signals tend to be found low in the band and slower ones above.

The busiest CW calling frequencies are those for QRP (see **www.qrparci.org**) and FISTS (**www.fists.org**). The convention for Morse is to conduct QSOs either directly on the calling frequency or on the closest clear frequency.

AM and SSB Phone

On the HF bands, SSB is by far the most common voice mode or phone signal. First introduced in the 1950s, SSB displaced AM as the preferred HF voice modulation method for several reasons. SSB uses less spectrum space than AM — a properly-adjusted SSB signal occupies about 3 kHz and an AM signal 6 kHz. This is because the carrier and "extra" sideband are suppressed and not transmitted on SSB.

No carrier is transmitted with an SSB signal, so all of the power is allocated to the speech information. In contrast, an AM signal's carrier consumes one-half or more of the total signal power but carries no information. The result is that, under equal conditions, an SSB signal will have a longer range than an AM signal.

Even with those disadvantages, AM has a role to play on the amateur bands. SSB transmitters tend to optimize the signal characteristics for strength at the expense of some fidelity. AM transmitters, on the other hand, tend to give a "warmer" sound to the speaker's voice. The AM signal detectors in older receivers tended to suffer from poor selectivity and interference, but modern receivers have better performance. AM calling frequencies can be found on many band plans, and a sizeable group of AM and antique radio enthusiasts are heard every day.

SSB is the more popular mode, but which of the sidebands is used? Because of technical considerations in early SSB radio design, the convention is to use the upper sideband (USB) on bands at or above 9 MHz (20 through 10 meters) and the lower sideband (LSB) elsewhere. On VHF and UHF, the upper sideband is used. Digital modes such as RTTY or PSK31 use LSB on all bands. Modern radios are set up to select the conventional sideband automatically. They can easily use either sideband on any band, but your signal won't be understood if you call or answer CQs on the "wrong" sideband!

FM phone signals are permitted only on the upper frequencies of the 10-meter HF band. As a result, there are many 10-meter repeaters that, when the band is open, provide cross-continent contacts! FM, in general, is not used on HF because the higher noise levels and wide bandwidth of the mode do not result in good signal-to-noise performance at HF.

Digital Phone

A new type of phone signal is coming to the Amateur Radio HF bands — digital phone! The operator's voice is converted to and from a stream of digital information by a modem or sound card, just like computer-generated digital signals. The modem or sound card then connects to a regular SSB transceiver's microphone input and speaker or headphone output. The digital phone transmissions have comparable fidelity to regular SSB signals but are less affected by fading and there is less noise in the recovered voice signal. This type of phone transmission is likely to become more popular as the technique is refined.

Digital Modes

You may have used packet radio on VHF or UHF to exchange digital data. There are plenty of digital signals on HF, as well. The oldest and still one of the most popular is *radioteletype* or *RTTY*. (Most hams pronounce it as "ritty.") In recent years, many operators have switched to PSK31 for low-speed keyboard to keyboard contacts, and to PACTOR for semi-automatic and automatic data communications. There are many more digital modes used on HF than on VHF.

On VHF and UHF, FM is usually used to carry digital information. Those signals are too wide for the HF bands — FCC rules do not permit wideband signals in the amateur bands below 30 MHz. On HF, SSB radios are used to send and receive the digital signals, which are transmitted as audio tones. The maximum bandwidth of an amateur digital signal on HF is currently limited to 1 kHz, with many modes narrower than that.

Image Modes

Image mode transmissions on HF encode pictures and graphics as tones. The tones are then reconstructed at the receiver to display the image on a computer screen or other display device. Image modes are permitted wherever phone transmissions are allowed, except on 60 meters where USB phone is the only authorized mode. Note that we are talking about transmitting still pictures and graphics, as opposed to full motion fast scan amateur television (ATV), which is used on the 70 cm and higher bands.

Amateurs commonly use two image modes on HF. Both are transmitted and received using SSB equipment following the same sideband conventions as for SSB phone. The most popular, slow-scan television (SSTV), was invented in the 1960s as a way of capturing a video image and sending it line-by-line over a voice channel. Sending an image (also called a *frame*) takes 8 seconds, thus the name "slow scan." In the early days, SSTV

Table 2-3
Mode Comparison

Mode	Bandwidth	Examples	Data Rate	Notes
CW	Up to 150 Hz		Up to 60 WPM	
AM	6 kHz			Can be higher fidelity than SSB
SSB	3 kHz			
Narrow Bandwidth HF Digital	Up to 500 Hz	RTTY, PSK31	Up to 100 WPM	Keyboard-to-keyboard
Medium Bandwidth HF Digital	Up to 1 kHz	PACTOR, Packet	Up to 1200 baud	Keyboard-to-keyboard and file transfer
VHF/UHF Digital	Up to 100 kHz	ASCII		Max bandwidth varies by band
Narrow Bandwidth Image	3 kHz max on HF	SSTV, Fax		
Video	6 MHz max	NTSC Video		UHF only

operation required special hardware. Computers and sound cards simplified greatly the process of sending and receiving these images, and software for SSTV operation is readily available. As a result, SSTV is reaching a new audience and is even being used in emergency situations to provide on-scene pictures.

Facsimile, or fax, is the very same mode that fax machines and computers use. If you've ever received a phone call from a fax machine, you already know that fax images are sent as audio tones. Those tones can also be sent over a radio voice channel. Amateurs have used fax for a variety of applications, such as weather maps and navigation reports, but its use on the air is declining in favor of digital data transmission.

Mode Comparison

Table 2-3 lists the common modes or types of modes and compares their basic characteristics. You'll learn about the details of these modes in Chapter 5. This table is intended to summarize the overview you've just read.

> *Before you go on, study test questions G2A01, G2A02, G2A03, G2A04, G2A05, G2A06, G2A07, G2A08 and G2A09. Review this section if you have difficulty.*

HF RECEIVING

Receiving an FM signal requires three basic controls: frequency (or channel), squelch and volume. SSB/CW receivers have many more adjustments such as those shown in **Figure 2-3** because they are designed for nonchannelized, continuous tuning operation. They must be able to receive desired signals in the presence of noise and interference from adjacent channels. Squelch is generally not used on amateur SSB and CW because of the higher noise levels on HF.

Selectivity, the ability to discriminate between closely-spaced signals, is more important on HF than *sensitivity*, the ability to detect a signal. This is because atmospheric noise, referred to as *QRN*, is much higher on the HF bands than on VHF and UHF.

Figure 2-3 — HF transceivers have a variety of controls to help minimize interference on crowded bands.

QRN is caused by storms or other natural atmospheric processes, and by man-made sources such as sparks from motors and appliances. As a result, high sensitivity is not required on bands below 15 meters because the noise on those bands masks very weak signals. *Preamplifiers* are rarely required except when inefficient antennas are used, although they may be useful on higher HF bands such as 15 though 10 meters.

On HF, very weak signals close to the noise level often need to be received in the presence of strong nearby signals that may be 10 million to 100 million times more powerful (70 to 80 dB). HF receivers use sharp filters to reject nearby signals. These filters may be supplied as discrete filter assemblies, often called crystal filters or mechanical filters. More recent radios use digital signal processing (DSP) ICs to handle the filtering, and some radios use a combination of discrete and DSP filters. Regardless of the technology used, the goal is to reject unwanted signals that are near the operating frequency. A typical receiver has at least one filter with response and bandwidth tailored for SSB reception, another for CW and a third for AM or FM.

Because HF operation is not channelized, you'll also encounter signals close enough to be audible as low- or high-pitched speech fragments or CW tones. This interference from other signals is called *QRM*. Along with the main VFO tuning control, HF receivers offer the ability to shift the receive frequency without changing the transmit frequency to fine-tune desired signals and avoid or minimize QRM. This is called *receiver incremental tuning* or *RIT*. Some transceivers also offer the ability to shift the *transmit* frequency without changing the receiver — *transmitter incremental tuning* or *XIT*.

As you'll learn in Chapter 5, transmitters can be misadjusted to create spurious output signals away from their intended channel. These unwanted signals are heard as noise by users of nearby channels and are difficult to filter out, although DSP filters can help. A steady tone from a station tuning up can be rejected by a *notch filter* that removes a narrow slice of signal from the channel.

Receivers can also be misadjusted to leave them susceptible to interference or even create interference-like effects from *overload* or *intermodulation* (signals mixing together and creating unwanted byproducts). A receiver's gain should be set so that it is just sensitive enough for the job and not more. Features like noise blankers and preamplifiers can make a receiver easy to overload and should only be used when necessary. Receiver technology is discussed in more detail in Chapter 5.

HF TRANSMITTING

While the receiver is used to find and select a suitable frequency for a contact, the transmitter is what generates the signal carrying your information. This section discusses methods of using the transmitter, and the details of adjusting a transmitter are covered in Chapter 5.

Phone

On HF phone, there are several ways to put your transceiver into transmit when you want to talk. If you're used to an FM mobile or handheld radio, you'll find *push-to-talk* (*PTT*) works just the same as on VHF and UHF. PTT is best for noisy environments. It's also simple and requires no special circuitry in the transmitter. HF operators sometimes

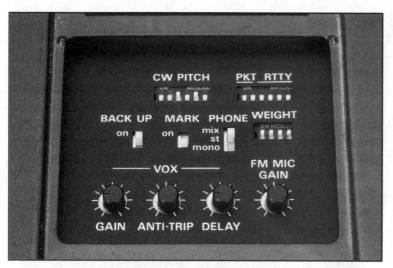

Figure 2-4 — VOX controls — Gain, Anti-VOX (called Anti-Trip on this transceiver) and Delay. Because they aren't often adjusted, many rigs place Gain and Anti-VOX out of the way or as menu items if controlled by software. Delay is used more often and is usually given a more prominent location. Some radios even have separate Delay controls for CW and phone.

use a footswitch rather than the PTT button on a microphone to key the transmitter during busy operating periods, particularly if an amplifier is used.

HF operators also frequently use *voice-operated transmit*, most often referred to as simply *VOX*. A special circuit in the transmitter uses audio from the microphone input to turn on ("key") the transmitter when the operator is speaking. VOX allows hands-free operation, which is more convenient for long periods of operation. Mobile operators use VOX to keep both hands on the steering wheel! (Note: It is unsafe to wear headphones while driving and illegal in many areas.)

There are three basic controls for the VOX circuit. They will be thoroughly described by your radio's operating manual and a typical set is shown in **Figure 2-4**. Get to know them so that you can adjust the VOX circuit properly at any time.

The first is a control called *VOX sensitivity*, or more often *VOX gain*. The more sensitive the VOX circuit, the less microphone audio it takes to key the transmitter. VOX gain is usually set first so that the transmitter keys when you speak at a comfortable voice level. Keying the transmitter with a VOX circuit is called "tripping the VOX." The VOX circuit's release of the transmitter is called "dropping out." The trick is to adjust the VOX gain so that it doesn't trip from stray noise in the shack and doesn't drop out while you are talking. Note that VOX operation allows the transmitter to be keyed from a cough or sneeze just as well as by speech!

Once the transmitter is keyed by the VOX circuit, *VOX delay* holds the transmitter on for a short time while the operator pauses or after the operator stops speaking. It keeps the transmitter from continually being turned on and off during pauses in the operator's speech, causing extra wear on switches and relays. VOX delay is adjusted after VOX gain has been set. Increasing VOX delay holds the transmitter on longer after speech ceases.

When you're using a speaker instead of headphones, the received signal can be picked up by the microphone, unintentionally keying the transmitter. The result is a continuous on/off cycling of the transmitter that sounds like a series of noise bursts to a listening station. The *anti-VOX* function subtracts a sample of the received signal from the microphone audio to prevent VOX cycling. Anti-VOX is usually adjusted following VOX gain and VOX delay. Increasing anti-VOX makes the VOX circuit less sensitive to received audio.

VOX can also be used for CW and digital transmissions. For CW, closing the external key trips the VOX circuit and VOX delay holds the transmitter on as for voice. VOX gain and anti-VOX have no effect for CW. For digital transmissions, the audio output from the modem or sound card used to convert computer data into audio tones activates the VOX just as a voice does. All three VOX controls have the same functions as for voice operation.

Phone Procedures and Abbreviations

You've already learned about the procedural signals "CQ" and "Break." From operating on VHF and UHF, you know when to use "Over" and "Clear." HF phone operation uses all of those signals and a few more. HF operators also make heavy use of the standard phonetics listed on the *General Class License Manual* Web page, **www.arrl.org/gclm**. Don't forget to give your call sign every 10 minutes and at the end of the contact.

You will also hear many operators using Q-signals on phone, even though they were really intended for use on CW. Their meaning is so widely understood, for example QRM and QRN that you met in the previous section, that it is hard to resist using them. A good reason to use Q-signals on phone is when you are in contact with a station who does not speak the same language. That is why Q-signals were developed so many years ago.

In any case, avoid the use of "10 codes" such as "10-4" since those are long obsolete and no longer used even by most police and fire departments. These professional radio users have decided it's better to use good old plain speech for clarity and understanding. If you're going to change frequency or close down the station, say just so.

CW

Morse contacts are far more common on HF than above 30 MHz. The code segments of open bands are busy with signals and sometimes filled to overflowing! Morse is not even close to dead on the ham bands. If you decide to learn it, you will add a powerful radio tool to your rapidly growing collection.

Most CW operators begin with a *straight key*, but soon graduate to the use of an electronic *keyer* for easier sending at higher speeds. A keyer, shown in **Figure 2-5**, generates Morse elements, the dits and dahs, with a small microprocessor or a digital logic circuit. The operator uses a *paddle* to tell the keyer which to generate. A paddle is a lever arm with large, flat knobs for the operator to touch. The lever arm has contacts on each side — move it one way to tell the keyer to make dits, and the other way to make dahs. Some paddles use a pair of back-to-back lever arms that can be squeezed to generate the dits and dahs. A skilled paddle operator can generate code at 50 WPM or more! Some radios have keyers built-in, too.

There are two choices as to how to set up a transceiver to switch between sending and receiving when using Morse. If you use the VOX circuit as described in the previous section on phone operating, the rig will switch back to receive after the VOX delay period expires. This is *semi break-in* operation. VOX delay can be set to a very short time to drop out between words or long enough that the transmitter stays on the whole time you're sending.

Under some circumstances, it is more con-

Figure 2-5 — An electronic keyer generates precisely formed and spaced dits and dahs under the control of a paddle. This combination makes it easy to send code at speeds over 15 words per minute with much less effort.

venient to be able to hear what is going on between the Morse characters and elements. You might want to do this when the station you're in contact with has to interrupt your transmissions or if interference is present. Most modern radios include a *full break-in* option in which the radio switches between transmit and receive in just a few milliseconds. When using full break-in, the operator can hear incoming signals between all transmitted code elements. Full break-in is also referred to as *QSK*, which is the Q-signal for break-in operation.

CW Procedures and Abbreviations

It is a lot of work to spell out the full text of all words and phrases, so telegraphers developed an extensive set of abbreviations and procedural signals called *prosigns*. Prosigns are two letters sent together as a single character. For example, the prosign $\overline{AR}$ (didahdidahdit) is used to indicate "End of Message."

Abbreviations are used to shorten common words, for example "GOING" becomes "GG" and "WEATHER" becomes "WX" in Morse code. This saves a lot of time and energy! Long lists of abbreviations and prosigns are available on the Web at **www.arrl. org/gclm**.

As mentioned before, calling CQ on CW follows the same form as on phone. "DE" is an abbreviation used in place of "from" and the procedural signal K replaces "over":

CQ CQ CQ DE W1AW W1AW W1AW K

A response to a CQ looks like this:

W1AW DE WB8IMY WB8IMY WB8IMY K

There's no need to send the CQing station's call more than once unless there is interference or the signal is weak! When signals are strong and clear, operators responding to a CQ may send their own call only once or twice.

Respond to a CQ at the speed of the calling station. If you are uncomfortable receiving at that speed, send the Q-signal "QRS" ("please send slower") before the final K. If you want to go faster, "QRQ" means "please send faster."

Remember to adjust your transmitting frequency so that your signal is "zero beat" with the other signal so that you will be on the same frequency. This means the two signals produce the same audio tone in a receiver. Check your radio's operating manual for instructions on how to zero beat another signal.

Once you are in contact with another station, the prosign $\overline{KN}$ is used instead of K to prevent other stations from breaking in during the contact. It means, "Only the station with whom I am in contact should respond." When asked if you are ready to receive information, "QRV" means "I am ready to copy." After receiving the message, "QSL" means "I acknowledge receipt."

When it's time to end the QSO, the prosign $\overline{SK}$ is used to let any listener know that the contact is completed:

WB8IMY DE W1AW SK

If you are going off the air, add CL for "closing station." As always, be sure to give your call sign every ten minutes and at the end of the contact.

Before you go on, study test questions G2A10, G2A11, G2F01, G2F02, G2F03, G2F04, G2F05, G2F06, G2F07, G2F08, G2F09, G2F10 and G2F11. Review this section if you have difficulty.

2.2 Digital Modes

DEFINITIONS

A *digital mode* is one in which data is exchanged as individual characters encoded as digital bits. For example, instead of sending "A" as didah in Morse code, it is exchanged as the bit pattern 01000001 in the ASCII code (ASCII is defined below). There are many digital modes used in Amateur Radio. Some are quite old, such as radioteletype which was invented in the 1930s. Others are adaptations of modes used commercially and some, such as PSK31, are purely amateur creations. New digital modes are being added regularly — an area in which amateur inventiveness shines. Books such as *The ARRL Handbook* and the *ARRL's HF Digital Handbook* provide detailed information about amateur digital communications.

A *digital mode* consists of two things; a *protocol* and a method of modulation. A protocol is the set of rules that control the encoding, packaging, exchanging and decoding of digital data. For example, packet radio uses the AX.25 protocol standard. That standard specifies how each packet is constructed, how packets are exchanged, what characters are allowed and so forth. The protocol standard doesn't say what kind of transmitter to use or what the signal will sound like on the air. The method of modulation, such as SSB or FM, is determined by conventional operating practices.

Where to Find Activity

Digital mode signals are restricted to the CW/data segments of each band. Most digital mode operation is found close to the top of the CW segment. Calling frequencies for the popular digital modes are incorporated into the band plans and are usually the lowest frequency of operation with operators moving up in frequency as activity increases. For example, on 20 meters most PSK31 signals are clustered around 14.070 MHz. RTTY and other digital mode signals are found above that.

Segments of the HF bands where you'll find signals of the popular digital modes are listed in **Table 2-4**. The modems used for digital signals often do not recognize signals from CW or other digital modes, so it is important that the human operator listen to the channel before transmitting to avoid causing QRM.

Table 2-4
Digital Signal Band Plan

Band (Meters)	Where to Find Digital Signals (MHz)	Notes
160	1.800 - 1.810	
80	3.570 - 3.600	
60	Data not permitted	
40	7.080 - 7.125	RTTY DX calling frequency 7.040 MHz
30	10.130 - 10.150	
20	14.070 - 14.0995 and 14.1005 - 14112	PSK31 calling frequency 14.070 MHz
17	18.100 - 18.110	
15	21.070 - 21.110	
12	24.920 - 24.930	
10	28.070 - 28.189	

Calling frequencies can be found on the ARRL Band Plan Web page (**www.arrl.org/FandES/field/regulations/bandplan.html**) or at the link on the *General Class License Manual* Web page (**www.arrl.org/gclm**).

Before you go on, study test questions G2E04, G2E08, G2E09 and G8B11. Review this section if you have difficulty.

DIGITAL MODE OVERVIEWS

The following paragraphs present a short summary of some popular digital modes. Exact definitions are covered in Chapter 5. Maximum data rates and signal bandwidths are specified by the FCC rules in §97.307 to limit signal bandwidth on congested bands. The FCC rules identify several types of digital codes (the method of encoding the characters for transmission) [§97.309]. If you intend to use a digital code other than those specified, you must first make sure that the protocol rules are public (amateurs are not allowed to use secret or private codes) and you must comply with bandwidth limitations.

Radioteletype

Radioteletype or RTTY is specially identified in the FCC rules as "narrowband, direct-printing telegraphy." It is a mode that was originally designed to be copied and printed off the air by a mechanical teleprinter. Today, amateurs use a computer instead. Amateur RTTY signals use the Baudot code, which encodes each character as five bits plus a start and stop bit to synchronize the sending and receiving stations. Baudot is the origin of the term *baud* (see the sidebar, "Bits or Bauds?").

RTTY uses *frequency-shift keying* or *FSK* to encode the digital ones and zeros. The signal shifts between a pair of tones to indicate 1 or 0. The two tones are called *mark* (1) and *space* (0) and the rate of shifting between them determines the character speed. On HF, the most common speeds are 60, 75 and 100 WPM (corresponding to 45, 56 and 75 bauds). You should always answer a RTTY station at the same speed it is using. Most RTTY conversations on HF are conducted at 45 bauds, and the most common shift between the mark and space frequencies is 170 Hz.

The Baudot code only has five bits, so only 32 unique characters can be represented. ($2^5 = 32$ distinct combinations)

To get around that limitation, two of the characters are used to select between sets of characters. The FIGS character causes every character to be received after it to be treated as a numeral, punctuation or control character. The LTRS character returns the characters to those of normal text.

RTTY operation is popular on all of the HF amateur bands when they are open. Most stations try to stay within the limits shown in Table 2-4, toward the bottom of the range.

Bits or Bauds?

There is a lot of confusion about bit rate and baud. Is it 300 bits per second or 300 baud? Bit rate refers to the number of bits per second (bps) carried by the transmission. Baud (just "baud" or "bauds," not "baud rate") refers to the number of digital symbols sent each second. Simple coding methods such as Baudot or ASCII carry one bit in each symbol sent by the transmitter. More sophisticated codes that use complex audio signals to carry the data encode more than one bit in every separate combination of signals, called a *symbol*. That is how modems faster than 9.6 kbps exchange data at such high rates over a narrow voice channel — each symbol sent by the transmitter at 9600 baud carries 2 bits (19.2 kbps), 4 bits (38.4 kbps) or 6 bits (56.6 kbps) of data. If each symbol carries a single bit, then bit rate and baud are the same.

PACTOR

PACTOR stands for PACket Teletype Over Radio. This mode improves on RTTY with the ability to detect and correct errors. PACTOR uses advanced modulation and packet methods to make the transmitted data easier to recover from the noisy and fade-prone HF channel.

There are currently three versions: PACTOR I, II and III. PACTOR I uses FSK modulation while PACTOR II and PACTOR III use more advanced *PSK (Phase Shift Keying)* modulation techniques. PACTOR III can achieve data bit rates as high as 5 kbps. The various PACTOR modes are the most popular on HF radio today for exchanging large amounts of information. PACTOR is the preferred method of data transmission for the popular *WinLink* Amateur Radio e-mail system (**www.winlink.org**).

ASCII and Packet Radio

Pronounced "as-key," ASCII is shorthand for American National Standard Code for Information Interchange. The ASCII code has a much larger set of characters than does Baudot because each character is represented by 7 bits, for a total of $2^7 = 128$ characters. (There is also an 8-bit ASCII code that is sometimes called *binary*.) ASCII characters also include start, stop and *parity* bits. (Parity is a count of how many 1 or 0 bits are present.) ASCII-coded transmissions are usually sent at 110 or 300 baud in the same part of the band as RTTY transmissions.

ASCII is most commonly encountered in the digital mode known as *packet radio*. (Packet radio is defined by the AX.25 protocol standard.) ASCII characters are transmitted as a group of characters called a *packet*. The packet starts with a *header* that provides information about the packet for routing and handling functions. Packets also include a *checksum* that allows the receiving system to detect errors in the packet's characters. The packets can move independently over a network of relay stations and are reassembled at the receiving station. Packet radio is most common on VHF and UHF because transmission errors from the noise encountered on HF greatly reduces the effectiveness of this mode. VHF and UHF packet radio systems usually operate at 1200 or 9600 bps.

PSK31

The "31" in PSK31 refers to the speed at which the protocol operates — 31 baud. This may sound quite slow, but PSK31 is designed for keyboard-to-keyboard communication and is sufficient to keep up with most typists. Instead of a fixed-length character code of 5, 7 or 8 bits, PSK uses a variable length code called *varicode* that assigns shorter codes to common characters, just like Morse code.

PSK31 has several attractive features. It requires a very narrow bandwidth (<100 Hz) and performs very well even as a weak signal on HF. PSK31 can be generated and decoded with an inexpensive PC sound card. No special equipment is required; you need only an audio interface to connect the radio and sound card. As shown in **Figure 2-6**, PSK31 signals are generally found on or near the calling frequency because the mode has such a narrow bandwidth.

Miscellaneous Digital Modes

There are numerous other digital modes on the HF, VHF and UHF bands. Here are some of the better known modes:

● *MFSK16*. MFSK16 stands for *multi-frequency shift keying* with 16 different tones being transmitted. On the air, an MFSK16 signal sounds like a set of whistles all being played simultaneously in a narrow bandwidth. By carefully shaping the signal and controlling how the tones are turned on and off, MFSK16 modulation is able to better withstand the fading and distortion associated with sky-wave signals. MFSK16 offers good

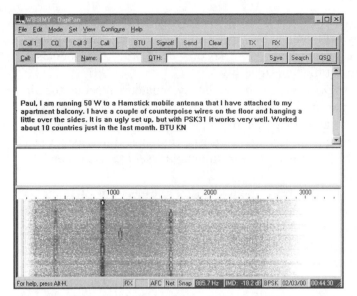

Figure 2-6 — PSK31 is a popular digital mode for keyboard-to-keyboard chats. To tune in PSK31 signals, the receiver is parked on the calling frequency. All of the signals in the receiver's passband show up as lines on a "waterfall display" and are selected by clicking the line with a computer mouse.

performance with weak signals even though the mode does not use error correction. Its bandwidth is slightly higher than 300 Hz and data is exchanged at about 42 WPM.

● *MT63*. MT stands for *multi-tone*. The data signal is composed of 64 tones and uses advanced DSP techniques. Bandwidth is 1 kHz, making it one of the wider digital modes, and data is exchanged at up to 100 WPM.

● *WSJT and JT44/JT65*. These modes are for VHF/UHF meteor scatter and moonbounce communications, respectively. Both use computer sound cards and DSP technology to perform advanced signal processing.

● *Hellschreiber*. Related to facsimile or fax, data is sent as dots that make up an image that is then read by a human operator.

Initiating and Terminating Contacts

Digital QSOs usually follow the general structure established by the long tradition of RTTY operating. A CQ on a digital mode looks similar to the other modes:

CQ CQ CQ DE W1AW W1AW W1AW
CQ CQ CQ DE W1AW W1AW W1AW K

The usual method of responding looks like this:

W1AW W1AW W1AW DE WB8IMY WB8IMY WB8IMY K

As on CW, if signals are loud and clear, you may reduce the number of times you send the call signs.

Digital operators often use Q-signals and other abbreviations common to CW. For example, K is used at the end of a transmission to indicate the other station is to transmit as shown above. SK is used to indicate "signing off" or "end of contact" and CL means "clear" or "closing station."

> *Before you go on, study test questions G2E02, G2E03, G2E05, G2E06, G2E07, G2E10 and G2E11. Review this section if you have difficulty.*

2.3 Nets and Emergency Operation

Nets are one of the oldest radio activities, originally started to help relay messages from point to point when radio communications did not cover long distances easily. Net procedures are actually derived from the even earlier operating practices of telegraphers who had to share a single line between many stations. A mainstay of operating on HF, learning the basics of net operation is important for all General class licensees.

DEFINITIONS AND STRUCTURE

There are three basic types of nets. Although they have different purposes, the basic procedures are common to all three. Each type has some special procedures that optimize its efficiency and effectiveness.

● *Traffic*. These nets exist to relay messages, also called *handling traffic*. Messages, usually in *radiogram* format, are exchanged for delivery or relay by the net members. Messages to be relayed are accepted by net members who act as liaisons to other nets through which the messages will be passed. There is a whole series of special procedural signals and Q-signals to help keep a traffic net flowing smoothly.

- *Emergency Communications* or *Emcomm.* In an emergency, amateurs meet on the air to facilitate communications to support needs of organizations involved in the recovery effort. Emcomm nets can handle formal messages, assign operators and equipment and coordinate the activities of hams in the field. Emergency traffic (messages) may be passed between public safety agencies or health-and-welfare traffic may be sent to friends and families outside the affected area.

- *Social or Topical.* By far the majority of nets are just on-the-air meetings of amateurs with a common interest or affiliation. Clubs frequently have a weekly net for the members to meet and exchange information. There are local swap-and-shop nets for hams to sell or trade equipment. Hobby nets (yes, hams have other hobbies!) meet regularly on every topic under the sun. These nets tend to be much less formal than traffic or emcomm nets.

You can find nets by using the ARRL online net lookup service at **www.arrl.org/ FandES/field/nets/client/index.html**. This is a good way to find a specific net, nets in your area or nets with a specific topic. You can also look up the purpose of a net that you encounter on the air. Some organizations publish net times and frequencies on their Web sites or in their newsletters.

Net Control Station

All of these nets have a Net Control Station (NCS) whose job it is to organize the net and lead it through its necessary business. The NCS should have a strong signal that can be heard by all of the net members, if possible. The NCS is in charge of all activity on the net frequency until the net is closed — he or she is The Boss!

On an informal net, the NCS may be a Master of Ceremonies, introducing net members and calling the roll. On formal nets, such as those that handle traffic, the NCS must manage the queue of messages to be relayed and keep track of the location and presence of stations that have joined the nets. On emcomm nets, the NCS may also have a leadership position within the emergency teams and not only manage the net, but resources in the field, too.

Checking In and Out

If you want to participate in a net, joining the net is called *checking in* and leaving is *checking out.* The best way to learn how to check in and out properly is to listen to the other members do it and follow their example. Most nets will also make a call for visitors to check in as part of regular net procedures. When you do check in, ask the NCS for more information about the net. Net procedures are covered in detail in the *ARRL Operating Manual.*

Traffic

If you are intrigued by the idea of traffic handling, there is an extensive amount of information in the ARRL's *Public Service Communication Manual*, available online at **www. arrl.org/FandES/field/pscm/index.html**. Messages are exchanged in the form of radiograms, derived from the telegram forms they resemble. While the format has been around a long time, it has shown itself to be exceptionally reliable for relaying messages by radio.

Traffic handling nets need a solid, wide-area organization in order to be effective and that job is done by the *National Traffic System* (NTS). This organization manages traffic nets across North America in an effective system that allows a radiogram to be generated, transmitted and delivered quickly and with a minimum amount of handling. **Figure 2-7** shows the general organization of local, regional and area nets.

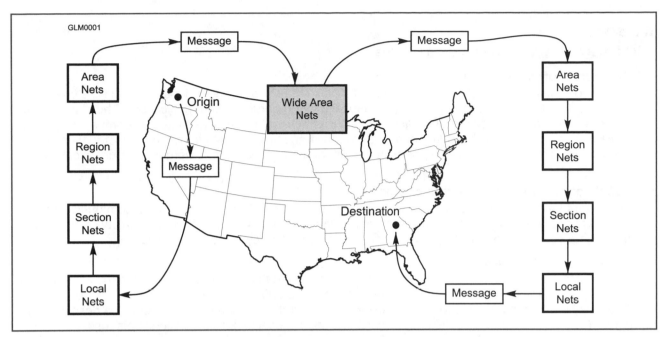

Figure 2-7 — The National Traffic System (NTS) is set up to handle messages in ARRL radiogram format and relay them anywhere in North America and Canada. Messages originate and are delivered from local and Section nets. Region and Area nets relay the messages across long distances.

EMERGENCY OPERATION

Emergency communications is a significant factor in the decision of many people to become hams and more importantly, to stay hams. Recent events around the world clearly demonstrate that Amateur Radio is needed and is an important part of our operation, just as much as technical experimentation and operator knowledge.

Amateurs should be familiar with emergency rules and procedures so that they can contribute effectively when normal communications are knocked out. Even if you are not affected by the emergency or disaster directly, you may receive emergency communications from an amateur who is. Emergency communications in any form take priority over *all* other types of amateur communication. Regardless of what else is happening on a frequency, all other operators must stand by and wait for the emergency communications to occur. You should be prepared to respond effectively.

Emergency Communications Definitions

Let's start by defining what the FCC considers emergency communications to be (see **Table 2.5**). FCC rule §97.111(a)(2) states that during an emergency or disaster, an amateur station may make "transmissions necessary to meet essential communication needs and to facilitate relief actions." These routine emergency communications are conducted on any frequencies authorized to the station control operator.

There are two exceptions to the rules that allow amateurs to use any means and any frequency necessary to provide emergency communications. The first exception is when there is an *immediate* threat to the safety of life or property. From FCC rule §97.403, "No provision of these rules prevents the use by an amateur station of any means of radiocommunication at its disposal to provide essential communication needs ..." That means you may use *any* frequency and mode, regardless of your license class if there is a *real* emergency, one that is an immediate threat to life or property. FCC rule §97.111(a)(3) even allows you to make contact with non-amateur stations, but *only* when a true emergency

Table 2-5

FCC Emergency Communications Rules

§97.401 Operation during a disaster.

A station in, or within 92.6 km (50 nautical miles) of, Alaska may transmit emissions J3E and R3E on the channel at 5.1675 MHz (assigned frequency 5.1689 MHz) for emergency communications. The channel must be shared with stations licensed in the Alaska-Private Fixed Service. The transmitter power must not exceed 150 W PEP. A station in, or within 92.6 km of, Alaska may transmit communications for tests and training drills necessary to ensure the establishment, operation, and maintenance of emergency communication systems.

§97.403 Safety of life and protection of property.

No provision of these rules prevents the use by an amateur station of any means of radiocommunication at its disposal to provide essential communication needs in connection with the immediate safety of human life and immediate protection of property when normal communication systems are not available.

§97.405 Station in distress.

(a) No provision of these rules prevents the use by an amateur station in distress of any means at its disposal to attract attention, make known its condition and location, and obtain assistance.

(b) No provision of these rules prevents the use by a station, in the exceptional circumstances described in paragraph (a), of any means of radiocommunications at its disposal to assist a station in distress.

§97.407 Radio amateur civil emergency service.

(a) No station may transmit in RACES unless it is an FCC-licensed primary, club, or military recreation station and it is certified by a civil defense organization as registered with that organization, or it is an FCC-licensed RACES station. No person may be the control operator of a RACES station, or may be the control operator of an amateur station transmitting in RACES unless that person holds a FCC-issued amateur operator license and is certified by a civil defense organization as enrolled in that organization.

(b) The frequency bands and segments and emissions authorized to the control operator are available to stations transmitting communications in RACES on a shared basis with the amateur service. In the event of an emergency which necessitates invoking the President's War Emergency Powers under the provisions of section 706 of the Communications Act of 1934, as amended, 47 U.S.C. 606, RACES stations and amateur stations participating in RACES may only transmit on the frequency segments authorized pursuant to part 214 of this chapter.

(c) A RACES station may only communicate with:

  (1) Another RACES station;

exists. That includes situations when you are at risk or when you are assisting someone else at risk.

The other exception is for stations in distress. If you are in distress, FCC rule §97.405(a) says, "No provision of these rules prevents the use by an amateur station in distress of any means at its disposal..." And if you hear another station in distress, "No provision of these rules prevents the use by a station ... of any means of radiocommunications at its disposal to assist a station in distress." [§97.405(b)] Again, these rules cover only the most extraordinary situations during a real emergency.

As you know from your Technician exam studies, you may not assist organizations such as the news media in acquiring or disseminating information. The only exception is that "... communications directly related to the immedi-

Figure 2-8 — In time of emergency, when normal communications are disrupted, Amateur Radio Emergency Service volunteers set up portable stations to assist emergency management agencies and relief organizations.

(2) An amateur station registered with a civil defense organization;

(3) A United States Government station authorized by the responsible agency to communicate with RACES stations;

(4) A station in a service regulated by the FCC whenever such communication is authorized by the FCC.

(d) An amateur station registered with a civil defense organization may only communicate with:

(1) A RACES station licensed to the civil defense organization with which the amateur station is registered;

(2) The following stations upon authorization of the responsible civil defense official for the organization with which the amateur station is registered:

(i) A RACES station licensed to another civil defense organization;

(ii) An amateur station registered with the same or another civil defense organization;

(iii) A United States Government station authorized by the responsible agency to communicate with RACES stations; and

(iv) A station in a service regulated by the FCC whenever such communication is authorized by the FCC.

(e) All communications transmitted in RACES must be specifically authorized by the civil defense organization for the area served. Only civil defense communications of the following types may be transmitted:

(1) Messages concerning impending or actual conditions jeopardizing the public safety, or affecting the national defense or security during periods of local, regional, or national civil emergencies;

(2) Messages directly concerning the immediate safety of life of individuals, the immediate protection of property, maintenance of law and order, alleviation of human suffering and need, and the combating of armed attack or sabotage;

(3) Messages directly concerning the accumulation and dissemination of public information or instructions to the civilian population essential to the activities of the civil defense organization or other authorized governmental or relief agencies; and

(4) Communications for RACES training drills and tests necessary to ensure the establishment and maintenance of orderly and efficient operation of the RACES as ordered by the responsible civil defense organizations served. Such drills and tests may not exceed a total time of 1 hour per week. With the approval of the chief officer for emergency planning the applicable State, Commonwealth, District or territory, however, such tests and drills may be conducted for a period not to exceed 72 hours no more than twice in any calendar year.

---

ate safety of human life or the protection of property may be provided by amateur stations to broadcasters for dissemination to the public where no other means of communication is reasonably available...." [§97.113(b)]

ARES and RACES

Amateurs have organized themselves in order to respond effectively to emergencies. There are two primary organizations for this purpose: the *Amateur Radio Emergency Service* (ARES) and the *Radio Amateur Civil Emergency Service* (RACES). ARES is sponsored by the ARRL and RACES is sponsored by government agencies. The ARES and RACES missions are similar and may overlap in many areas, but they have very different operating rules.

ARES is organized and managed by members of the ARRL's Field Organization (**www.arrl.org/FandES/field/pscm/sec1-ch1.html**). Membership in ARES is open to any licensed amateur, whether an ARRL member or not, although League membership is required to hold an official appointment. ARES teams are led by Emergency Coordinators (ECs) at the local level. District Emergency Coordinators (DECs) lead the local teams in a larger area (such as a county), and ARES leadership for the entire ARRL Section is handled by the Section Emergency Coordinator (SEC). The SEC reports to the ARRL Section Manager. The mission of ARES is to provide communications assistance to local and regional government and relief agencies. Served agencies include organizations such as the American Red Cross, Salvation Army and National Weather Service. ARES may also assist local and regional emergency management agencies or even the Federal Emergency Management Agency (FEMA) if normal communications systems fail.

RACES is a specific part of the Amateur Service governed by FCC rule §97.407 to provide communications for civil defense purposes during local, regional, or national civil emergencies (**www.arrl.org/FandES/field/pscm/sec1-ch4.html**). Although RACES is sponsored by the Federal Emergency Management Agency (FEMA), it is usually administered by local, county and state emergency management agencies.

To participate in RACES and operate as a RACES station, you must register with a local civil defense organization. Only FCC-licensed amateurs may be the control operators of RACES stations [§97.407(a)]. RACES stations may communicate only with other RACES stations and certain government stations. All RACES communications must be carried out under the direction of a civil defense organization. FCC rules provide for RACES members to conduct regular training and drills so that they can provide orderly and efficient communications for the civil defense organizations they serve [§97.407(c), (d), (e)]. Furthermore, the FCC is empowered to restrict the operating frequencies of RACES stations if the War Emergency Powers have been activated [§97.407(b)].

Distress Calls

Because amateurs operate from so many locations and on so many frequencies, distress calls are often made to amateurs. It's important that each amateur know what to do if a distress call is received or if one is to be made.

What would you do if you heard a call for help? Your responsibility is to react to the call for help and do your best to obtain assistance for the station in distress. First, immediately suspend your existing contact, if any. Then:

1) Immediately acknowledge to the station calling for help that you hear them.

2) Stand by to receive the location of the emergency and the nature of the assistance required.

3) Relay the information to the proper authorities and stay on frequency for further information or until help arrives.

If you are the station making the distress call:

1) On a voice mode, say "Mayday Mayday Mayday" or on CW send "SOS SOS SOS" (Mayday should not be confused with the Pan-Pan urgency call) followed by "any station come in please."

2) Identify the transmission with your call sign.

3) Give your location with enough detail to be located and state the nature of the situation.

4) Describe the type of assistance required and give any other pertinent information.

As mentioned before, FCC rule §97.405 allows a station in distress and requesting emergency help to use *any* means of radiocommunication at their disposal to attract attention and request help. Any frequency on which you think you will be heard, any mode, any power level necessary — even those outside your normal privileges — may be used as long as the emergency exists. Even unidentified transmissions outside of amateur bands, such as to allow direction finding, are permitted if required to provide the necessary communications. Similarly, if you hear a distress call, the same permission to respond by any means necessary applies to you.

> *Before you go on, study test questions G1B04, G2C01, G2C02, G2C03, G2C04, G2C05, G2C07, G2C08, G2C09, G2C10, G2C11 and G2C12. Review this section if you have difficulty.*

Chapter 3

Rules and Regulations

In this chapter, you'll learn about:
- **International operating rules**
- **The ITU, FCC and FAA**
- **Rules for exams and examiners**
- **Frequency privileges**
- **Managing interference issues**
- **Third-party rules**
- **Technical rules and standards**
- **Good amateur practices**

As a General class licensee, your frequency privileges expand dramatically from those of the Technician class. You'll be operating on a whole new set of HF bands and probably using new modes. Along with different propagation and procedures, there are also new regulations and frequency limits that apply. We'll build on the rules and regulations you learned to pass your Technician exam.

The exact text of the FCC Part 97 regulations won't be reproduced in this book in most cases. You can quickly access the exact wording of the regulation through the ARRL's Web site (**www.arrl.org**) by entering the regulation number, such as "97.301" in the search function window. For a complete copy of Part 97, see **www.arrl.org/FandES/field/regulations/rules-regs.html**.

You are encouraged to access the regulations discussed in the book, not only to help remember them, but to gain experience in reading the regulations governing the Amateur Service. This will help when you refer to them with questions after you've received your General class license.

3.1 Regulatory Bodies

On the HF bands, signals routinely travel long distances and cross international borders with ease. That makes the international rules and regulations much more than an academic exercise! The rules for the Amateur Service vary around the world, sometimes dramatically. Let's start by asking the question, who's in charge here?

INTERNATIONAL TELECOMMUNICATION UNION (ITU)

The *International Telecommunication Union* or *ITU* is the organization responsible for all international radio regulations. Individual nations agree by treaty to abide by those regulations. Each country decides how to administer and implement those regulations and may even add additional regulations, as long as they do not conflict with the ITU regulations.

The ITU has created three administrative areas, called *regions*. Each region has its own set of frequency *allocations* or divisions of the radio spectrum. **Figure 3-1** shows the three ITU regions. The continental United States, Alaska, Hawaii and most US territories and possession are in Region 2. Certain US-administered Pacific islands (American Samoa, the Northern Mariana Islands, Guam and Wake Island) are in Region 3.

ITU regions have their greatest effect on amateurs in frequency allocations around the world. For example, the 75-meter allocation varies from 50 kHz in Region 1 to 250 kHz in Region 2. (Individual country allocations vary even more.) Section 97.301 contains a complete listing of frequency allocations by region. Parts (a) and (d) of that section contain the frequency allocations that apply to amateurs operating from the US.

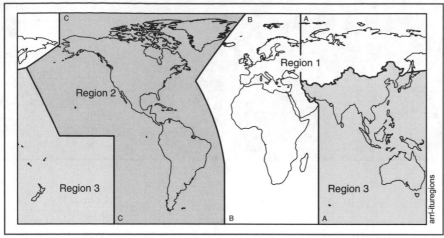

Figure 3-1 — This map shows the world divided into three ITU regions.

FCC STRUCTURE AND AUTHORITY

The Federal Communications Commission (FCC) is the agency in the United States charged with writing and administering the rules for US amateurs. FCC regulations apply to any amateur (US or foreign) operating where the FCC has jurisdiction. Outside the 50 states, that includes all US possessions and territories, as well as operation from US-flagged vessels operating in international waters.

Frequency sharing arrangements on the different bands are controlled by §97.303, and §97.305(f)(11) applies to US amateurs using phone in the Pacific and Caribbean. US amateurs operating abroad are required to abide by the appropriate regional frequency limits, subject to their host government's regulations.

Amateur Auxiliary

The Amateur Service prides itself on being largely *self-policing* so that amateurs follow FCC regulations with as little government monitoring and supervision as possible. The ARRL's Official Observer program (**www.arrl.org/FandES/field/org/oo.html**) was created to provide feedback to amateurs on operating practices and signal quality. In 1982, an additional step was taken when the *Amateur Auxiliary* was formally created so that amateurs could assist the FCC. These volunteers monitor the amateur frequency bands for rule violations and intruders not licensed to use amateur frequencies. The mission of both the ARRL's Official Observers and the Amateur Auxiliary is to encourage amateur self-regulation and compliance with the FCC rules.

Tally-Ho, the Fox Hunt!

One activity that is becoming more and more popular is fox-hunting or radio direction-finding (RDF). The basic premise is to locate hidden transmitters (the fox) and it combines radio skills with outdoor orienteering. It's a great combination of radio, geography and exercise. The hunt can be a friendly local competition for practice or a large scale sporting event attended by amateurs from around the world! However the event is organized, direction-finding skills can be used by the Amateur Auxiliary to locate stations violating FCC rules, intentionally or not. More information about fox-hunting and direction-finding is available at **members.aol.com/homingin/index.htm**l.

FAA RULES

Along with the FCC, there is one other federal agency that has jurisdiction in amateur affairs and that is the *Federal Aviation Administration* or *FAA*. Amateurs who want to construct an antenna structure more than 200 feet in height must notify the FAA and register the tower with the FCC to avoid unknowingly creating hazards to aircraft. Additional restrictions apply if the antenna is within about 4 miles of a public use airport or heliport.

Before you go on, study test questions G1B01, G2D01, G2D02 and G2D03. Review this section if you have difficulty.

3.2 Amateur Licensing Rules

As a Technician class licensee, you've already experienced a unique aspect of the Amateur Service — the volunteer-administered licensing program. Along with being largely self-policing, amateurs and amateur organizations keep licensing and examination services widely available in a time of shrinking government services. After you receive your General class license, you'll be able to fully participate in this program. This section covers the regulations that govern the volunteer licensing program and the individuals who make it a success.

LICENSE ELEMENTS

You passed Element 2 to get your Technician license. To reach General class, you must now pass Element 3. This is the General class written exam with 35 multiple-choice questions. The Amateur Extra exam is Element 4. There is no Element 1; that was the 5 WPM Morse code exam no longer required for any license class.

So You Want to be a VE?

The requirements to become a Volunteer Examiner (VE) are listed in §97.509(b). To become a VE you must:

✔ Be accredited by a VEC

✔ Be at least 18 years of age

✔ Hold a General class or higher license (must be listed in the FCC database)

✔ Have never had your amateur license suspended or revoked

EXAMINER RULES

The volunteer licensing program is administered by *Volunteer Examiner Coordinators* (VECs). VECs are organizations that have entered into an agreement with the FCC to coordinate amateur license examinations. The ARRL is the largest VEC (**www.arrl.org/arrlvec**), but there are 13 other VECs. You can find them on the FCC's Universal Licensing Service Web site (**wireless.fcc.gov/uls**) — enter "VEC" into the search window to find the list.

To become accredited by the ARRL VEC program, you must meet the FCC's requirements (see the sidebar, "So You Want to be a VE?") and must pass a short multiple-choice test based on the *Volunteer Examiner's Manual*. Becoming accredited costs nothing and you can then administer amateur license exams. You don't have to be a US citizen to be accredited as a VE as long as you hold a General class or higher US amateur license and meet all the criteria.

Not all license exams can be administered by any VE. As a General class licensee, you are only allowed to administer the Element 2 Technician class exam. **Table 3-1** shows which exams can be administered by VEs holding the various license classes.

Table 3-1
Allowed License Exams by VE License Class

VE License Class	Allowed Examinations
General	Technician (Element 2)
Advanced	General (Element 3), Technician (Element 2)
Amateur Extra	Amateur Extra (Element 4), General (Element 3), Technician (Element 2)

Before you go on, study test questions G1D02, G1D05, G1D10, G1D11, G1D12 and G1D13. Review this section if you have difficulty.

EXAMINATION RULES

No matter what licensing elements are available in the exam session, the rules are always the same. Every exam session must be coordinated by one of the VECs and conducted by three VEs accredited by that VEC. (Other VEs may assist, but at least three VEs from the coordinating VEC must be present.) At least three VEs must hold the necessary license class shown in Table 3-1 to give the exam elements.

The VEs are in charge of administering all parts of the exam session. The three primary VEs (if there are more than three) must be present and must observe all aspects of the exam session. VEs grade all exams and are responsible for determining the correct answers. There are other requirements, all spelled out in §97.509.

Once the exams are completed, the VEs must also supply the necessary paperwork. Each successful applicant is given a *Certificate of Successful Completion of Examination* (CSCE) showing what elements the examinee has passed. (**Figure 3-2** shows a filled out CSCE.) The CSCE is good for 365 days and can be presented at any other exam session as evidence of having obtained credit for specific elements. Use the CSCE until your new license arrives from the FCC. An NCVEC Quick-Form 605 (shown in **Figure 3-3**) is also filled out for each candidate who successfully acquires or upgrades their amateur license class.

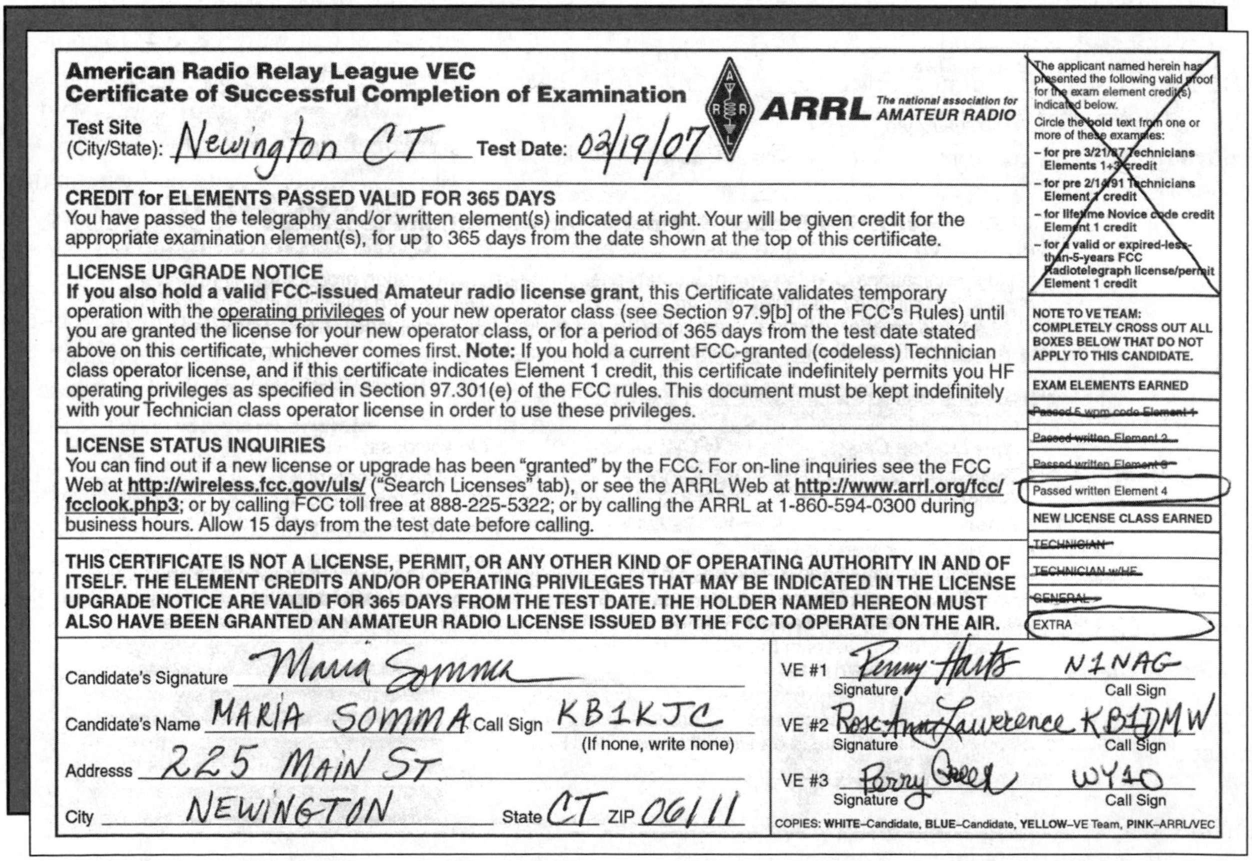

American Radio Relay League VEC
Certificate of Successful Completion of Examination

ARRL The national association for AMATEUR RADIO

Test Site (City/State): Newington CT Test Date: 02/19/07

CREDIT for ELEMENTS PASSED VALID FOR 365 DAYS
You have passed the telegraphy and/or written element(s) indicated at right. Your will be given credit for the appropriate examination element(s), for up to 365 days from the date shown at the top of this certificate.

LICENSE UPGRADE NOTICE
If you also hold a valid FCC-issued Amateur radio license grant, this Certificate validates temporary operation with the operating privileges of your new operator class (see Section 97.9[b] of the FCC's Rules) until you are granted the license for your new operator class, or for a period of 365 days from the test date stated above on this certificate, whichever comes first. **Note:** If you hold a current FCC-granted (codeless) Technician class operator license, and if this certificate indicates Element 1 credit, this certificate indefinitely permits you HF operating privileges as specified in Section 97.301(e) of the FCC rules. This document must be kept indefinitely with your Technician class operator license in order to use these privileges.

LICENSE STATUS INQUIRIES
You can find out if a new license or upgrade has been "granted" by the FCC. For on-line inquiries see the FCC Web at **http://wireless.fcc.gov/uls/** ("Search Licenses" tab), or see the ARRL Web at **http://www.arrl.org/fcc/fcclook.php3**; or by calling FCC toll free at 888-225-5322; or by calling the ARRL at 1-860-594-0300 during business hours. Allow 15 days from the test date before calling.

THIS CERTIFICATE IS NOT A LICENSE, PERMIT, OR ANY OTHER KIND OF OPERATING AUTHORITY IN AND OF ITSELF. THE ELEMENT CREDITS AND/OR OPERATING PRIVILEGES THAT MAY BE INDICATED IN THE LICENSE UPGRADE NOTICE ARE VALID FOR 365 DAYS FROM THE TEST DATE. THE HOLDER NAMED HEREON MUST ALSO HAVE BEEN GRANTED AN AMATEUR RADIO LICENSE ISSUED BY THE FCC TO OPERATE ON THE AIR.

The applicant named herein has presented the following valid proof for the exam element credit(s) indicated below.
Circle the bold text from one or more of these examples:
- **for pre 3/21/87 Technicians Elements 1+3 credit**
- **for pre 2/14/91 Technicians Element 1 credit**
- **for lifetime Novice code credit Element 1 credit**
- **for a valid or expired-less-than-5-years FCC Radiotelegraph license/permit Element 1 credit**

NOTE TO VE TEAM: COMPLETELY CROSS OUT ALL BOXES BELOW THAT DO NOT APPLY TO THIS CANDIDATE.

EXAM ELEMENTS EARNED
~~Passed 5 wpm code Element 1~~
~~Passed written Element 2~~
~~Passed written Element 3~~
Passed written Element 4

NEW LICENSE CLASS EARNED
~~TECHNICIAN~~
~~TECHNICIAN w/HF~~
~~GENERAL~~
EXTRA

Candidate's Signature Maria Somma
Candidate's Name MARIA SOMMA Call Sign KB1KJC (If none, write none)
Addresss 225 MAIN ST
City NEWINGTON State CT ZIP 06111

VE #1 Signature Call Sign N1NAG
VE #2 Signature Call Sign KB1DMW
VE #3 Signature Call Sign WY1O

COPIES: WHITE–Candidate, BLUE–Candidate, YELLOW–VE Team, PINK–ARRL/VEC

Figure 3-2 — The CSCE (Certificate of Successful Completion of Examination) is your test session receipt that serves as proof that you have completed one or more exam elements. It can be used at other test sessions for 365 days.

After the exam session, the VEs send the paperwork to their VEC. There it is reviewed and information is sent on to the FCC so that licenses and upgrades can be issued.

Before you go on, study test questions G1D04, G1D07, G1D08 and G1D09. Review this section if you have difficulty.

IDENTIFICATION REQUIREMENTS

As soon as you receive a CSCE showing that you've achieved General class, you can start using *all* of your new privileges right away. As long as you already have a call sign in the FCC database, you don't have to wait for the FCC to update your license class! You must, however, add an *indicator* to your call sign whenever you operate outside Technician privileges. This tells a listener that you are operating legally. On phone, say your call sign followed by "temporary (or slash) AG." On CW or digital modes, add "/AG" to your call sign. (If you pass the General class exam before your first call sign is added to the FCC database, congratulations on the quick work, but you'll have to wait for your call sign to be assigned before you can operate.)

One new wrinkle to operating on HF is that you may be able to practice your foreign language skills with amateurs in other countries! This is an excellent use of Amateur Radio. The only restriction on speaking foreign languages on the air is that you are required to identify your station in English or by using the English language alphabet.

Before you go on, study test questions G1D01, G1D03, G1D06 and G1E09. Review this section if you have difficulty.

3.3 Control Operator Privileges

Along with all of your new privileges comes the responsibility to operate within them. This section covers the basic requirements that a General class licensee must satisfy on the air. Some, such as the prohibition against broadcasting, you'll find familiar from your Technician class studies. Others, such as third-party rules, are new and may take a little study to understand clearly. Nevertheless, since you have already passed the Technician exam, you already know how radio "works" — that will make understanding easier!

FREQUENCY PRIVILEGES

While General class licensees gain access to all those new frequencies on HF, you are also expected to know what those frequencies are. Relax — it's not necessary to have every individual band segment memorized! The way most General licensees operate is to have a frequency chart at the operating position, such as the one shown in **Figure 3-4**. (For reference and study, download your own full color copy of the chart from **www.arrl. org/FandES/field/regulations/bands.html**.) When you tune the bands, check the chart to be sure you're within the proper band segment before transmitting. Of course, you're allowed to *listen* anywhere and are encouraged to do so.

You should learn the basic frequency limits of each band as shown in **Table 3-2**. This is easier than you might think because most of the amateur HF bands are *harmonically related*. For example, it's easy to remember the sequence "1.8 - 3.5 - 7 - 14 - 21 - 28 MHz" because the frequencies are close to being integer multiples of 1.8 MHz. These are the "traditional" HF amateur bands. You can convert the frequencies to wavelength as 300 / f (frequency in MHz) to get "160 - 80 - 40 - 20 - 15 - 10." (For example, 300 / 21 = 14.3.)

NCVEC QUICK-FORM 605 APPLICATION FOR
AMATEUR OPERATOR/PRIMARY STATION LICENSE

SECTION 1 - TO BE COMPLETED BY APPLICANT

PRINT LAST NAME	SUFFIX (Jr., Sr.)	FIRST NAME	INITIAL	STATION CALL SIGN (IF ANY)
MORIN		Joanne	B	KA1JPA

MAILING ADDRESS (Number and Street or P.O. Box)
225 Main St.

SOCIAL SECURITY NUMBER (SSN) or (FRN) FCC FEDERAL REGISTRATION NUMBER
987-654-321

CITY	STATE CODE	ZIP CODE (5 or 9 Numbers)	E-MAIL ADDRESS (OPTIONAL)
Newington	CT	06060	

DAYTIME TELEPHONE NUMBER (Include Area Code) OPTIONAL | FAX NUMBER (Include Area Code) OPTIONAL | ENTITY NAME (IF CLUB, MILITARY RECREATION, RACES)

Type of Applicant: ☒ Individual ☐ Amateur Club ☐ Military Recreation ☐ RACES (Modify Only)

CLUB, MILITARY RECREATION, OR RACES CALL SIGN

I HEREBY APPLY FOR (Make an X in the appropriate box(es))

SIGNATURE OF RESPONSIBLE CLUB OFFICIAL (not trustee)

☐ EXAMINATION for a **new** license grant

☒ EXAMINATION for **upgrade** of my license class

☐ CHANGE my **name** on my license to my new name

Former Name: _____
(Last name) (Suffix) (First name) (MI)

☐ CHANGE my mailing address to **above** address

☐ CHANGE my station **call sign** systematically

Applicant's Initials: _____

☐ RENEWAL of my license grant.

Do you have another license application on file with the FCC which has not been acted upon?	PURPOSE OF OTHER APPLICATION	PENDING FILE NUMBER (FOR VEC USE ONLY)

I certify that:
* I waive any claim to the use of any particular frequency regardless of prior use by license or otherwise;
* All statements and attachments are true, complete and correct to the best of my knowledge and belief and are made in good faith;
* I am not a representative of a foreign government;
* I am not subject to a denial of Federal benefits pursuant to Section 5301of the Anti-Drug Abuse Act of 1988, 21 U.S.C. § 862;
* The construction of my station will NOT be an action which is likely to have a significant environmental effect (See 47 CFR Sections 1.1301-1.1319 and Section 97.13(a));
* I have read and WILL COMPLY with Section 97.13(c) of the Commission's Rules regarding RADIOFREQUENCY (RF) RADIATION SAFETY and the amateur service section of OST/OET Bulletin Number 65.

Signature of applicant (Do not print, type, or stamp. Must match applicant's name above.) (Clubs: 2 different individuals must sign)

X _Joanne B Morin_   Date Signed: 2/23/07

SECTION 2 - TO BE COMPLETED BY ALL ADMINISTERING VEs

Applicant is qualified for operator license class:

☐ NO NEW LICENSE OR UPGRADE WAS EARNED

☐ TECHNICIAN   Element 2

☒ GENERAL   Elements 2 and 3

☐ AMATEUR EXTRA   Elements 2, 3 and 4

DATE OF EXAMINATION SESSION
EXAMINATION SESSION LOCATION
VEC ORGANIZATION
VEC RECEIPT DATE

I CERTIFY THAT I HAVE COMPLIED WITH THE ADMINISTERING VE REQUIRMENTS IN PART 97 OF THE COMMISSION'S RULES AND WITH THE INSTRUCTIONS PROVIDED BY THE COORDINATING VEC AND THE FCC.

1st VEs NAME (Print First, MI, Last, Suffix)	VEs STATION CALL SIGN	VEs SIGNATURE (Must match name)	DATE SIGNED
Steven R. Ewald	WV1X	Steven R. Ewald	2/23-07
2nd VEs NAME (Print First, MI, Last, Suffix) Rose-Anne Lawrence	KB1DMW	Rose-Anne Lawrence	2-23-07
3rd VEs NAME (Print First, MI, Last, Suffix) Penny E Harts	N1NAC	Penny E Harts	2.23.07

DO NOT SEND THIS FORM TO FCC – THIS IS NOT AN FCC FORM.
IF THIS FORM IS SENT TO FCC, FCC WILL RETURN IT TO YOU WITHOUT ACTION.

NCVEC FORM 605 - February 2007
FOR VE/VEC USE ONLY - Page 1

ARRL0138

Figure 3-3 — This sample NCVEC Quick Form 605 shows how your form will look after you have completed your upgrade to General.

AMATEUR RADIO LICENSE LEVELS AND REQUIREMENTS

In the US, there are three license levels, or "license classes" which are Technician class, General class and Extra Class. The Federal Communications Commission (FCC) grants these licenses.

LEVEL 1: Technician Class License
EXAM: 35-question Technician Written Exam (Element 2)
PRIVILEGES: All VHF/UHF amateur bands (frequencies above 30 MHz) and certain HF frequencies on the 80, 40, and 15 meter bands using CW, and on the 10 meter band using CW, voice, and digital modes.

LEVEL 2: General Class License (upgrade from Technician)
EXAM: 35-question General Written Exam (Element 3)
PRIVILEGES: All VHF/UHF amateur bands and most HF privileges (10 through 160 meters).
In addition to the Technician privileges, General Class operators are authorized to operate on any frequency in the 160, 30, 17, 12, and 10 meter bands. They may also use significant segments of the 80, 40, 20, and 15 meter bands.

LEVEL 3: Extra Class License (upgrade from General)
EXAM: 50-question Extra Written Exam (Element 4)
PRIVILEGES: All amateur privileges.

Should you have any question, please contact your local volunteer examiner team, or contact one of the 14 volunteer examiner coordinator (VEC) organizations. For contact information for the VECs, or to contact the FCC, call 888-225-5322 (weekdays), or write to FCC, 1270 Fairfield Road, Gettysburg PA 17325-7245. Also see the FCC web at **http://wireless.fcc.gov/services/index.htm?job=service_home&id=amateur**. ARRL, the national association for Amateur Radio, has additional information and resources at **www.arrl.org** or 1-888-277-5289.

ARE WRITTEN TESTS AN FCC-LICENSE REQUIREMENT? ARE THERE EXEMPTIONS?

As of April 15, 2000, you may be examined on only three classes of operator licenses, each authorizing varying levels of privileges. The Amateur Operator/Primary Station License class for which an examinee qualifies for is determined by the exams taken at a VE test session. The exams cover regulations, operating practices, and electronics theory. There is no exemption from the written exam requirements for persons with difficulty in reading, writing, or because of a handicap or disability. There are exam accommodations that can be afforded examinees. Most new amateur operators start at the Technician class and then advance one class at a time. The VEs give examination credit for the license class currently (and in some cases, previously) held so that examinations required for that license need not be repeated. The written examinations are constructed from question pools that have been made public (see: **www.arrl.org/arrlvec/pools.html**). Helpful study guides and training courses are also widely available. To locate examination opportunities in your area, contact your local club, VE group, one of the 14 VECs or see the online listings at: **www.arrl.org/examsearch**.

IS KNOWLEDGE OF MORSE CODE AN FCC-LICENSE REQUIRMENT?

Beginning February 23, 2007, the FCC no longer requires passing a Morse code examination for any Amateur Radio license class.

SOCIAL SECURITY NUMBER

Under the Debt Collection Act of 1996 your Taxpayer ID Number (TIN), which is your Social Security Number, is required on this application -- or your FCC-assigned Federal Registration Number (FRN). An FRN is assigned by the FCC registration system as soon as your SSN is registered.

RENEWING OR MODIFYING YOUR AMATEUR RADIO OPERATOR/PRIMARY STATION LICENSE

NCVEC FORM 605

The NCVEC form 605 may also be used to renew or modify your Amateur Radio Operator/Primary Station license. License renewals (with associated fee for vanity renewals) may only be completed during the final 90 days prior to license expiration, or up to two years after expiration. Changes to your mailing address, name and requests for a sequential change of your station call sign appropriate for your license class may be requested at any time. This form may not be used to apply for a new specific "Vanity" station call sign. Do not send or provide this form to the FCC - this form is for VE / VEC use only.

THE FCC APPLICATION FORM 605

The FCC version of the form 605 may not be used for applications submitted to a VE team or a VEC since it does not request information needed by the administering VE's. The FCC Form 605 may however, be used to routinely renew or modify your license without charge. New vanity license requests and vanity license renewals require a FCC regulatory fee. FCC form 605 should be sent to the FCC, 1270 Fairfield Rd., Gettysburg PA 17325-7245. FCC forms can be obtained via the FCC web at **http://www.fcc.gov/formpage.html** or by fax at 202-418-0177 (request Form 000605). The FCC Forms Distribution Center will accept orders by calling 800-418-3676.

RENEWING OR MODIFYING YOUR AMATEUR LICENSE

You can submit your renewal or license modifications to FCC via the internet at: **http://wireless.fcc.gov/uls/**. If you are already registered in ULS and have obtained a FRN (Federal Registration Number), you can choose the "ONLINE FILING / LOG IN" link to perform your on-line transaction with the FCC. If you do not have a FRN, you must first register in the ULS by following the "New Users / Register" link and complete your registration information. You can then choose the "Online Filing / LOG IN" link. Direct any on-line filing or password questions to FCC Tech Support weekdays at 202-414-1250.

CLUB STATION CALL SIGN ADMINISTRATORS (CSCSA)

The NCVEC Form 605 is also used for the processing of applications for Amateur Service club and military recreation station call signs and for the modification of RACES stations. This form may not be used to apply for a new specific "Vanity" station call sign. The Club Station Call Sign Administrators are: ARRL/VEC (225 Main St., Newington, CT 06111), W4VEC (3504 Stonehurst Pl., High Point, NC 27265) and the W5YI-VEC (PO Box 565101, Dallas TX 75356) Please return this form to one of these three CSCSAs.

NCVEC FORM 605 – FOR VE / VEC USE ONLY
February 2007 - Page 2

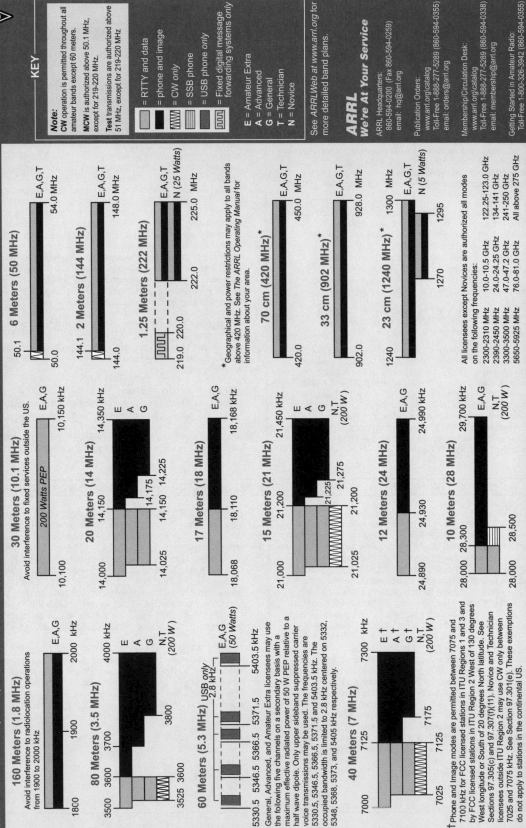

Figure 3-4 — Amateur operating privileges.

Too Close for Comfort

When you operate phone using SSB, it's important to know where your actual signals appear on the band. Nearly all radios show the carrier frequency of a SSB or AM transmission. On SSB, that means your actual signal lies entirely above or below the displayed frequency. If the sidebands occupy about 3 kHz of spectrum, you'll need to be sure that you stay far enough from the edge of your frequency privileges to avoid transmitting a signal outside them. For example, Generals are permitted to use up to 14.350 MHz, so the displayed carrier frequency of a USB signal should be no higher than 14.347 MHz. If you transmit higher than that, the sidebands begin to intrude on non-amateur frequencies above 14.350 MHz!. Similarly, using LSB on 40 meters, Generals should operate with the carrier frequency no lower than 7.178 MHz.

Table 3-2
Summary of Amateur HF Bands

Wavelength (meters)	Frequency (MHz)
160	1.800-2.00
80 and 75	3.500-3.750 and 3.750-4.000
60	5.332, 5.348, 5.368, 5.373 and 5.405 (center frequency)
40	7.000-7.300
30	10.100-10.150
20	14.000-14.350
17	18.068-18.168
15	21.000-21.450
12	24.890-24.990
10	28.000-29.700

The conversion isn't exact — it's just a handy approximation.) Practice those two sequences and you're more than halfway home!

Other HF bands have been made available to amateurs since 1980: the "WARC" bands and 60 meters. (WARC stands for World Administrative Radio Conference.) At the 1979 WARC, amateurs were granted allocations at 30, 17 and 12 meters (10, 18 and 24 MHz). Amateurs also gained access to five fixed-frequency channels on 60 meters (5 MHz) in 2003.

General class license privileges extend across most of these frequency bands, but not completely. As the frequency chart shows, for all bands where Generals have only partial access, their privileges for each mode are located at the top of the band where that mode is permitted. For example, on 40 meters Generals are only restricted from using CW, RTTY and data at the lowest frequencies of 7000-7025 kHz. On 40 meter phone, General privileges begin at 7175 kHz and extend to the top of the band at 7300 kHz. Even though Generals may not have full access to all parts of some bands, they are not prohibited from using any mode by their frequency restrictions. On HF, Generals have all amateur privileges on the 160, 30, 17, 12 and 10 meter bands.

There are two HF bands that have special regulations. The 60 meter band privileges permit channelized USB phone *only* with a power limit of 50 W ERP (see the Technical Rules and Standards section later in this chapter for details). This is the only amateur band in which CW is *not* permitted. The 30 meter band privileges permit only CW, RTTY and data signals. The 60 meter and 30 meter bands are also *secondary amateur allocations*, meaning that stations in the *primary services* have priority and must be avoided. All other HF bands are primary amateur allocations and no other services, such as Citizens Band, land mobile, or government stations are allowed.

Before you go on, study test questions G1A01, G1A02, G1A03, G1A04, G1A05, G1A06, G1A07, G1A08, G1A09, G1A10, G1A11, G1A12 and G1A13. Review this section if you have difficulty.

TRANSMISSION DEFINITIONS

Emission Designators

The FCC uses alphanumeric codes called *emission mode designators* to identify specific transmission modes. The first character (a letter) designates the type of modulation, such as A for amplitude or F for frequency. The second character (a numeral) designates the type of signal that is doing the modulating, such as 1 for a single digital signal or 3 for a single analog signal. The third character (another letter) designates the type of information to be transmitted, such as A for telegraphy received by ear or E for voice. Fourth and fifth characters are added in special cases. Here are three common modes and their designators:

- A1A — amplitude-modulated telegraphy for aural reception
- F3E — frequency-modulated telephony
- J3E — single-sideband, suppressed-carrier telephony

It is not necessary to memorize these codes, but it is a good idea to know where to look them up if you need to. A table of designators for the most common amateur emission types can be found at **www.arrl.org/gclm**.

Beacons

Beacon transmissions are very useful on the HF bands, just as they are on VHF and UHF. Beacons are used for observation of propagation and reception, as well as for other related activities. They alert operators to band openings that might otherwise be missed and provide a source of on-air signals for amateurs to calibrate and adjust their equipment. The sidebar "A System of DX Beacons" describes a worldwide system of beacons operating in a coordinated manner on several bands. Many individuals operate beacons on the 10 meter (28 MHz) band. The *General Class License Manual* Web site (**www.arrl.org/gclm**) provides links to beacon directories.

Perhaps you would like to put up your own beacon station. The rules, contained in §97.203, are quite simple. The most important are that there must be no more than one beacon signal in the same band from a single location and beacons are limited to 100 W PEP output. The FCC rule also lists the frequency ranges in which beacon operation is permitted.

A System of DX Beacons

Contacting stations around the world is one of the pleasures largely unique to the HF amateur bands, but how can an individual tell if the bands are open and to where? To be sure, there are terrific propagation software packages, but nothing substitutes for real on-the-air experience. That's where the international beacon system established by the Northern California DX Foundation (NCDXF) and operated in cooperation with the International Amateur Radio Union (IARU) comes in handy.

The NCDXF operates and maintains a system of beacons operating on 14.100, 18.110, 21.150, 24.930 and 28.200 MHz. (**www.ncdxf.org/beacons.html**). Special licenses were obtained from the FCC for the beacons operating below 28 MHz. There are 18 beacons distributed around the world on every continent except Antarctica. The beacons all take turns transmitting on each of the five frequencies at different power levels so that the listener can gauge propagation in that direction. Take a listen and see what you can hear!

Before you go on, study test questions G1B02, G1B03 and G1B10. Review this section if you have difficulty.

INTERFERENCE DEFINITIONS

Managing interference skillfully is the hallmark of a good operator and amateur licensee. This is especially true on the HF bands, where propagation can range from local to worldwide over the course of a few hours. While this is exciting from the standpoint of being able to make contacts over long distances, it also means that your signals have the potential to impact many other amateurs and vice versa.

Unintentional

Most interference between amateur stations is *unintentional*, meaning not intended to disrupt communications. Perhaps propagation changed and stations that were previously able to share a frequency can no longer do so since they can now hear each other. Sometimes procedural mistakes are made and one station transmits too close to an existing contact. A misadjusted transmitter can create spurious outputs that interfere with nearby signals. When this sort of thing happens, use common sense and calm judgment to resolve the situation. Take advantage of the Amateur Service's frequency agility and move to another frequency. Improve your operating procedures and learn how to operate your receiver and transmitter properly to reduce the amount of interference you cause or are susceptible to.

The amplitude modulated signals (both AM and SSB) common on the HF bands can cause audible or visible interference in nearby audio/video equipment and telephones. This interference is unintentional, of course, but is still disruptive to the equipment owners. Amateurs have become skilled in mitigating and eliminating RF interference (RFI) so there are lots of resources for you to rely on should you find yourself causing RFI. (See the *General Class License Manual* Web site for links to interference resources.)

Harmful

When persistent interference disrupts ongoing communication — amateur, broadcast, commercial and so on — it becomes *harmful interference*. The interference does not have to prevent communications, only degrade or interrupt it. When harmful interference occurs between amateur stations, both have the responsibility to make the effort to resolve the situation. Harmful interference does not become an enforcement issue unless it is done *willfully* as described in the next section.

Harmful interference can occur to consumer equipment (televisions, telephones, VCRs and so forth) as well as among operators on the amateur bands. If harmful interference to consumer equipment cannot be resolved, try consulting the ARRL's interference resolution resources, such as the Technical Information Service at **www.arrl.org/tis** or articles on RFI, such as **www.arrl.org/news/rfi/neighbors.html**. The FCC also provides the *Television Interference Handbook* (**www.arrl.org/fcc/tvibook.html**) that can provide guidance.

The FCC does rarely take steps to restrict amateur operation in cases of persistent interference that cannot be resolved any other way. In the case of interference to broadcast receivers, for example, the

---

Special Circumstances

Amateurs are required to take special steps to mitigate interference in the following circumstances:

✔ When operating within one mile of an FCC Monitoring Station

✔ When transmitting spread spectrum emissions

✔ When using a band where the Amateur Service is secondary

FCC Monitoring Stations require an environment free of strong or spurious signals that can interfere with their receivers. The location of monitoring stations can be determined from a regional FCC office. Spread spectrum (SS) transmissions, because of their nature, have the potential to interfere with fixed frequency stations, so SS users should be sure their transmissions will not cause interference. And remember that Amateur Radio is not the primary service on 60 and 30 meters. On those bands, we are a secondary service and need to avoid interfering with primary users.

FCC is empowered to restrict amateur station operation to times other than 8 PM to 10:30 PM local time every day, as well as on Sundays from 10:30 AM to 1 PM local time. This is quite unusual since there are nearly always ways to manage the interference if the receiver is reasonably well designed.

It is also important to manage your own expectations regarding interference. Operators who are used to a repeater-based environment may find it difficult at first to copy SSB signals in the presence of atmospheric noise (QRN) and relatively small amounts of interference heard from signals nearby on the band (QRM). That difficulty does not automatically make QRM and QRN harmful interference, however. The solution is for the operator new to HF to improve his or her receiving skills through practice.

Band conditions and occupancy vary dramatically from day to day, as well. On a weekday, when the band is relatively uncrowded, signals can sound as if they were on a local repeater. But on a weekend or during a contest, the band might be quite crowded. This is not necessarily harmful interference and you can avoid unpleasant surprises by taking advantage of on-line calendars, newsletters and bulletins to inform yourself about upcoming conditions.

Regardless of how the interference comes about and whose fault it is, try to resolve it in such a way as to maintain the good image of the Amateur Service. Work with other amateurs in good faith and remember that no one "owns" a frequency, including you! Have a Plan B and take advantage of Amateur Radio's flexibility.

Willful

Occasionally, harmful interference can't be easily resolved. When the parties involved persist in their behavior, it can become *willful interference* (or *intentional interference*). This is expressly forbidden by the FCC rules. There are *no* circumstances when it is acceptable to intentionally interfere with ongoing communications.

Repeater Coordination

Repeaters are installed in locations that provide long range coverage, so interference between repeaters would be quite a problem if not managed properly. To minimize repeater-to-repeater interference, *regional repeater coordinators* or *frequency coordinators* have been established. Coordinators work with local amateurs to assign repeater input and output frequencies so as to minimize interference between repeaters.

Volunteer frequency coordinators help to minimize interference among repeaters.

These volunteer frequency coordinators are a good example of the self-organizing nature of Amateur Radio. They derive their authority voluntarily from the amateurs in the areas they serve. The ARRL is not a frequency coordinator, nor does the ARRL "certify" coordinators. Anyone planning on installing a repeater should check with the local frequency coordinator prior to such installation. A listing of frequency coordinators can be found on the National Frequency Coordinator's Council Web site, **www.arrl.org/nfcc/**.

Not all repeater owners choose to participate in the coordination process. If the frequencies selected do not cause interference, no harm is done. If interference does occur between a *noncoordinated* and a *coordinated* repeater systems, though, the licensee of the noncoordinated repeater has the primary responsibility of resolving the interference. The FCC has made it quite clear that they expect amateurs to use and respect the local frequency coordination process as a matter of "good amateur practice."

Primary versus Secondary

Amateurs have primary status on most of their bands. The exceptions are the 60 meter, 30 meter and 70 cm bands, as well as several microwave bands. As secondary users, amateur stations are allowed to use the frequency band only if they do not cause harmful interference to primary users. For example, amateurs operating on the 60 meter band must not cause harmful interference to stations operating in other radio services with primary status. Similarly, amateur stations have no protection from interference caused by primary service users. If you are operating on a band for which amateurs have a secondary allocation, listen carefully for a primary service station before transmitting. If you hear a station from a primary status service, you should change frequencies to avoid causing harmful interference to the other station.

Before you go on, study test questions G1A14, G1A15, G1A16, G1B13, G1E04 and G1E06. Review this section if you have difficulty.

THIRD-PARTY TRAFFIC

Amateur Radio is often used to send messages on behalf of someone who is not an amateur. This is called *third-party communication*. Because Amateur Radio can bypass the normal telephone and postal systems, particularly over the long-distance HF bands, many foreign governments have a legitimate interest in limiting this loss of revenue. Similarly, the Amateur Service should not be used as a noncommercial messaging system.

The FCC recognizes that third-party communication is part of the ham radio mission, specifically to train operators and to provide an effective emergency communications resource. Handling messages, also called "handling traffic," is part of both normal and emergency communications. As a result, third-party communications may be exchanged between any two amateur stations operating under FCC rules with the constraint that the communications must be noncommercial and of a personal, unimportant nature or be messages relating to emergencies or disaster relief.

Definitions and Rules

Let's start by defining third-party communications. Any time that you send or receive information via ham radio on behalf of any unlicensed person or organization, even if the person is right there in the station with you — that's third-party communications. Here are some clarifying points:

● The entity on whose behalf the message is sent is the "third party" and the control operators who make the radio contact are the first and second parties.

● A licensed ham generates third-party traffic by communicating a message to someone who is not a licensed amateur. A message from one ham to another ham is not third-party communications, whether directly transmitted or relayed by other stations.

● A licensed amateur capable of being a control operator at either station is not considered a third party regardless of whether he or she is at the station.

● The third party need not be present in either station. A message can be taken to a ham station or a ham can transmit speech from a third-party's telephone call over ham radio (this is called a *phone patch*).

● The communications transmitted on behalf of the third party need not be written. Spoken words, data or images can all be third-party communications.

● The third party may participate in transmitting or receiving the message at either station. An unlicensed person in your station engages in third-party communications when they speak into the microphone, send Morse code or type on a keyboard. Letting an unlicensed friend make a contact under your supervision is third-party communications, even if the contact is short and for demonstration or training purposes.

● An organization, such as a church or school, can also be a third party.

● Third-party traffic may never be exchanged on behalf of someone whose amateur license has been suspended or revoked.

International Considerations

When signals cross national borders, the rules change. International third-party communications are prohibited unless the country in question specifically allows third-party communications to and from US hams. **Table 3-3** shows which countries have third-party agreements with the United States. If the other country isn't on this list, third-party communication to or from that country is not permitted. This is important to remember because hams like to be helpful and can inadvertently violate third-party rules if not careful.

If you contact a DX station who then asks you to pass a message to his family, doing so would be third-party communications. Check to be sure the DX station's country has a third-party agreement with the US before accepting the message.

Making a contact to allow a visiting student to talk to his family in South America is

Table 3-3
Third-Party Traffic Agreements List

Occasionally, DX stations may ask you to pass a third-party message to a friend or relative in the States. This is all right as long as the US has signed an official third-party traffic agreement with that particular country, or the third party is a licensed amateur. The traffic must be noncommercial and of a personal, unimportant nature. During an emergency, the US State Department will often work out a special temporary agreement with the country involved. But in normal times, never handle traffic without first making sure it is legally permitted.

US Amateurs May Handle Third-Party Traffic With:

C5	The Gambia	J7	Dominica	VK	Australia
CE	Chile	J8	St Vincent and the	VP6	Pitcairn Island*
CO	Cuba		Grenadines	XE	Mexico
CP	Bolivia	JY	Jordan	YN	Nicaragua
CX	Uruguay	LU	Argentina	YS	El Salvador
D6	Federal Islamic Rep. of	OA	Peru	YV	Venezuela
	the Comoros	PY	Brazil	ZP	Paraguay
DU	Philippines	TA	Turkey	ZS	South Africa
EL	Liberia	TG	Guatemala	3DA	Swaziland
GB	United Kingdom	TI	Costa Rica	4U1ITU	ITU - Geneva
HC	Ecuador	T9	Bosnia-Herzegovina	4U1VIC	VIC - Vienna
HH	Haiti	V2	Antigua and Barbuda	4X	Israel
HI	Dominican Republic	V3	Belize	6Y	Jamaica
HK	Colombia	V4	St Kitts and Nevis	8R	Guyana
HP	Panama	V6	Federated States of	9G	Ghana
HR	Honduras		Micronesia	9L	Sierra Leone
J3	Grenada	V7	Marshall Islands	9Y	Trinidad and
J6	St Lucia	VE	Canada		Tobago

Notes:
*Since 1970, there has been an informal agreement between the United Kingdom and the US, permitting Pitcairn and US amateurs to exchange messages concerning medical emergencies, urgent need for equipment or supplies, and private or personal matters of island residents.

Please note that Region 2 of the International Amateur Radio Union (IARU) has recommended that international traffic on the 20 and 15-meter bands be conducted on 14.100-14.150, 14.250-14.350, 21.150 -21.200 and 21.360-21.450 MHz. The IARU is the alliance of Amateur Radio societies from around the world; Region 2 comprises member-societies in North, South and Central America and the Caribbean.

At the end of an exchange of third-party traffic with a station located in a foreign country, an FCC-licensed amateur must transmit the call sign of the foreign station as well as his own call sign.

Current as of January 2007; see **www.arrl.org/FandES/field/regulations/io/3rdparty.html** for the latest information.

third-party communications even if both the student and the family are present at the stations involved. Be sure there is a third-party agreement in place.

Before you go on, study test questions G1E01, G1E05, G1E07, G1E08 and G1E10. Review this section if you have difficulty.

PROHIBITED AND RESTRICTED COMMUNICATIONS

The FCC has given amateurs a lot of room to operate, so to speak, giving hams a free hand to transmit what they like. There are a few general prohibitions. For example, transmitting a false distress signal is absolutely prohibited under all circumstances, as is obscene or indecent speech. Some other prohibitions have special exceptions, however.

You're already aware that transmitting music is prohibited, even music that is just part of the background noise in your station or your vehicle. (Turn down the broadcast audio when you're on the air!) Is it ever permitted? Only when it is an incidental part of a space shuttle retransmission. That means that you're listening to a space shuttle transmission and retransmitting it for other amateurs to hear, which is permitted. If music happens to be part of the space shuttle audio, it's okay for it to be included in the retransmission.

Another type of prohibited transmission is codes that are intended to obscure the meaning of the message. What about Q-signals and pro-signs? Those are well-known abbreviations intended to make normal communications more efficient and not more obscure, so they're perfectly acceptable. Are encryption or "secret codes" ever allowed? Only when used to control a space station (not the ISS, but any station operating in space, such as an amateur satellite [§97.3(a)(40)]) or a radio-controlled model aircraft. In the first instance, codes are necessary to prevent unauthorized stations from transmitting commands to the space station. In the second, the FCC has ruled that the coded commands are not intended to obscure the message — they are the message!

Transmitting false distress signals, obscene or indecent speech is absolutely prohibited.

Speaking of space stations, some satellites have uplinks or downlinks in the 10-meter amateur band. If the downlink is on 10 meters, is it okay for a Technician licensee to transmit on the VHF or UHF uplink and have the satellite retransmit their signals on the 10 meter band? The satellites are acting as repeater stations that simultaneously retransmit the signals of other stations on another frequency. The same question applies to terrestrial *cross-band repeaters* that receive signals on one frequency band and retransmit them on another frequency band. Such transmissions are permitted if the control operator of the repeater transmitter that operates on the HF band has a General class license or higher.

Much is made as well over the prohibition of business-related activity on the amateur bands. In your Technician studies, you learned about what is considered business and what is incidental personal interest in a communication. Among the most common such situations are the regular "swap nets" held in many areas for amateurs to trade or sell equipment related to Amateur Radio. This is perfectly legitimate as long as other amateurs are being notified of the sale of apparatus normally used in an amateur station and such activity is not done on a regular basis. That means no household goods and no selling radios every week for profit.

Before you go on, study test questions G1B05, G1B06, G1B07, G1B08, G1B09, G1E02 and G1E03. Review this section if you have difficulty.

What's in a Log?

Most amateurs keep a record of the following information for HF QSOs:

✔ The date and time of the contact

✔ The band and/or frequency of the contact

✔ The call sign of station contacted

✔ The signal report given

This is by no means the only useful information to keep. The station operator's name, the station location, your power level and many types of other notes are stored.

WRITTEN RECORDS

In Chapter 2, we discussed station records and why it is a good idea to keep a log of your HF contacts. A detailed log is an asset to any amateur station. Practically, the log can help with a reply if the FCC requests information on who was control operator of your station at a given date and time.

Even so, there are only two types of written records that the FCC requires you to keep:

● The call signs of other amateurs operating your station.

● For 60 meter operation only, if you are using an antenna other than a dipole, record the antenna gain calculations or manufacturer's data for antennas used — this is to ensure that the 50 W ERP level restriction is met.

Before you go on, study test questions G2D08, G2D09 and G2D12. Review this section if you have difficulty.

3.4 Technical Rules and Standards

Two sets of technical rules receive the most attention on the General class exam — those for transmitted power and for digital transmissions. These two areas represent the biggest changes for operators new to HF operating and practices.

GOOD AMATEUR PRACTICES

To be sure, there are many operating procedures and technical areas not covered by the exam or even by the FCC Part 97 rules. Setting exact rules for every type of operating would result in an impenetrable thicket of regulation and would work against one of the basic tenets of the Amateur Service — technical experimentation and innovation. What has worked well for amateurs is the general requirement by the FCC that in the absence of a specific rule, amateur stations should be operated in conformance with good engineering and good amateur practice. While the FCC reserves the right to rule on what is and isn't "good engineering and good amateur practice," amateurs themselves set the day-to-day operating standards.

How can you find out what those standards are? Amateurs are expected to educate themselves and assist others in doing so. To that end, the ARRL publishes a number of respected references, such as the *ARRL Handbook* and the *ARRL Antenna Book*. (The complete on-line catalog of ARRL publications is available at **www.arrl.org/catalog**.) Other publishers offer their own lines of publications, and there are ham Web sites for every technical topic you can think of. The *General Class License Manual* Web site lists several sources for technical reference information.

Before you go on, study test questions G1B11 and G1B12. Review this section if you have difficulty.

TRANSMITTERS AND AMPLIFIER POWER

Because HF QSOs are primarily made directly from point to point without the assistance of repeaters, transmitter power becomes a more significant issue on the HF bands. Many HF operators use a *linear amplifier* to increase the transmitter output power and their signal's readability at the receiving end.

General, Advanced and Amateur Extra licensees are limited to a maximum transmitter output power of 1500 W peak envelope power or PEP. This level of power is sometimes known as a "full gallon." Novice and Technician licensees operating on HF are limited to 200 W PEP output. (See Chapter 4 for the definition of PEP.) Of course, amateurs are always required to use the *minimum* power necessary to carry out the desired communication.

The power measurement must be made at the output of the transmitter or amplifier, whichever is the final piece of equipment that generates RF power before the connection to the antenna system. The antenna system includes feed lines and any impedance matching devices.

There are two restrictions on where maximum power may be used:
- Amateurs are restricted to 200 W PEP on the 30 meter band (10 MHz)
- Amateurs are restricted to 50 W ERP on the 60 meter band (5 MHz) with a maximum signal bandwidth of 2.8 kHz.

To determine your ERP (effective radiated power), multiply your transmitter output power by the gain of your antenna. For example, if your antenna has a gain of 3 dB relative to a dipole (3 dBd, a factor of 2) and your transmitter output power is 100 watts, then your ERP is 100 × 2 = 200 watts. To use this antenna on the 60 meter band, your transmitter output power should be no more than 25 watts because 25 × 2 = 50 watts ERP.

Prior to the release of the FCC's Report and Order 04-140 in late 2006, *all* amateurs were restricted to 200 W PEP output power on the Novice segments of the 80, 40 and 15 meter bands. Because of rule changes in that Report and Order, and in the subsequent Report and Order eliminating Morse code testing, Novice and Technician licensees are now allowed the same 80, 40 and 15 meter CW frequency privileges as General class licensees. On 10 meters, Novices and Techs are allowed the same CW, RTTY and data privileges as other operators in the 28.0 to 28.3 MHz segment, plus SSB phone and CW operation from 28.3 to 28.5 MHz. In all cases, Novice and Technician licensees operating on HF are limited to 200 W PEP output, and General, Advanced and Extra licensees are no longer restricted to 200 W in the former Novice segments on 80, 40 and 15 meters.

> *Before you go on, study test questions G1C01, G1C02, G1C03, G1C04, G1C05, G1C06, G1C07, G1C13 and G2D10. Review this section if you have difficulty.*

DIGITAL TRANSMISSIONS

Technical standards for digital transmissions are primarily concerned with the bandwidth of the transmitted signal. There are also requirements that the protocol be public so that any amateur can monitor it or use it to engage in communications. [§97.309(a)] The transmitted signal bandwidth is closely tied to its *symbol rate* which is a measure of how many individual signaling events take place every second (see the sidebar "Bits or Bauds" in Chapter 2). In general, the higher the symbol rate, the wider the bandwidth required to transmit the signal. Bandwidth has a very specific definition in FCC rule §97.3(a)(8) — the frequency range outside of which the signal components are at least 26 dB (400 times) below the average (mean) power of the signal inside that range.

FCC rules §97.305(c) and §97.307(f) restrict the symbol rate of transmitted signals to make sure that digital signals do not consume too much bandwidth at the expense of other modes. **Table 3-4** shows the limits by band. On the HF bands, symbol rate and bandwidth are restricted because those bands are relatively narrow. A wide bandwidth signal would cause a lot of interference. As the size of the amateur bands increases with frequency, faster (wider) signals are allowed. At 33 cm (902 MHz) and above, there is no limit except for the band edges themselves, creating the "autobahn" of amateur digital signaling.

Table 3-4

Maximum Symbol Rates and Bandwidth

Band	Symbol Rate (baud)	Bandwidth (kHz)
Below 10 m	300	1
10 m	1200	1
6 m, 2 m	19.6k	20
1.25 m, 70 cm	56k	100
33 cm and above	no limit	no limit

Before you go on, study test questions G1C08, G1C09, G1C10, G1C11 and G1C12. Review this section if you have difficulty.

Chapter 4

Components and Circuits

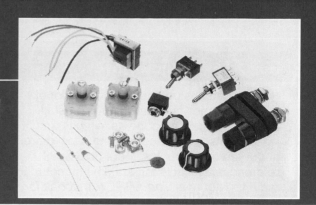

In this chapter, you'll learn about:

- **Review of basic electrical concepts**
- **Decibels, RMS and PEP**
- **Resistors, capacitors and inductors**
- **Series and parallel circuits**
- **Transformers and vacuum tubes**
- **Reactance, impedance and resonance**
- **Diodes, transistors, ICs and microprocessors**
- **Basic test equipment**

Get ready to "lift the hood" and learn more about electronics, the heart and soul of what makes a radio go! As a General, you'll understand the basic mechanics of how simple circuits work and how the components work together. That understanding enables to you to adjust your equipment and maintain your station knowledgeably. Even more importantly, you'll be able to respond effectively when things aren't working exactly right or when you need to operate under field or emergency conditions.

You've already learned the fundamentals of electricity and radio to pass the Technician exam and we'll dive one layer deeper for the General. Turn the ignition key and get warmed up with a short refresher of what you learned to pass the Technician exam.

4.1 Review

VOLTAGE, CURRENT AND POWER

Electric current (I) is the flow of electrons, atomic particles that each carry one unit of negative electric charge. Current is measured in *amperes* (A or amps) with an *ammeter*. *Voltage* (E) is the force that makes electrons move and is measured in *volts* (V) with a *voltmeter*. *Power* (P), measured in *watts* (W) is the product of voltage and current.

$$P = E \times I$$

$$E = \frac{P}{I}$$

$$I = \frac{P}{E}$$

RESISTANCE AND OHM'S LAW

The opposition of a material to current flow is called *resistance* (R) and is measured in *ohms* (Ω) with an *ohmmeter*. Georg Ohm discovered that voltage, current and resistance are proportional. *Ohm's Law* states that R = E ÷ I. If you know any two of I, E or R, you can determine the missing quantity:

$$R = \frac{E}{I}$$

$$I = \frac{E}{R}$$

$$E = I \times R$$

The voltage caused by current flowing through a resistance ($E = I \times R$) is called a *voltage drop*.

Substituting the Ohm's Law equivalents for voltage ($E = I \times R$) and current ($I = E \div R$) allows power to be calculated using resistance:

$$P = I^2 \times R$$

$$P = \frac{E^2}{R}$$

The drawing in **Figure 4-1** is an aid to remembering Ohm's Law in any of its forms. Here are a few examples:

To find out how many watts of electrical power are used if 400 V dc is supplied to an 800 Ω resistor:

$$P = \frac{E^2}{R} = \frac{400 \times 400}{800} = \frac{160,000}{800} = 200 \text{ W}$$

To find out how many watts of electrical power are used by a 12 V dc light bulb that draws 0.2 A:

$$P = I \times E = 0.2 \times 12 = 2.4 \text{ W}$$

To find out how many watts are being dissipated when a current of 7.0 mA of current flows through a 1.25 kΩ resistor:

$$P = I^2 \times R = 0.007 \times 0.007 \times 1250 = 0.06125 \text{ W} = 61.25 \text{ mW}$$

Remember that 7 mA (milliamperes) is equal to 0.007 A, 1.25 kΩ (kilohms) is equal to 1250 Ω and 0.06125 W is equal to approximately 61 mW (milliwatts).

AC AND DC WAVEFORMS

Current that flows in one direction all the time is called *direct current*, abbreviated dc. Current that reverses direction is called *alternating current*, abbreviated ac. A voltage that has the same polarity all the time is a *dc voltage*. A voltage that reverses polarity is an *ac voltage*.

Frequency

A complete sequence of ac current flowing, stopping, reversing and stopping again is called a *cycle*. The number of cycles per second is the current's *frequency* (f) measured in *Hertz* (Hz). A *harmonic* is a frequency that is some integer multiple (2, 3, 4 and so on) of a lowest or

Figure 4-1 — This simple diagram will help you remember the Ohm's Law relationships. If you know any two of the quantities, you can find the third by covering up the unknown quantity. The positions of the remaining two symbols show if you have to multiply (side-by-side) or divide (one above the other).

ARRL0005

fundamental frequency. The harmonic at twice the fundamental frequency is called the *second harmonic*, at three times the fundamental frequency the *third harmonic*, and so forth.

Wavelength

All radio waves travel at the *speed of light* (c) in whatever media they are traveling. The speed of light in space and air is 300 million (3×10^8) meters per second and somewhat slower in wires and cables. The *wavelength* (λ) of a radio wave is the distance it travels during one complete cycle.

$$\lambda = \frac{c}{f} \qquad f = \frac{c}{\lambda}$$

$$\lambda \text{ (in meters)} = \frac{300}{f \text{ (in MHz)}}$$

A radio wave can be referred to by wavelength or frequency because the speed of light is constant. As frequency increases wavelength decreases and vice-versa.

Components

The three most basic types of electronic components are *resistors*, *capacitors* and *inductors* (coils). Resistors, designated with an R, have a resistance specified in ohms (Ω), kilohms (kΩ) or megohms (MΩ). Capacitors, designated with a C, store electric energy and have values measured in picofarads (pF), nanofarads (nF) and microfarads (μF). Inductors, designated L, store magnetic energy and have values measured in nanohenrys (nH), microhenrys (μH), millihenrys (mH) and henrys (H).

SERIES AND PARALLEL CIRCUITS

A *circuit* is any complete path through which current can flow. If two or more components are connected in a circuit so that the same current flows through all of the components, that is a *series circuit*. If two or more components are connected so that the same voltage is applied to all of the components, that is a *parallel circuit*.

Before you go on, study test questions G5B03, G5B04 and G5B05. Review this section if you have difficulty.

4.2 Power Measurements

DECIBELS

You were introduced to the decibel (dB) in your studies for the Technician class exam. As you become more and more experienced in ham radio, you'll notice the "deebee" everywhere — it's the standard way of referring to power or voltage ratios.

The formula for computing decibels is:

$$dB = 10 \log_{10} \text{(power ratio)}$$

$$dB = 20 \log_{10} \text{(voltage ratio)}$$

If you are comparing a measured power or voltage (P_M or V_M) to some reference power (P_{REF} or V_{REF}) the formulas are:

$$dB = 10 \log_{10} \frac{P_M}{P_{REF}}$$

$$dB = 20 \log_{10} \frac{V_M}{V_{REF}}$$

Positive values of dB mean the ratio is greater than 1 and negative values of dB indicate a ratio of less than 1. Ratios greater than 1 can be referred to as *gain*, while ratios less than 1 can be called a *loss* or *attenuation*.

For example, if an amplifier turns a 5 watt signal into a 25 watt signal, that's a gain of:

$$10 \times \log_{10}\left(\frac{25}{5}\right) = 10 \times \log_{10}(5) = 10 \times 0.7 = 7 \text{ dB}$$

On the other hand, if by adjusting a receiver's volume control the audio output signal voltage is reduced from 2 volts to 0.1 volt, that's a loss of:

$$20 \times \log_{10}\left(\frac{0.1}{2}\right) = 20 \times \log_{10}(0.05) = 20 \times -1.3 = -26 \text{ dB}$$

Any time you double the power (or cut it in half), there is a 3 dB change. A two-times increase (or decrease) in power results in a gain (or loss) of:

$$10 \times \log_{10}\left(\frac{2}{1}\right) = 10 \times \log_{10}(2) = 10 \times 0.3 = 3 \text{ dB}$$

Calculating a Power or Voltage Ratio from dB

You already know how to turn power and voltage ratios into decibels. What if you are given a ratio in dB and asked to calculate the power or voltage ratio? Here are the formulas:

$$\text{Power ratio} = \text{anti}\log\frac{\text{dB}}{10}$$

$$\text{Voltage ratio} = \text{anti}\log\frac{\text{dB}}{20}$$

Example 1: A power ratio of 9 dB = antilog (9 ÷ 10) = antilog (0.9) = 8

Example 2: A voltage ratio of 32 dB = antilog (32 ÷ 20) = antilog (1.6) = 40

Antilog, or inverse logarithm, is sometimes written as the logarithm raised to the negative 1 power ($\log_{10}^{-1}$). On scientific calculators this button may be labeled LOG⁻¹, ALOG or 10ˣ, which means "raise 10 to the power of this value." Some calculators require a two-button sequence such as INV then LOG.

Reference Values for dB

There are several commonly used reference powers and voltages, such as 1 V or 1 mW. When a dB value uses one of them as the references, dB is followed with a letter. Here are the most common:

✔ dBV means dB with respect to 1 V ($V_{REF} = 1$ V)

✔ dBμV means dB with respect to 1 μV ($V_{REF} = 1$ μV)

✔ dBm means dB with respect to 1 mW

Converting dB to Percentage and Vice Versa

$$\text{dB} = 10 \log\frac{\text{Percentage Power}}{100\%}$$

$$\text{dB} = 20 \log\frac{\text{Percentage Voltage}}{100\%}$$

$$\text{Percentage Power} = 100\% \times \text{anti}\log\frac{\text{dB}}{10}$$

$$\text{Percentage Voltage} = 100\% \times \text{anti}\log\frac{\text{dB}}{20}$$

Here's a practical application. Suppose you are using an antenna feed line that has a signal loss of 1 dB. You can calculate the amount of transmitter power that's actually reaching your antenna and how much is lost in the feed line.

$$\text{Percentage Power} = 100\% \times \text{anti}\log\left(\frac{-1}{10}\right) = 100\% \times \text{anti}\log\,(-0.1) = 79.4\%$$

So 79.4% of your power is reaching the antenna and 20.6% is lost in the feed line.

Example 3: A power ratio of 20% = 10 log (20% ÷ 100%) = 10 log (0.2) = –7 dB

Example 4: A voltage ratio of 150% = 20 log (150% ÷ 100%) = 20 log (1.5) = 3.52 dB

Example 5: –3 dB represents a percentage power = 100% × antilog (–3 ÷ 10) = 50%

Example 6: 4 dB represents a percentage voltage = 100% × antilog (4 ÷ 20) = 158%

Before you go on, study test questions G5B01 and G5B13. Review this section if you have difficulty.

RMS: DEFINITION AND MEASUREMENT

As ac electrical power became common, it was important to know how much ac voltage delivered the same average power in comparison to a dc voltage. The power equation is quite clear for dc: $P = E^2 \div R$. But what value for E should be used for ac power? The peak voltage, an average…or what? The answer turns out to be the *root mean square* (RMS) voltage (often abbreviated V_{RMS}). If RMS voltage is used in the equations shown above for calculating power, the result for the ac signal is the same as for an unvarying dc voltage.

"Root mean square" refers to the method used to calculate the RMS voltage — it is the square root of the sum of the squares of the average (*mean*) values of the signal voltages that are present. If the voltages of more than one waveform are added together, first square the amplitude of each voltage ("square"), then sum them together and compute the average ("mean"), and take the square root of the mean ("root").

The RMS value of voltage can be calculated for any waveform, but for a sine wave, the most common ac waveform of all, the RMS value is simply 0.707 times the sine wave's peak voltage as shown in **Figure 4-2**.

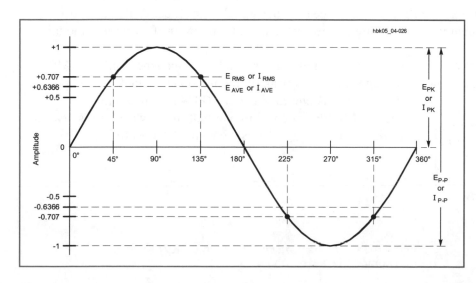

Figure 4-2 — The relationships between RMS, average, peak and peak-to-peak values of ac voltage and current for a sine wave.

For sine waves , use the following equations:

$$V_{RMS} = 0.707 \times V_{PEAK} = 0.707 \times \frac{V_{PK-PK}}{2}$$

$$V_{PEAK} = 1.414 \times V_{RMS}$$

$$V_{PK-PK} = 2 \times 1.414 \times V_{RMS} = 2.828 \times V_{RMS}$$

Do not use these formulas for waveforms such as a speech waveform, square waves or dc voltages combined with ac voltages that are not sine waves!

Example 7: A sine wave with a peak voltage of 17 V has an RMS value of

$$V_{RMS} = 0.707 \times 17 = 12 \text{ V}$$

Example 8: A sine wave with a peak-to-peak voltage of 100 V has an RMS value of

$$V_{RMS} = 0.707 \times \frac{100}{2} = 35.4 \text{ V}$$

Example 9: A sine wave with an RMS voltage of 120 V has a peak-to-peak voltage of

$$V_{PK-PK} = 2 \times 1.414 \times 120 = 2.828 \times 120 = 339.4$$

It is particularly important to know the relationship between RMS and peak voltages to choose components that have sufficient voltage ratings. Capacitors are often connected across ac power leads to perform RF filtering. The capacitor must be rated to withstand the ac peak voltage. For example, a capacitor placed across a 120 V ac power line will experience a peak voltage of 120 × 1.414 = 169.7 V. A capacitor with a 200 V rating or higher should be used.

> *Before you go on, study test questions G5B07, G5B08 and G5B09. Review this section if you have difficulty.*

PEP: DEFINITION AND MEASUREMENT

You are sure to agree that the full amateur power limit of 1500 watts certainly has a lot of "pep," but PEP (or *peak envelope power*) has a more formal definition. PEP is the average power during one RF cycle at the peak of the signal's envelope. PEP is used because it is a convenient way to measure or specify the maximum power of amplitude-modulated signals.

To calculate average ac power, you need to know the load impedance and the RMS voltage. Measure the RF voltage at the very peak of the modulated signal's envelope — this is the *peak envelope voltage* (PEV) as shown in **Figure 4-3**. PEV is equal to one-half of the waveform's peak-to-peak voltage, V_{PK-PK}. PEP is then calculated as follows:

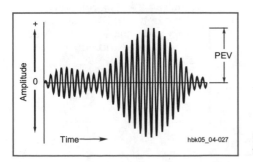

Figure 4-3 — The peak envelope voltage (PEV) for a composite waveform.

$$PEP = \frac{\left(\dfrac{0.707 \times V_{PK-PK}}{2}\right)^2}{R} = \frac{(PEV \times 0.707)^2}{R} = \frac{V_{RMS}^2}{R}$$

Example 10: If PEV is 50 V across a 50 Ω load, the PEP power is

$$PEP = \frac{(50 \times 0.707)^2}{50} = 25 \text{ W}$$

Example 11: If a 50 Ω load is dissipating 1200 W PEP, the RMS voltage is

$$V_{RMS} = \sqrt{PEP \times R} = \sqrt{1200 \times 50} = 245 \text{ V}$$

Example 12: In example 11, the peak voltage is

$$V_{PEAK} = 245 \text{ V} \times 1.414 = 346 \text{ V}$$

Example 13: If an oscilloscope measures 200 V_{PK-PK} across a 50 Ω load, the PEP power is

$$PEP = \frac{\left(\dfrac{0.707 \times 200}{2}\right)^2}{50} = \frac{4999}{50} = 100 \text{ W}$$

For 500 V_{PK-PK}, the PEP power is

$$PEP = \frac{\left(\dfrac{0.707 \times 500}{2}\right)^2}{50} = \frac{31241}{50} = 625 \text{ W}$$

PEP is equal to the average power if an amplitude-modulated signal is not modulated. This is the case when modulation is removed from an AM signal (leaving only the steady carrier) or when a CW key is closed. Likewise, an FM signal is a constant-power signal, so PEP is always equal to average power for FM signals. So if an average-reading wattmeter connected to your transmitter reads 1000 W when you close the key on CW, your PEP output is also 1000 W.

> *Before you go on, study test questions G5B06, G5B11, G5B12, G5B14 and G5B15. Review this section if you have difficulty.*

4.3 Components

You were introduced to electronic components while studying for your Technician exam. In this section, you'll learn some of the characteristics of each common type of component. The symbols that represent each type of component on electronic schematics are presented in **Figure 4-4** for reference. Refer to this figure as you read this section.

There are several attributes that are common to most components. They describe the electrical characteristics of the component. When selecting a component for a design or

Common Schematic Symbols Used in Circuit Diagrams

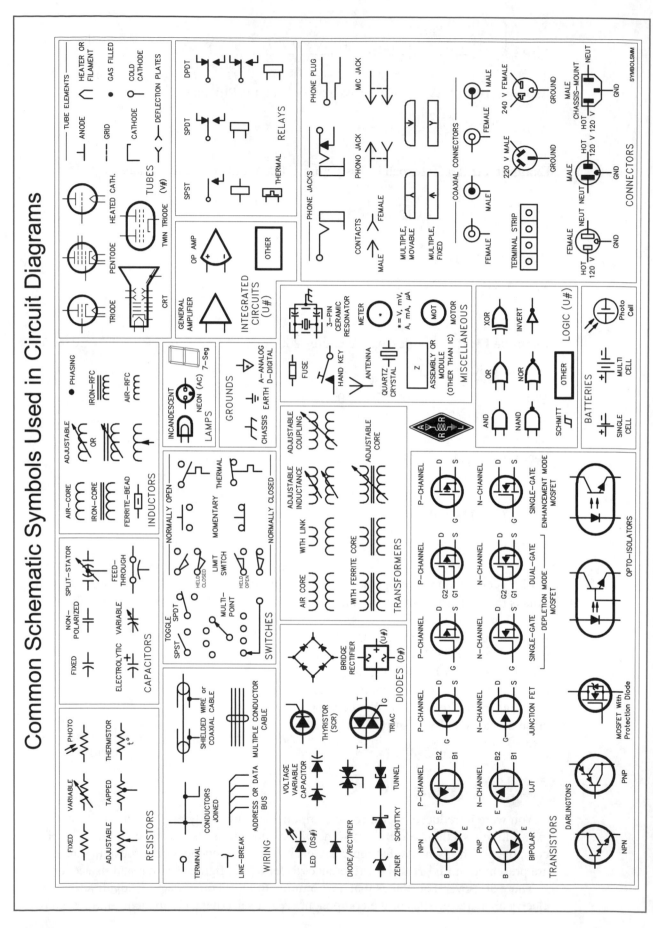

Figure 4-4 — These are the standard symbols used by the ARRL on schematic diagrams.

for repair, it's important to consider these characteristics:

- *Nominal value* — the rated amount of ohms, farads, henrys and so forth that the component is supposed to present to a circuit
- *Tolerance* — the amount the actual value is allowed to vary from the nominal value, usually expressed in percent
- *Temperature coefficient* — the type of variation of the component's actual value with temperature
- *Power (or voltage or current) rating* — the rated ability of the component to withstand heat or dissipate energy

There are additional characteristics specific to each type of component, but the preceding characteristics generally apply to all components. A more complete description of electronic components can be found in *The ARRL Handbook* and the Web site for this study guide contains links to more information.

RESISTORS AND RESISTANCE

A selection of resistors is shown in **Figure 4-5** ranging from subminiature resistors in *surface-mount* packages to a *power resistor* that can dissipate several watts of power. Although all of the resistors could have the same nominal value, they obviously vary in other characteristics. There are several common types of resistors. **Table 4-1** illustrates how their characteristics differ and in what applications they are most commonly used.

Resistors of all types are available with nominal values from 1 Ω or less to more than 1 MΩ. The nominal value is printed directly on the body of the resistor as text or by using colored bands of paint. (This book's Web site, **www.arrl.org/gclm**, has links to more information on component marking.) Several tolerances are available, from precision resistors with tolerances of 1% or less, to general-purpose resistors with tolerances of 5% or 10%.

Table 4-1
Characteristics of Resistor Types

Resistor Type	Power Ratings	Applications
Carbon composition	⅛ - 2 watt	General use, wire leads
Carbon film	⅒ - ½ watt	General use, wire leads and SMT package
Metal film	⅒ - ½ watt	Low-noise, wire leads and SMT package
Wirewound	1 watt - 100 watts or more	Power circuits
Metal oxide	½ - 10 watts	Noninductive for RF applications

Temperature coefficients (or "tempco") may be either positive or negative, depending on the material from which the resistor is made. For a positive temperature coefficient, as temperature increases so does resistance. Oppositely, resistors with a negative tempco will decrease in resistance as temperature decreases. Most resistor types are available with several different values of tempco, specified in ohms per degree Centigrade (Ω/°C). A special type of resistor, the *thermistor*, has a very precisely controlled change in value with temperature and is used as a temperature sensor.

In radio electronics uses, the parasitic inductance of a resistor is important. Wire-wound power resistors are made by winding resistive wire on a ceramic form, making a small coil. This type of construction results in significant amounts of inductance that is generally unimportant at low frequencies or dc. If such a resistor is used in a radio frequency circuit, though, the inductance is often enough to disrupt the circuit's operation or affect

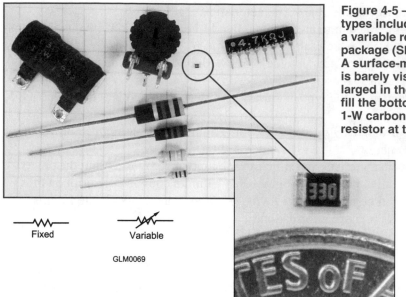

Figure 4-5 — These examples of common resistor types include a 10-W power resistor at the upper left, a variable resistor at top center and a single in-line package (SIP) of several resistors at the upper right. A surface-mount technology (SMT) resistor package is barely visible next to the variable resistor but is enlarged in the inset photo. Several low-power resistors fill the bottom half of the photograph, from the large 1-W carbon composition resistor to the small ¼ W resistor at the bottom.

Fixed   Variable

GLM0069

its tuning. Be sure to use one of the noninductive resistor types for radio circuits, such as carbon composition, carbon film or metal oxide.

Sometimes a circuit needs an adjustable amount of resistance, such as for a volume control or to adjust a current or voltage. Variable resistors are used in those cases. They are called "potentiometers" or "pots." Larger pots have shafts and bushings so that they can be attached to panels and adjusted manually. Very small pots that are mounted on a circuit board and not adjusted regularly are called "trimmers."

Before you go on, study test questions G6A01, G6A06, G6A13 and G7A19. Review this section if you have difficulty.

INDUCTORS AND INDUCTANCE

Figure 4-6 shows several common types of inductors and their corresponding schematic symbols. Double lines next to the inductor symbol indicate the presence of a magnetic core, as opposed to an air core inductor. The variable inductor in the middle also has a magnetic core — showing the double lines in the variable inductor symbol is optional.

Miniature inductors (not shown in the figure) have the same style of package and are easily confused with resistors. (This book's Web site, **www.arrl.org/gclm**, has links to more information on component marking and will take you to more information how these inductors are identified.)

The inductance of an inductor, the measure of its ability to store magnetic energy, is directly pro-

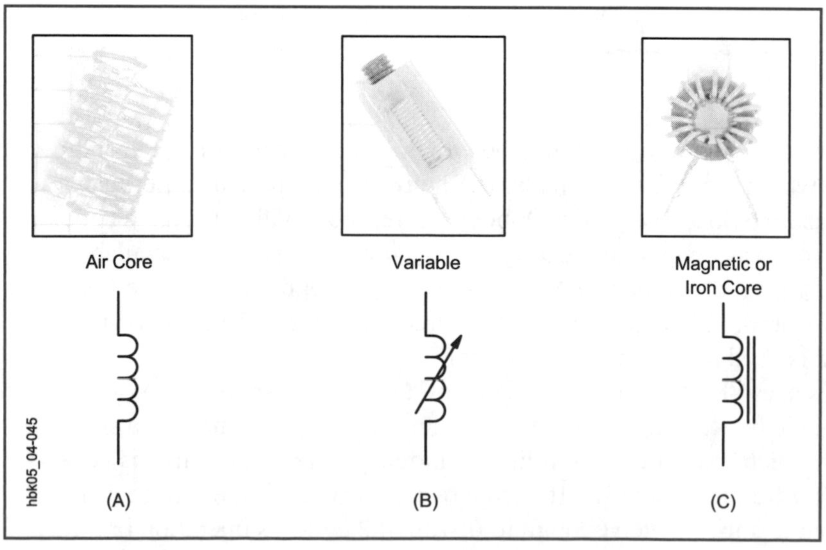

Air Core   Variable   Magnetic or Iron Core

(A)   (B)   (C)

hbk05_04-045

Figure 4-6 — Photos and schematic symbols for common inductors.

portional to the square of the number of turns and the area enclosed by each turn. Making an inductor longer without changing the number of turns or diameter reduces inductance. The higher the inductance, the greater the amount of magnetic energy is stored for a given amount of current. Increasing the core's ability to store magnetic energy, called its *permeability*, also increases its inductance. Large inductors called *filter chokes* are used to filter and smooth power supply output voltages similarly to large filter capacitors.

The type of core and winding of an inductor are important to the type of circuit in which it is to be used. Here is a list of several common types of inductors you'll encounter:
- *Laminated iron core* — dc and ac power and filtering
- *Powdered iron solenoid* — power supplies, RF chokes, audio and low-frequency radio circuits
- *Powdered iron and ferrite toroids* — audio and radio circuits
- *Air core* — RF transmitting

Variable inductors are encountered in low-power receiving and transmitting applications. Low-power variable inductors are adjusted by moving a magnetic core in and out of the inductor. The core is threaded and moves when turned. In a transmitter or impedance matching circuit, high-power variable inductors are adjusted by moving a sliding contact along the inductor.

After its inductance, the most important rating of an inductor is its current rating. Current rating is important for two reasons. First, because an inductor is really a long piece of wire, it can have up to several ohms of resistance. This causes heat to be dissipated inside the inductor. Too much current may cause the wire to burn out and "open" the inductor.

The second reason current rating is important is to avoid *core saturation*. The core of an inductor can only store so much magnetic energy. When the limit is reached, the inductor is *saturated*. If more current is forced through the inductor, the inductor suddenly loses its inductance! Imagine a bucket of water, with the water representing the stored energy. As long as the bucket is not filled, water can be added to and drained from the bucket. If water continues to be added, eventually the bucket's limit is reached and any additional water overflows as if the bucket was not even there, just as a saturated inductor cannot store any additional energy.

Inter-turn capacitance in an inductor is created by adjacent turns of wire separated by air or their insulation. Even though the turns of wire are connected, the small separation between the wire surfaces creates a small capacitance. In a coil of many turns, the inter-turn capacitance can become significant. At high frequencies, the combination of the coil's inductance and the inter-turn capacitance can become a series- or parallel-resonant circuit!

While resistors dissipate energy entirely within their bodies, the stored energy of an inductor is not quite so tame. As **Figure 4-7** shows, when two inductors are placed close together with their axes aligned, the magnetic field from one inductor can also pass through the second inductor, sharing some of its energy. This is called *coupling*. The ability of inductors to share or transfer magnetic energy is called *mutual inductance*. This property can be useful, such as in a transformer, but otherwise is generally unwanted.

Mutual inductance can be minimized in several ways. Small inductors can be shielded by wrapping them with a thin layer of magnetic material such as iron. If the coils are wound along a

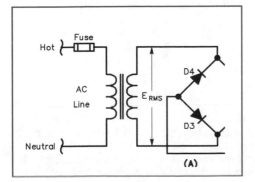

Figure 4-7 — When the switch, S, is closed, current flows through coil number 1, setting up a shared magnetic field that causes a voltage to be induced in the turns of coil number 2.

straight axis as shown in the figure (called a *solenoidal winding*), the coils may be placed so that their axes are at right angles to each other.

Another way is to use a *toroidal winding* as shown at the right in Figure 4-6. The toroid core contains nearly all of the inductor's magnetic field. Since the field does not extend outside of the core, toroidal inductors (or "toroids") can be placed next to each other in nearly any orientation with minimal mutual inductance. This property makes them ideal for use in RF circuits, where you do not want interaction between nearby inductors. Toroids may be wound on ferrite or powdered iron cores. (Ferrite is a ceramic containing iron compounds.) These core materials have high permeabilities, making it possible to obtain large values of inductance in a relatively small package (as compared to the number of turns that would be required with an air-core inductor). The material used to make the core can be optimized to work best on a specific range of frequencies.

Before you go on, study test questions G6A07, G6A08, G6A09, G6A10 and G6A12. Review this section if you have difficulty.

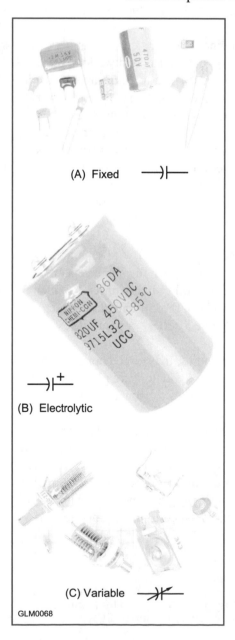

(A) Fixed —)|—

(B) Electrolytic —)|+—

(C) Variable —)|⧸—

GLM0068

CAPACITORS AND CAPACITANCE

Several types of capacitors or "caps" used in radio electronics are shown in **Figure 4-8** and additional symbols for capacitors in Figure 4-4. All capacitors have the same basic structure — two conducting surfaces separated by a *dielectric* that stores electrical energy while preventing dc current flow between the surfaces. The larger the surfaces, the closer the separation, and the more electrical energy the dielectric can store, the larger the resulting capacitance. (The dielectric's ability to store energy is specified by a quantity called the *K factor*.)

The simplest capacitor is a pair of metal plates separated by air. You can see examples of this type of capacitor in Figure 4-8C. These variable capacitors have two sets of plates, one fixed and the other moveable, so that as the moveable plates are rotated between the fixed plates, the changing area of overlap varies the capacitance as well.

Other types of capacitors use thin foils as the conducting surfaces. The foils are separated by a plastic film and rolled up. These are the film capacitors and as you might guess from the "rolled up" aspect of their construction, they have a significant amount of parasitic inductance. The ceramic capacitor is made from thin plates of ceramic with one side plated by a metal film and many such layers stacked together. As a result of this construction, ceramic capacitors have relatively little parasitic inductance. Ceramic and film

Figure 4-8 — Photo A shows fixed value capacitors, including aluminum electrolytic capacitors near the center. Film and mica capacitors are shown on the left and ceramic units on the right. Photo B shows a large "computer grade" electrolytic capacitor used in power supply filters. Photo C shows several small adjustable or "trimmer" capacitors.

capacitors are used in both audio and radio circuits with ceramics more common at high frequencies. Ceramic capacitors are also popular because of their low cost.

Two other popular styles of capacitors are designed to optimize their energy storage capabilities: electrolytic and tantalum capacitors. Electrolytic capacitors use metal foil for the conducting surfaces, but the dielectric is a wet paste or gel of chemicals (the electrolyte) that create an insulating layer on the foils. Tantalum capacitors are similar in that a porous mass of tantalum is immersed in an electrolyte. The electrolyte and the large surface area of electrolytic and tantalum capacitors create large capacitances in comparatively small volumes. Electrolytic capacitors can be seen near the center of Figure 4-8A and in Figure 4-8B. The small "gumdrop" shaped capacitor toward the lower left of Figure 4-8A is a tantalum capacitor. Tantalum and electrolytic capacitors are also *polarized*, meaning that a dc voltage may only be applied in one direction without damaging the electrolyte in the capacitor. Electrolytics use the "rolled up" method of construction and have a high parasitic inductance. Tantalum capacitors have relatively little parasitic inductance compared to electrolytics.

After their value of capacitance, the most important rating for capacitors is their voltage rating. Practical capacitors have a voltage limit above which the dielectric material's insulating ability breaks down and an arc occurs between the capacitors' conducting surfaces. Except for air dielectric capacitors, this usually destroys the capacitor.

The parasitic inductance of a capacitor reduces its effective capacitance at high frequencies. For this reason, physically large electrolytic and tantalum capacitors are used in circuits designed for signals with frequencies below 1 MHz. Film capacitors are generally useful up to several tens of MHz. Ceramic capacitors are used into the VHF and UHF range, but the parasitic inductance of their leads reduces the effective capacitance.

There are many uses of capacitors in radio circuits. Each requires different characteristics that are satisfied by the various styles of capacitor construction. Here are some examples of common capacitor types and their uses:

- *Ceramic* — RF filtering and bypassing at high frequencies, inexpensive
- *Plastic film* — circuits operating at audio and lower radio frequencies
- *Silvered-mica* — highly stable, low-loss, used in RF circuits
- *Electrolytic and tantalum* — rectifier and power supply filter circuits
- *Air and vacuum dielectric* — transmitting and RF circuits

Capacitors have many uses, but several are common enough to have a special name. *Blocking* capacitors pass ac signals while blocking dc signals. *Bypass* capacitors provide a low impedance path for ac signals around a higher-impedance component or circuit. *Filter* capacitors smooth out the voltage pulses of rectified ac to an even dc voltage. *Suppressor* capacitors absorb the energy of voltage transients or "spikes." *Tuning* capacitors vary the frequency of resonant circuits or filters or adjust impedance matching circuits.

> **Before you go on, study test questions G6A02, G6A03, G6A04, G6A05, G6A11 and G7A22. Review this section if you have difficulty.**

SERIES AND PARALLEL CIRCUITS AND COMPONENTS

Now that you know about the common electronic components, the next step is to learn how to combine them! First, let's review the two fundamental circuit rules illustrated in **Figure 4-9**:

- Voltages add in a series circuit, and
- Currents add in a parallel circuit.

Returning to the analogy between electricity and water pressure and flow, if a pump

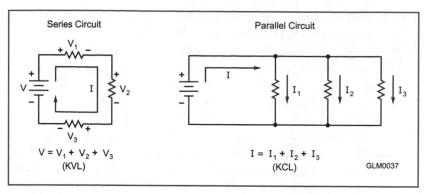

Figure 4-9 — In series circuits, the current is the same in all components and voltages are summed. In parallel circuits, voltage across all components is the same and currents into and out of circuit junctions must be equal.

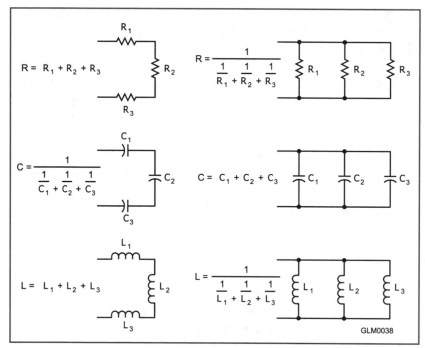

Figure 4-10 — This drawing illustrates how components in series and parallel can be combined into a single equivalent component value.

Table 4-2

Calculating Series and Parallel Equivalent Values

Component	In Series
Resistor	Add values, R1 + R2 + R3 +...
Inductor	Add values, L1 + L2 + L3 +...
Capacitor	Reciprocal of Reciprocals, 1/(1/C1 + 1/C2 + 1/C3 +...)

Component	In Parallel
Resistor	Reciprocal of Reciprocals, 1/(1/R1 + 1/R2 + 1/R3 +...)
Inductor	Reciprocal of Reciprocals, 1/(1/L1 + 1/L2 + 1/L3 +...)
Capacitor	Add values, C1+C2+C3+...

---

supplies pressure to a closed water system, the pressure drops around the system must add up to equal the pressure supplied by the pump. There can be no "spare" or "leftover" pressure. Whether voltage is applied by a battery, power supply or ac outlet, around a series circuit the voltages across the various components must add up to be equal to the voltage applied to the circuit. This is *Kirchoff's Voltage Law*.

Parallel circuits also have a water analogy. Where several pipes come together, the sum of water flows entering the junction must be equal to the sum of water flows leaving the junction. Stated in a different way, the sum of water flows entering and leaving the junction must equal zero. Water in must equal water out. Electrical current works in just the same way: The total current entering a circuit junction must equal the sum of currents leaving the junction. This is *Kirchoff's Current Law*.

Components connected in series or parallel can be replaced with a single *equivalent* component. The rules for determining the equivalent component's value are summarized in **Table 4-2** and shown graphically in **Figure 4-10**. There are really only two formulas to remember — a simple sum (add the values) and the "reciprocal of reciprocals." For capacitors, the reciprocal of reciprocals equation looks like this:

$$C_{EQU} = \frac{1}{\frac{1}{C1} + \frac{1}{C2} + \frac{1}{C3} + ... + \frac{1}{C_N}}$$

When there are only two components, the reciprocal of reciprocals equation simplifies quite a bit, shown here for resistors:

$$R_{EQU} = \frac{R1 \times R2}{R1 + R2}$$

Example 14: What is the total resistance of three 100 Ω resistors in series?

$$R_{EQU} = 100 + 100 + 100 = 300 \ \Omega.$$

In parallel?

$$R_{EQU} = \frac{1}{\dfrac{1}{100} + \dfrac{1}{100} + \dfrac{1}{100}} = \frac{1}{\dfrac{3}{100}} = \frac{100}{3} = 33.3 \ \Omega$$

Example 15: What is the total resistance of a 25 Ω, a 50 Ω and a 75 Ω resistor in series?

$$R_{EQU} = 25 + 50 + 75 = 150 \ \Omega.$$

In parallel?

$$R_{EQU} = \frac{1}{\dfrac{1}{25} + \dfrac{1}{50} + \dfrac{1}{75}} = 13.6 \ \Omega$$

Example 16: What is the total resistance of a 1.5 kΩ and a 2.2 kΩ resistor in parallel?

$$R_{EQU} = \frac{1.5 \ k\Omega \times 2.2 \ k\Omega}{1.5 \ k\Omega + 2.2 \ k\Omega} = 0.89 \ k\Omega$$

Example 17: What is the total inductance of a 10 mH, a 15 mH and a 25 mH inductor in series?

$$L_{EQU} = 10 \ mH + 15 \ mH + 25 \ mH = 50 \ mH.$$

In parallel?

$$L_{EQU} = \frac{1}{\dfrac{1}{10} + \dfrac{1}{15} + \dfrac{1}{25}} = 4.8 \ mH$$

Example 18: What is the total capacitance of two 1 µF and one 4.7 µF capacitors in series?

$$C_{EQU} = \frac{1}{\dfrac{1}{1} + \dfrac{1}{1} + \dfrac{1}{4.7}} = 0.45 \ \mu F$$

In parallel?

$$C_{EQU} = 1 \ \mu F + 1 \ \mu F + 4.7 \ \mu F = 6.7 \ \mu F.$$

Table 4-3
Effect on Total Value of Adding Components in Series and Parallel

Component	Adding In Series	Adding In Parallel
Resistor	Increase	Decrease
Inductor	Increase	Decrease
Capacitor	Decrease	Increase

Table 4-3 shows what happens to the total value of resistance, capacitance and inductance when additional components are added in series or parallel.

TRANSFORMERS

In the previous discussion on inductors, mutual inductance was introduced along with various methods of avoiding it. Mutual inductance is put to good use in the *transformer*. Transformers transfer power between two or more inductors sharing a common core (see Figure 4-4 for schematic symbols). The inductors are called *windings*. The winding to which power is applied is called the *primary winding* and the winding from which power is extracted is called the *secondary winding*. When voltage is applied to the primary winding, mutual inductance causes voltage to appear across the secondary winding. Transformers work equally well "in both directions," so the primary and secondary winding assignments are mostly for convenience.

Transformers can change power from one combination of ac voltage and current to another by using windings with different numbers of turns. (Transformers can only transfer ac power, not dc.) This transformation occurs because all windings share the same magnetic field by virtue of being wound on the same core. If the energy in all windings is the same, but the number of turns are different, then the current in each winding must change so that the total power into and out of the transformer are equal. This occurs regardless of what load is attached to the secondary windings.

The ratio of the number of turns in the primary winding, N_P, to the number of turns in the secondary winding, N_S, determines how current and voltage are changed by the transformer. Most electronic circuits are primarily concerned with voltage, so the most common transformer equations are those that relate transformer input (or primary) voltage, E_P, to output (or secondary) voltage, E_S:

$$\frac{E_S}{E_P} = \frac{N_S}{N_P} \quad \text{or} \quad E_S = E_P \times \frac{N_S}{N_P}$$

Example 19: What is the voltage across a 500-turn secondary winding if 120 V ac is applied across the 2250-turn primary winding?

$$E_S = 120 \times \frac{500}{2250} = 26.7 \text{ V ac}$$

Example 20: What would be the secondary-to-primary turns ratio to change 115 V ac to 500 V ac?

$$\frac{N_S}{N_P} = \frac{E_S}{E_P} = \frac{500}{115} = 4.35$$

A transformer transfers energy, but it changes the combination of voltage and current while doing so. The ratio of voltage to current in an ac circuit is impedance, so the transformer also changes impedance between the primary and secondary circuits. In this way, the transformer acts similarly to an automobile's transmission, changing one combination of torque and speed (mechanical power) at the drive wheels to a different combination at the engine's drive shaft. Electrically, the transformer changes the impedance connected to the secondary winding, Z_S, to a different impedance when measured through the primary winding, Z_P. Again, turns ratio is key (a good analogy is the ratio of gear teeth in a mechanical gearbox or transmission).

$$Z_P = Z_S \left(\frac{N_P}{N_S} \right)^2 \text{ or } \sqrt{\frac{Z_P}{Z_S}} = \frac{N_P}{N_S}$$

Example 21: What is the primary impedance if a 100 Ω load is connected to the secondary of a transformer with a 5:1 secondary-to-primary turns ratio?

$$Z_P = 100 \left(\frac{1}{5} \right)^2 = 4 \, \Omega$$

Example 22: What turns ratio is required to change a 600 Ω impedance to a 4 Ω impedance? In this case, take the square root of the impedance radio:

$$\text{Turns ratio} = \sqrt{\frac{Z_P}{Z_S}} = \sqrt{\frac{600}{4}} = \sqrt{150} = 12.25$$

Note that the impedance to be changed (in this case 600 Ω) can be connected to the primary or secondary, but turns ratios are always stated with the larger number first. In this example, it is stated as 12.25:1, not 1:12.25.

If there is no load connected to a transformer's secondary winding (or windings), there will still be some current flow in the primary. This *magnetizing current* establishes a magnetic field, just as if there was only one winding on the transformer.

Transformers used in ac power circuits are often rated in *volt-amperes* (abbreviated VA) as a measure of their power handling capability. VA are used instead of watts because the voltage and current are often not precisely in phase with each other due to the reactance of the windings and possibly the load. (Reactance is discussed in the next section.)

> *Before you go on, study test questions G5C01, G5C02, G5C03, G5C06, G5C07 and G7A23. Review this section if you have difficulty.*

VACUUM TUBES

The vacuum tube, the oldest device capable of amplification, still makes a valuable contribution to the amateur's shack in high-power amplifiers. In addition to power amplifiers, many amateurs enjoy using antique "tube gear," just as audiophiles do. As a General class licensee, you're likely to encounter vacuum tubes and so you'll need to know how they operate.

A vacuum tube has three basic parts: a source of electrons, an electrode to collect the electrons, and intervening electrodes that control the electrons traveling from source to collector. Each electrode of the tube is called an *element*. **Figure 4-11** shows the schematic symbol for a tube and the tube's elements. A tube with two elements is a diode, three elements a triode, four elements a tetrode and so forth. The most common tubes in amateur service today are triodes and tetrodes. Some tube terminology:

- *Filament or heater* — heats the cathode, causing it to emit electrons
- *Cathode* — the source of electrons
- *Control grid* — the grid closest to the cathode, used to regulate electron travel between the cathode and plate

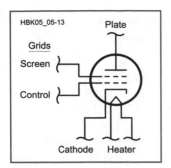

Figure 4-11 — A vacuum tube tetrode schematic symbol includes a heater, cathode, the control and screen grids and the anode or plate. The heavy circle is sometimes used to refer to the tube's envelope.

● *Screen grid* — an electrode that reduces grid-to-plate capacitance that diminishes the tube's ability to amplify at high frequencies

● *Suppressor grid* — an electrode that prevents electrons from traveling from the plate to the control or screen grid

● *Plate* — the electrode that collects electrons, called plate current

All amplifying tubes have at least three electrodes — a cathode (and a filament to heat it), a grid and a plate. Heated to a high temperature by a heater or filament, the cathode emits electrons into the vacuum of the tube. The plate is placed at a positive voltage with respect to the cathode (plate-to-cathode voltage) to attract the electrons. The electrons travel toward the plate through holes in the control grid. If the control grid is at a negative voltage with respect to the cathode (grid-to-cathode voltage), the electrons are repelled and are either slowed down, decreasing plate current, or stopped altogether, called *cutoff*. Conversely, a positive grid-to-cathode voltage accelerates the electrons toward the plate, increasing plate current. Varying the control grid's voltage therefore varies plate current, amplifying the input signal.

Because the control grid is a fine mesh of wires with lots of empty space, relatively few electrons are collected by the grid, even when the grid-to-cathode voltage is positive. This means that grid current is low even for swings of tens of volts. Since impedance is the ratio of voltage to current, that means the grid impedance is quite high — from several hundred ohms in large power tubes to more than a megohm in sensitive amplifiers. Compared to different types of semiconductors, the tube is most like the field-effect transistor (FET).

Vacuum tubes typically operate at voltages that are hazardous to humans, as high as two or three thousand volts in power amplifiers. Equipment that uses high-voltage has numerous safety features to prevent electrical shock. Lower-voltage tube equipment relies on the operator or technician to exercise the proper procedures. Take extra safety precautions when servicing or maintaining tube equipment.

Before you go on, study test questions G6B10, G6B11 and G6B12. Review this section if you have difficulty.

4.4 Impedance

REACTANCE

Capacitors and inductors resist the flow of ac differently than they do dc. The resistance to ac current flow caused by capacitance or inductance is called *reactance* (symbolized by X) and is measured in ohms, like resistance. Reactance occurs because capacitors and inductors store energy. Let's find out how by starting with the capacitor.

Capacitive Reactance

If a dc voltage is applied to a capacitor that is fully discharged (that is, there is no stored energy and the voltage across the capacitor is zero), at first the current rushes in and the capacitor begins to store energy in its internal electric field. This causes the voltage across the capacitor to rise, opposing the voltage causing current to flow into the capacitor. This reduces the amount of current flowing into the capacitor. As shown in **Figure 4-12**, the more energy is stored and the higher the voltage across the capacitor, the smaller the current that flows. Eventually the capacitor charges to the same voltage as the source of the current and current flow stops. When voltage is initially applied, the capacitor looks like a short circuit

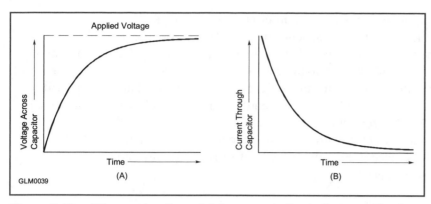

Figure 4-12 — When a circuit containing a capacitor is first energized, the voltage across the capacitor is zero, and the current is very large. As time passes, the voltage across the capacitor increases, as shown at A, and the current drops toward zero, as shown at B.

to dc signals. After the capacitor is charged, it looks like an open circuit to dc signals and that is how a capacitor blocks dc current.

For ac current, the situation is different. If the ac voltage is at a low enough frequency, it acts like a slowly varying dc voltage and the capacitor can stayed charged enough to reduce current to a small value. If the ac voltage is at a higher frequency, however, it is continually changing and the capacitor never gets sufficiently charged to reduce current very much. So a capacitor blocks dc current, resists low-frequency ac current and passes high-frequency ac current.

The opposition to ac current flow from the stored energy in a capacitor is called *capacitive reactance* and is denoted with a subscript, X_C. Its behavior with frequency is described by the following equation:

$$X_C = \left(\frac{1}{2\pi f C} \right)$$

where f = frequency in Hz and C is the capacitance in farads

As frequency of the applied signal increases, capacitive reactance decreases and vice-versa. Be sure to account for the units of frequency (such as kHz and MHz) and capacitance (such as pF, nF and μF).

Example 23: What is the reactance of a 1 nF capacitor at 2 MHz?

$$X_C = \left(\frac{1}{2 \times 3.14 \times (2 \times 10^6) \times (1 \times 10^{-9})} \right) = 79\,\Omega$$

Inductive Reactance

Inductors also resist ac current, but in a complementary way. If a dc voltage is applied to an inductor with no stored energy, the resulting current causes a magnetic field to be established that opposes the incoming current. Initially, the current flow in the inductor is very small, but gradually builds up, storing more and more energy until opposition to the current disappears and the inductor is "fully charged" with magnetic energy. This is illustrated in **Figure 4-13**. When voltage is originally applied, the inductor looks like an open circuit to dc voltage. After the magnetic field is

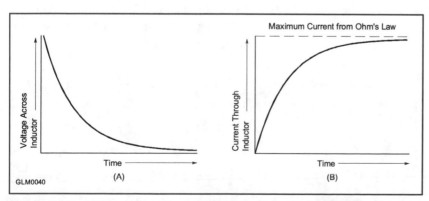

Figure 4-13 — When a circuit containing an inductor is first energized, the initial current is zero and the full applied voltage appears across the inductor. As time passes, the voltage drops toward zero as shown at A, and the current increases, as shown at B.

at full strength, the inductor looks like a short circuit to dc voltage.

This behavior is the opposite of a capacitor that blocks dc currents. If an ac voltage with a high frequency is applied to an inductor, the resulting current changes too quickly for the magnetic field to build up and so the current is always opposed. If the frequency of the ac voltage is low, the inductor's magnetic field can be established and the opposition to current is low. So an inductor blocks high-frequency and passes low-frequency ac currents while acting like a short circuit to dc currents.

The opposition to ac current flow from the stored energy in a inductor is called *inductive reactance* and is denoted with a subscript, X_L. Its behavior with frequency is described by the following equation:

$$X_L = 2\pi f L$$

where f = frequency in Hz and L is the inductance in henrys.

As the frequency of the applied signal increases, inductive reactance increases and vice-versa. As with the formula for capacitive reactance, be sure to account for the units of frequency and inductance.

Example 24: What is the reactance of a 10 μH inductor at 5 MHz?

$$X_L = 2 \times 3.14 \times (5 \times 10^6) \times (1 \times 10^{-5}) = 314 \ \Omega$$

Here's another way to look at the effect of the stored energy in capacitors and inductors: Capacitors oppose changes in voltage, while inductors oppose changes in current. Both oppose the flow of ac current, but in complementary ways.

Before you go on, study test questions G5A02, G5A03, G5A04, G5A05, G5A06 and G5A09. Review this section if you have difficulty.

IMPEDANCE

Impedance is a general term for the opposition to current flow in an ac circuit caused by resistance, reactance or any combination of the two. Impedance is symbolized by the letter Z and it is also measured in ohms, just like resistance and reactance. Like resistance, impedance is the ratio of voltage to current. For example, in **Figure 4-14**, the impedance of whatever is in the "black box" is computed as the applied voltage of 250 V ac divided by the measured current of 2 A. The result is 125 Ω, regardless of whether the impedance is the result of a 125 Ω resistor or an inductor or a capacitor with a reactance of 125 Ω at the frequency of the ac voltage or even a combination of resistance and reactance that limited current to 2 A. How could you tell what was inside the box? Changing frequency and remeasuring current would be useful, since resistance does not change with frequency, while reactances do!

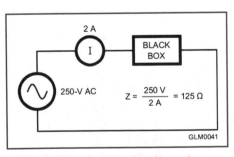

Figure 4-14 — In this circuit, we know that the box presents 125 Ω of opposition to the current, but we don't know what's in the box.

Before you go on, study test questions G5A01 and G5A10. Review this section if you have difficulty.

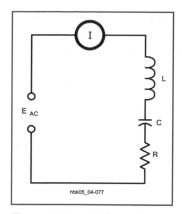

Figure 4-15 — This series circuit is resonant when the capacitive reactance of C equals the inductive reactance of L. At resonance the reactances cancel, leaving R as the only impedance in the circuit.

RESONANCE

In its broadest definition, *resonance* is the condition in which there is a match between the frequency at which a circuit or antenna naturally responds and that of an applied signal. Resonance in a circuit occurs when the capacitive and inductive reactances present are equal. When a circuit's capacitive and inductive reactances are equal, their effects on ac current cancel out. In a resonant series circuit, such as shown in **Figure 4-15**, the reactances of L and C cancel, forming a short circuit, leaving only the resistance, R, as the circuit's impedance. In a resonant parallel circuit of L, C and R the reactances cancel, but this time L and C form an open circuit and again only R is left as the circuit impedance.

Resonance is put to good use in filters and tuning circuits to select or reject specific frequencies at which resonance occurs. In some circumstances, though, resonance can cause problems. For example, the parasitic inter-turn capacitance of inductors causes them to become *self-resonant* when the parasitic capacitive reactance equals the inductive reactance. This can form either a series resonance in which the inductor looks like a short circuit or a parallel resonance in which the inductor looks like an open circuit. In either case, this is probably not what the circuit designer had in mind! Avoiding unwanted resonances requires careful selection and construction of inductors.

SOURCE AND LOAD IMPEDANCE AND MATCHING

Knowing the impedance of a circuit is particularly important when the goal is to deliver the maximum power from a power source (such as a transmitter) to a load (such as an antenna). According to the *Maximum Power Transfer Theorem*, maximum power transfer occurs when the source and load impedances are equal.

The impedance of a source is its internal impedance that limits its ability to deliver power. For example, a hearing aid battery and a D-cell may both supply 1.5 V, but the internal impedance of the hearing aid battery is much higher, limiting the current it can supply to a low value. The D-cell's lower internal impedance enables it to supply high currents.

Amateur transmitting equipment is designed so that the source impedance at the output (or output impedance) is 50 Ω. Most coaxial cables have a 50 Ω characteristic impedance. Most antennas are designed to have a feed point impedance of 50 Ω, but they rarely present that impedance over an entire amateur band. This *mismatch* results in an SWR greater than 1:1. If the difference between the load impedance and the transmitter output impedance is great enough, the transmitter may reduce its output power to avoid damage. The solution is an *impedance-matching circuit* that *transforms* the undesired impedance to the desired value.

Most impedance-matching circuits are *LC circuits* made of inductors and capacitors. **Figure 4-16** shows two popular LC circuits used for impedance matching: the Pi network (a *network* is a formal name for circuit) and the Tee network. The names are derived from the letters π and T, which the circuit schematics resemble. These can be made entirely of fixed-value components for loads such as a single-band antenna. Adjustable components can also be used, allowing the circuit to be used at different frequencies or loads.

Another popular method of performing impedance matching was introduced in the section on transformers. Special RF *impedance transformers* are often employed in this role, equalizing impedances of source and load to maximize the transfer of power. Impedance-

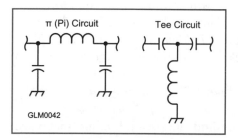

Figure 4-16 — The Pi (π) and Tee circuits are named for the letters that they resemble. The Pi-circuit is often used to transform the impedances between transistors or tubes in amplifiers and feed lines. The Tee-circuit is common in standalone "antenna tuners" or "transmatches."

matching can also be performed by special lengths and connections of transmission line.

Regardless of what method is employed, it is important that the ratings of the components, transformer cores or transmission lines not be exceeded. Large transformation ratios (typically of 10:1 or more) or high power can put a lot of stress on the components used in the circuit. For example, using an impedance transformer at high power can result in core saturation, creating harmonics and causing signal distortion. Stay within the limit of the manufacturer's specification.

Before you go on, study test questions G5A07, G5A08, G5A11, G5A12, G5A13 and G5A14. Review this section if you have difficulty.

4.5 Semiconductor Components

Semiconductors are materials that conduct electricity better than an insulator but not as well as a metal. Silicon (chemical symbol Si) and germanium (Ge) are examples of semiconductors used in radio electronics. The electrical properties of semiconductors can be controlled by the addition of small amounts of other materials such as indium (In) or phosphorus (P). These impurities are called *dopants* and adding them to the base material is called *doping*. If the impurity's presence creates more electrons to conduct electricity, the result is N-type material. Otherwise, the impurity creates P-type material. All semiconductors are created from combinations of N-type and P-type material. Where the two types of material are in contact, that is a *PN junction*.

DIODES AND RECTIFIERS

A semiconductor diode, like its vacuum tube equivalent, only allows current flow in one direction. The *junction diode* is created from a layer of P-type (the *anode*) and N-type (the

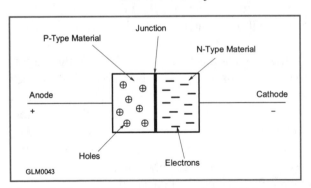

Figure 4-17 — A PN-junction consists of P-type (not enough electrons) and N-type (too many electrons) material in direct contact. The junction is formed at the boundary between the layers of material.

cathode) material as shown in **Figure 4-17** with wire leads attached to each layer. Current flows when positive voltage is applied from the P-type to the N-type material, called *forward bias*, forcing electrons across the junction. Voltage applied in the reverse direction from N-type to P-type, called *reverse bias*, pulls electrons away from the junction so that no current flows. The voltage required to force electrons across the junction is the diode's *forward voltage* or *junction threshold voltage* and is abbreviated V_F. For silicon diodes, V_F is approximately 0.7 V and for germanium 0.3 V. Typical diode packages are shown in **Figure 4-18**. (For more information about semiconductors, follow the links on the *General Class License Manual's* Web site.)

A semiconductor diode has several ratings that place limits on how it may be used. These are the two most important ratings:

● *Peak inverse (or reverse) voltage (PIV)* — the maximum reverse voltage (voltage in the nonconducting direction) that may be applied before *reverse breakdown* occurs, allowing current to flow in the reverse direction

● *Average forward current (I_F)* — because of the forward voltage, current through the diode generates heat equal to $I_F \times V_F$. Exceeding this rating will destroy the diode.

Another parameter that affects how a diode works at high frequencies is its *junction*

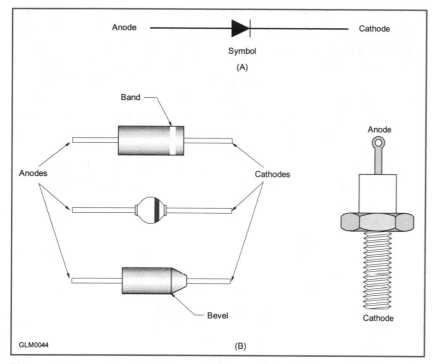

Figure 4-18 — The schematic symbol for a diode is shown at A. Several common diode and rectifier package styles are shown at B

capacitance (C_J). When reverse-biased, the layers of P- and N-type material act like the plates of a small capacitor. The larger C_J becomes, the longer it takes the diode to switch from being reverse-biased to conducting forward current.

Different methods of construction creates diodes with a different set of characteristics useful for certain types of circuits.

- *PIN diode* — conducts ac signals with low forward voltage drop, used for RF switching and control
- *Schottky diode* — low junction capacitance allows operation at high frequencies
- *Varactor* — the reverse-biased junction acts like a capacitor and can be used as a small variable capacitor
- *Zener diode* — extra levels of doping allow Zeners to be used as voltage regulators while in reverse breakdown

Diodes that are designed for circuits with low-power signals are called *signal* or *switching diodes*. Heavy-duty diodes for use in high-power circuits must carry high currents, withstand high voltages or dissipate a lot of power. These diodes are called *rectifiers* and may have PIV and I_F ratings as high as 1000 V or 100 A!

Before you go on, study test questions G6B01, G6B02, G6B03, G6B05 and G6B06. Review this section if you have difficulty.

BIPOLAR AND FET TRANSISTORS

The back-to-back layers of P- and N-type material enable the diode's unidirectional current flow. Adding another layer of semiconductor material, however, creates a device capable of amplifying a signal — the transistor. **Figure 4-19** illustrates the basic structure of a *bipolar* transistor. (Bipolar transistors are made from P- and N-type material and use current to control their operation. Semiconductor diodes are *passive* devices, needing no external power to perform their current routing function. Unlike the diode, the transistor is an *active* device, requiring power to function.

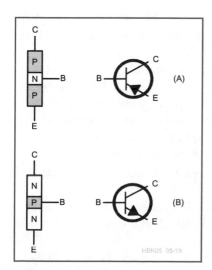

Figure 4-19 — Bipolar transistors are made from three layers of P- and N-type material. At A, a thin layer of N-type material is sandwiched between two layers of P-type material, forming a PNP transistor. The schematic symbol has three leads: collector (C), base (B) and emitter (E), with the arrow pointing in toward the base. At B, the opposite construction creates an NPN transistor, with the emitter arrow pointing out away from the base.

Bipolar transistors have three electrodes — the collector (C), emitter (E) and base (B). The collector and emitter leads carry the current that is controlled by the transistor. Transistor operation is controlled by current flowing between the base and emitter. The thin base layer of material creates a pair of back-to-back PN junctions that would seem to prevent current flow through the transistor no matter which way voltage is applied because one junction is always reverse-biased. When current flows between the base and emitter, however, the base is so thin that the current causes both junctions to break down, allowing full current flow between collector and emitter.

The amount of base-emitter current required for collector-emitter current to flow is quite small. The control of a large current by a smaller current is amplification and the ratio of the collector-emitter current to base-emitter current is called *current gain*. Current gain for dc signals is represented by the symbol β (beta). Current gain for ac signals is represented by the symbol h_{fe}.

Even though the transistor's base is very small, it is still large enough that the base-emitter and collector-base junctions form small capacitances. These capacitances cause the ac current gain (h_{fe}) of the transistor to be reduced as frequency increases. The ability of a transistor to amplify high frequency signals is measured by its *gain-bandwidth product* f_T that has units of MHz. It is also known as the transistion frequency, the frequency at which current gain equals unity. A "fast" transistor has a large f_T and is capable of amplifying signals to high frequencies.

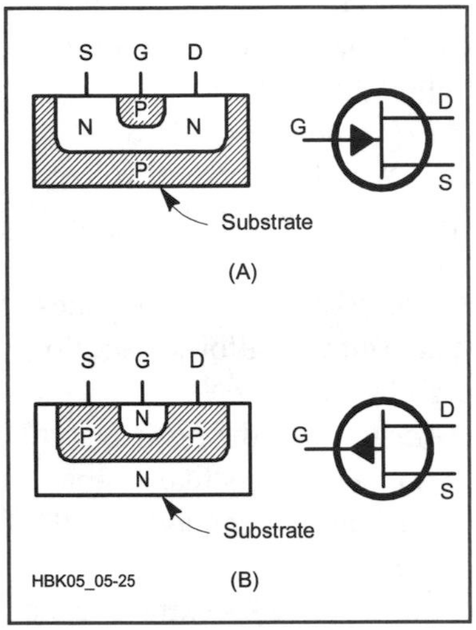

Another type of transistor, shown in **Figure 4-20** is the *field effect transistor* (FET). The FET has three electrodes like the bipolar transistor — the drain (D), source (S) and gate (G). Instead of controlling drain-source current with gate-source current, the voltage between the gate and source is used. Instead of current gain, the FET has *transconductance* (g_m) — the ratio of source-drain current to gate-source voltage. A junction-FET (JFET) is constructed with the gate material in direct contact with the material that connects the source and drain electrodes. A metal-oxide-semiconductor FET (MOSFET) and a related device, the insulated-gate FET (IGFET) has an insulating layer of oxide between the gate and the rest of the transistor. Both JFETs and MOSFETs are very sensitive, with small amounts of voltage able to control the source-drain current. Their operation is quite similar to a vacuum tube in this regard.

Transistors' high amplification also makes them ideal for use as switches for both voltage and current. By applying enough base-emitter current or gate-source voltage, the transistor can be driven into *saturation* where further increases in input result in no output change. Similarly, the input signal can reduce output current to zero — the condition of *cutoff*. These two states make an excellent representation of digital ON/OFF signals in logic circuits.

Transistors come in many types of pack-

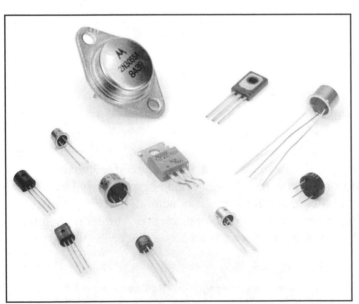

Figure 4-20 — JFET devices are made from P- and N-type material like bipolar transistors, but use a gate embedded in a channel to control electron flow. An N-channel JFET is shown at A and a P-channel JFET at B.

Figure 4-21 — Transistors come in a variety of package styles. The smaller packages are used in low-power circuits for small signals. The larger packages are used in power-control and transmitter circuits.

ages. The different styles are often identified with package numbers beginning with "TO" (for Transistor Outline), such as the TO-3, TO-92 and TO-220 packages shown in **Figure 4-21**. Low-power transistors usually have insulated, plastic packages. Plastic packaging is unsuitable for transistors that must dissipate larger amounts of power. Their packages have metal surfaces through which excess heat can be easily removed. The metal surface is often connected internally to the collector or source of the transistor so a direct connection to a metal heat sink or equipment chassis would short out that voltage. Some sort of insulation is often required between the case and heat sink. Be cautious when installing or replacing high-power transistors to avoid short circuits.

Before you go on, study test questions G6B07, G6B08, G6B09 and G7A21. Review this section if you have difficulty.

ANALOG AND DIGITAL INTEGRATED CIRCUITS

If one transistor is good, more must be better! The processes that make transistors on thin wafers of silicon can just as easily create many diodes, transistors, resistors, capacitors and even tiny spiral inductors and connect them with wires made of thin plated-on metal. The result is an *integrated circuit* (IC) also known as a "chip." The two most common types of integrated circuits are *analog* (or *linear*) and *digital* (or *logic*).

Analog ICs are used for applications such as signal amplification, filtering, measurement and power control. They operate over a continuous range of voltages and currents. **Figure 4-22** shows the schematic symbol and connection diagrams for two of the most common analog ICs, the operational amplifier and the linear voltage regulator. The operational amplifier or "op amp" is widely used for dc and audio circuits as an inexpensive source of gain. Linear voltage regulators are used to maintain a power supply output at a constant voltage over a wide range of currents.

Digital ICs operate with discrete values of voltage and current that represent the binary number system values "0" and "1". It's easy to design digital circuits that have two stable states (ON and OFF) to represent either binary value. By combining digital circuits, those values can be used to perform computations or control functions.

The basic building block of digital circuits are circuits called *gates* that perform inversion (changing a 1 to a 0 and vice versa) and the OR and AND functions. Because of the way digital circuits are designed, the most common gates in actual use are the inverter, NAND and NOR. All three of these functions and their schematic symbols are shown in **Figure 4-23**. More complex functions — all the way up to microprocessors and digital signal processors — are constructed from combinations of these three functions. Digital circuits that use gates to combine binary inputs to generate a binary output or combination of binary outputs are called *combinational logic*.

Another class of digital circuits combines binary signals in a way that depends on time and on the sequence of inputs to the circuits. These circuits are called *sequential logic*. The basic building block of sequential logic is the *flip-flop*, which has two stable states. The flip-flop responds to a *clock* signal that causes its outputs to change based on the input signals. The two outputs, Q and $\overline{Q}$ (the overbar indicates that the signal is inverted), are always in opposite states. There are several kinds of flip-flops and the most common,

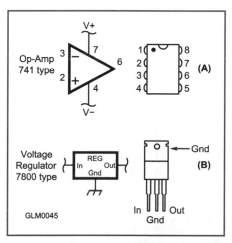

Figure 4-22 — The popular 741 op-amp symbol and dual in-line package (DIP) connections are shown at A. A common three-terminal voltage regulator, the 7800-series, is shown at B.

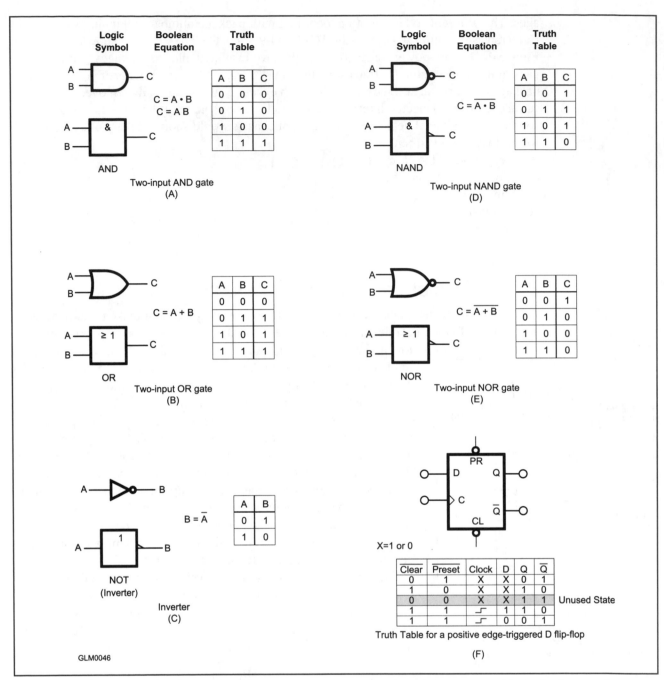

Figure 4-23 — These are the schematic symbols for the basic digital logic functions with the logic equations and truth tables that describe their operation. The two-input AND gate is shown at A, a two-input OR gate at B, an inverter at C, a two-input NAND gate at D and a two-input NOR gate at E. A D-type flip-flop is shown at F.

the D-type, is shown in Figure 4-23. When a digital signal, such as a pulse or square wave, is applied to the clock input, the rising edge (the edge that goes from low to high or from 0 to 1) causes the Q output to be 1 if the D input is 1 and vice versa. The Q and $\overline{Q}$ outputs stay in that state until the next rising edge is applied to the clock input.

By connecting flip-flops together so that one flip-flop's outputs feed the next flip-flop's input, two important types of circuits are created: *counters* and *shift registers*. In a counter, the outputs of the chain of flip-flops make up a binary number or state representing the number of clock signals that have occurred. Each flip-flop stores one bit of the total count. The highest number that a counter can represent is 2^n, where n is the number of flip-flops

Table 4-4

Logic Family Characteristics

Family Name	Maximum Frequency of Operation	Power Consumption	Power Supply
TTL	100 MHz	High	5 V
CMOS	1 GHz	Low	3-5 V
CMOS (CD4000)	1 MHz	Very Low	3-15 V

that make up the counter. For example, a 3-bit counter (one with three flip-flops) can count $2^3 = 8$ different states, a 4-bit counter can count 16 states, and so on.

Connecting the array of flip-flops slightly differently results in a shift register. The shift register stores a sequence of 1s and 0s from its input as the flip-flop outputs. Each clock signal causes the value at the shift register's input to pass or shift to the next flip-flop in the string. Some shift-register circuits can be configured to shift up or down (forward or backward) along the array. Shift registers are a simple form of digital memory. (For more information on flip-flops and digital circuits in general, see the *General Class License Manual* Web site.)

There are several different types or *families* of digital circuits. A family is a certain style of circuit design that is used to create all of the different logic functions. Different families may use different power supply voltages or have different voltage and current levels that represent the 0 and 1 values. To construct complex circuits from many gates, the same family of circuits must be used so that the voltage and current levels are compatible for all of the gates.

Characteristics of some common logic families are shown in **Table 4-4**. The oldest logic family is resistor-transistor logic (RTL) and is no longer in use. The transistor-transistor logic (TTL) logic family replaced RTL. The most popular logic family in use today is the *complementary metal-oxide semiconductor* (*CMOS*) logic family because of its high speed and low power consumption. CMOS devices are used in personal computers and in microprocessor-controlled equipment, such as most current amateur transceivers. There is also an older CMOS logic family represented by ICs with CD4000 part numbers that are designed for use in very low power circuits. Each major family has a variety of subfamilies that are optimized for a particular use. One example is LSTTL, a low-power version of TTL. Information about each logic family can be found on logic manufacturer's Web sites and in *The ARRL Handbook*.

> Before you go on, study test questions G6C01, G6C02, G6C03, G6C06, G7B01, G7B02, G7B03, G7B04, G7B05 and G7B06. Review this section if you have difficulty.

RF INTEGRATED CIRCUITS

RF ICs are specially designed for functions commonly required at radio frequencies, such as low-level high-gain amplifiers, mixers, modulators and demodulators, and even filters. RF ICs greatly reduce the number of discrete devices required to build radio circuits.

An MMIC (monolithic microwave integrated circuit) is a special type of RF IC that works through microwave frequencies. Taking advantage of integration to combine many RF devices into a single package, some MMICs perform several functions. One example is an MMIC that acts as an entire receiver front end. The MMIC is what enables communications engineers to construct low-cost cell phones, GPS receivers and other sophisticated examples of wireless technology.

MICROPROCESSORS AND RELATED COMPONENTS

Where digital control and computing functions were once performed by circuits composed of many discrete ICs, today these functions are performed by the miniature computers called *microprocessors* that contain thousands of gates in a single IC (often called a "chip"). Modern microprocessors are capable of performing millions of computing instructions per second and often include functions such as parallel and serial input-output ports, counters and timers right on the chip. Nearly all microprocessors are built from CMOS logic.

Microprocessors perform a sequence of operations described by a program. The program itself is in the form of *machine language* that is directly usable as instructions by the digital logic circuits in the microprocessor. Machine language is *binary data* and is created from the text statements written by a human programmer using a special program known as a *compiler*.

Memory

The machine language program must be stored in some kind of memory devices so that microprocessor can read the instructions. There are several kinds of memory. *Volatile* memory loses the data it stores when power is removed. *Nonvolatile* memory stores data permanently, even if the power is removed. *Random-access memory* (RAM) can be read from or written to in any order. *Read-only memory* (ROM) stores data permanently and cannot be changed. There are several common types of each as shown in **Table 4-5**. Memory devices or systems are connected to the microprocessor by a high-speed interface called a *memory bus* that can transfer data at high rates.

Table 4-5
Memory Types

Memory	*Volatile/Nonvolatile*
Static RAM (SRAM)	Volatile
Dynamic DRAM (DRAM)	Volatile, data must be continually refreshed
Programmable ROM (PROM)	Nonvolatile
EPROM (Erasable PROM)	Nonvolatile, can be erased by exposure to UV
EEPROM (Electrically-erasable PROM)	Nonvolatile, can be electrically erased, Flash EEPROM erased in sections
Mass storage	Nonvolatile, data stored on hard drive, CD-ROM or tape

Interfaces

Microprocessors and computers interact with the outside world through interfaces — special circuits, methods and connectors for data exchange. There are two types of interface, *serial* and *parallel*. Serial interfaces transfer one bit of data in each transfer operation. Parallel interfaces transfer multiple bits of data in each operation. The most common computer interfaces are listed in **Table 4-6**.

Serial interfaces are used as an inexpensive way of connecting two pieces of equipment to share digital data. The standard interface in amateur equipment has been the RS-232 interface (also known as a PC COM port). RS-232 refers to the industry standard

Table 4-6

Common Computer Interfaces

Interface	Type	Typical Speed (bits/sec)
RS-232	Serial	115 k
USB	Serial	USB 1.1, 1.5 M; USB 2.0, 480 M
Firewire	Serial	800 M
Centronics	Parallel	1 Mbytes/sec
IDE / ATA	Parallel	50 Mbytes/sec
SCSI	Parallel	100 Mbytes/sec
PC Card	Parallel	10 Mbytes/sec

that describes the interface's electrical characteristics. RS-232 is rapidly being replaced in most computers by the USB (universal serial bus) interface. RS-232 and USB serial interfaces in the ham shack are used to connect computers to transceivers, TNCs and multimode communications processors, as well as to accessories such as antenna switches and rotators.

Network connections are also serial interfaces. The most common physical network interface is Ethernet. For wireless connections, many computers use the popular WiFi interface, described by the IEEE 802.11 standard. Bluetooth and Zigbee wireless interfaces are used for short range "cable-replacement."

Parallel interfaces are used primarily to connect computers to mass storage devices such as hard drives. Inside computers, parallel interfaces are used to connect the microprocessor to hard drives and memory devices. The most common parallel interface outside of the computer is the Centronics printer interface, named for the company that created it.

> **Before you go on, study test questions G6C04, G6C05, G6C11 and G6C12. Review this section if you have difficulty.**

VISUAL INTERFACES

Amateur equipment uses two types of devices to present information visually, the *indicator* and the *display*. An indicator is a device that presents on/off information visually by the presence, absence or color of light. Common indicators are the incandescent light bulb and the light-emitting diode (*LED*). A display is a device that is capable of presenting text or graphics information in visual form. One example is the display showing frequency and operating information on the front panel of most transceivers.

Incandescent light bulbs have been largely replaced by LEDs in most amateur equipment. LEDs last longer, can be turned on and off far quicker, use less power and generate less heat than light bulbs. Some indicators include LEDs of different colors, creating more than one color or even white light. An LED is a diode made from special types of semiconductor material that emit light when the PN junction is forward biased.

The most common type of display is the *LCD* (liquid crystal display) created by sandwiching liquid crystal material between transparent glass panels. A pattern of electrodes is printed in a thin, transparent film on the front glass panel with a single electrode covering the rear panel. As voltage is applied to the electrodes on the front panel, the liquid crystals twist into a configuration that blocks light. LCDs require ambient or *back lighting* (a light source behind the liquid crystal layer) since the liquid crystal layer does not generate light on its own.

> **Before you go on, study test questions G6C07, G6C08 and G6C09. Review this section if you have difficulty.**

4.6 Practical Circuits

RECTIFIERS AND POWER SUPPLIES

Almost every piece of amateur equipment requires power. Electronic equipment requires dc to operate, so a *power supply* (either built-in or external) is required to run equipment from household ac power. Most amateur equipment uses +13.8 V dc power, a voltage chosen to be compatible with vehicle power systems for mobile operation.

A power supply has three basic parts — an input transformer, a rectifier and a filter-regulator output circuit. The input transformer converts the 120 V ac household power to a voltage closer to the desired 13.8 V. It also serves to isolate the power supply output from the ac power line. This is an important safety feature because the power supply's negative output is usually connected to the station's ground, frequently in direct contact with the operator.

Rectifier Circuits

After the ac voltage has been reduced to a lower value by the input transformer, a rectifier circuit converts the bipolar ac waveform into pulses of dc as shown in **Figure 4-24**.

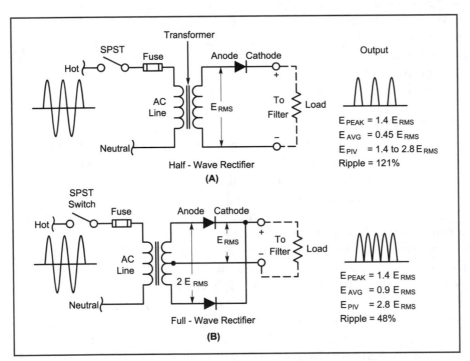

Figure 4-24 — Two fundamental rectifier circuits and the characteristics of their output voltage. (A) Half-wave. (B) Full-wave center-tap. The half-wave circuit converts only one-half of the input waveform (180°) while the full-wave circuit converts all of the input waveform (360°).

Don't confuse a single diode rectifier with the rectifier circuit — they both have the same name but one is a component and the other a circuit. There are two basic types of rectifier circuits — the *half-wave* and the *full-wave center-tapped*.

A half-wave rectifier shown in Figure 4-24A permits current flow during one-half of the input ac waveform (180°) from the transformer. That creates a series of pulses of current in the load at the same frequency as the input voltage. There is an equal duration between pulses when no current flows. The rectifier output waveform's average voltage is 0.45 times the transformer winding's output voltage, or $0.45\ E_{RMS}$.

There is also one diode forward voltage drop in series with the load current that reduces the peak output voltage by 0.6 V for regular silicon diodes.

The full-wave rectifier shown in Figure 4-24B is really two half-wave rectifiers operating on alternate half-cycles. The advantage of the full-wave rectifier is that output is produced during the entire 360° of the ac cycle. The output voltage from this rectifier circuit is $0.9\ E_{RMS}$ (minus one diode forward voltage drop). The output from full-wave rectifiers is a series of pulses at twice the frequency of the input voltage. To use the full-wave

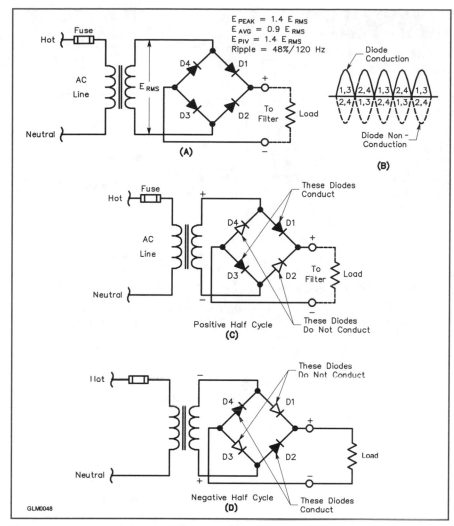

$$E_{PEAK} = 1.4\ E_{RMS}$$
$$E_{AVG} = 0.9\ E_{RMS}$$
$$E_{PIV} = 1.4\ E_{RMS}$$
Ripple = 48%/120 Hz

Figure 4-25 — The full-wave bridge rectifier has an equivalent output to the full-wave center-tap rectifier without a center-tapped transformer winding, but requires twice as many rectifier diodes.

rectifier, however, requires that the transformer output winding be center-tapped to provide a return path for current that flows in the load. Since the output winding is center-tapped, each half of the winding must be capable of generating the full output voltage, E_{RMS}, so the total winding must put out twice the full output voltage, $2\ E_{RMS}$.

There is a second type of full-wave rectifier, called a *full-wave bridge*, shown in **Figure 4-25**. This circuit adds two diodes (a total of four), but eliminates the need for a center-tapped, double-voltage transformer. The figure shows how it works, with a pair of diodes conducting on alternate half-cycles. The pairs of diodes work like a double-pole, double-throw switch synchronized to the ac waveform, connecting the winding to the load first with one polarity, then the other. Output voltage is again $0.9\ E_{RMS}$, but less a pair of forward voltage drops because there are two diodes in series with the current at all times.

There is a difference in voltage and current ratings needed for the diodes used in these three circuits.

• In the full-wave rectifier (using the center-tapped transformer winding), when a diode is not conducting, it must withstand not only the voltage from its own half of the winding, but the full voltage from the other winding of the opposite polarity. That doubles the required voltage rating for the diodes, so they should have a PIV rating of at least two times the normal peak output voltage of the supply.

• The diode in a half-wave rectifier circuit must withstand the full transformer peak output voltage. It is a good design practice to select a diode with a PIV rating of one to two times the normal peak output voltage of the supply.

• In the full-wave bridge, the diodes only have to withstand the transformer's peak output voltage.

• In the half-wave rectifier circuit, all of the load current goes through one diode and so it must be rated to carry the average load current.

• In both full-wave circuits, the diodes each supply only one-half of the load current, halving their current rating requirement.

Diodes in Parallel and Series

Power supply components must be sufficiently rated for the voltages and currents they must supply, especially the rectifier diodes. Sometimes, the combination of voltage and current would require an expensive component if a single diode were to be used. It is common in that case to replace a single diode with two or more much less expensive diodes.

If the current requirement is too high for a single diode, two diodes can be placed in parallel as shown in **Figure 4-26**. The diodes will share the current, but one often receives more than the other due to small variations in forward voltage. The solution is to place a small resistance (typically less than 0.1 Ω) in series with each diode. The small voltage drop of the resistor reduces the effect of the difference in the diode's voltage drops, greatly equalizing the current in each diode.

When high voltage rating is the issue, the solution is to place several diodes in series in a *rectifier string*. Again, it is important to equalize the voltage applied to each diode. This is done as shown in Figure 4-26 by placing a resistor string in parallel with the diode string. The resistors insure that when the rectifier string is reverse-biased, the diodes all experience close to the same reverse voltage.

The series and parallel resistors do dissipate some power, making the supply slightly less efficient. The tradeoff is that less expensive components can be used, making the equipment easier to maintain and construct.

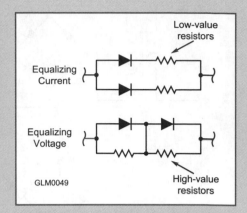

Figure 4-26 — Low-value resistors are used to equalize current between two diodes in parallel. If diodes are connected in series to withstand high voltages, high-value resistors equalize the voltage across each diode.

Table 4-7
Rectifier Diode Ratings

Rectifier Type	Number of Diodes	PIV Voltage Rating	Avg Forward Current Rating
Half-wave	1	1.4 to 2.8 E_{RMS} (2 E_{PK})	I_{LOAD}
Full-wave	2	2.8 E_{RMS} (2 E_{PK})	0.5 I_{LOAD}
Full-wave bridge	4	1.4 E_{RMS} (E_{PK})	0.5 I_{LOAD}

Table 4-7 summarizes the voltage rating requirements for the diodes in all three rectifier circuits.

Filter Circuits

The pulses of dc current into a load are unsuitable for use by electronic circuits. They must be filtered so that the voltage is supplied at a steady voltage. The variation in output voltage caused by the current pulses is called *ripple,* and it is measured as the percentage of the peak-to-peak variation compared to average output voltage. The most common way of reducing ripple is to use a large *filter capacitor* at the output of the rectifier. Seen in **Figure 4-27**, this is called a *capacitor-input filter.*

A sufficiently large capacitor maintains the power supply output voltage close to the average value of the rectifier output even for heavy load currents. (In practice, several capacitors in parallel may be used to increase the value of capacitance to the desired level.) The rectifier supplies current to the capacitor, charging it and raising its voltage whenever the rectifier output voltage is greater than the capacitor voltage. The capacitor then discharges the stored energy as current through the load until the rectifier can charge it up again. The percentage of variation in output voltage between no load and full load is called the supply's *regulation.*

For a properly sized filter capacitor, the rectifier charges the capacitor in short pulses

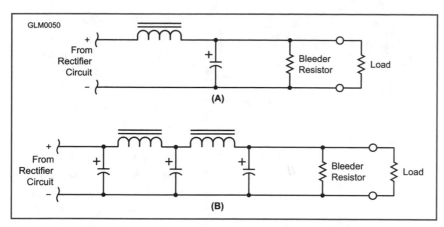

Figure 4-27 — Shown at A is a choke-input power supply filter circuit. B shows a capacitor-input, multisection filter. Bleeder resistors connected across the filter capacitors slowly discharge the stored energy when the supply is turned off.

of high current while the load draws current from the capacitor more slowly. Electrolytic capacitors are the usual choice for filter capacitors because they offer high capacitance in a relatively small volume.

The capacitor in a power supply output filter is continuously charging and discharging, with current flowing in and out of the capacitor. These currents can be quite high, so it is important to avoid losses caused by losses in the capacitor. There are several sources of capacitor losses such as the resistance of conducting surfaces and of the internal electrolyte paste. All of the losses are lumped together in a single parasitic resistance called the *equivalent series resistance* (ESR). Low ESR is desirable for filter capacitors.

An alternate type of filter circuit is also shown in Figure 4-27, the *inductor-input or choke-input filter*. You will recall that inductors oppose change in current and so the inductors in the filter help smooth pulses of rectifier output current, just as the capacitor smoothes voltage pulses. The combination of an inductor and a capacitor in the output filter circuit allows the use of a smaller capacitor for a given level of ripple. Inductors large enough to act as a filter at ac power frequencies are often quite large with many turns of wire on a substantial core. The resistance of the wire would cause too much voltage drop in a high-current, low-voltage supply so inductor-input filters are only found in high-voltage, low-current supplies such as those used for vacuum tube equipment.

Power Supply Safety

Safety is important in power supply design because of the connection to the ac line power and because a lot of energy is supplied by and stored in the supply. Fuses in the primary are used to protect against the hazard of excessive current loads or short circuits, and all power supplies should have an on/off switch to remove ac power when not in use.

Another hazard encountered in power supplies is the stored energy in filter capacitors. If the supply is simply turned off with no load connected, the energy stored in the capacitor has nowhere to go and a significant voltage will be present at the capacitor terminals. *Bleeder resistors* are used to discharge the stored energy when power is removed. Connected across the filter capacitors as shown in Figure 4-27, these resistors have a high enough value that they do not affect normal operation. When power is turned off, if there is no load, the resistors slowly dissipate the stored energy as heat, reducing the capacitor voltage to a safe value within a few seconds. If you are working on a power supply, be sure to wait long enough for the bleeder resistors to do their work after turning power off.

Switch-mode or Switching Supplies

Power supplies that use capacitor- or inductor-input filters and linear voltage regulators to provide filtering and regulation are called *linear supplies*. Another type of power supply filter and regulation circuit uses high-frequency pulses of current to control the output voltage. This is called a *switch-mode supply* or *switching supply*.

In the block diagram of a switching supply in **Figure 4-28**, the ac input is first rectified

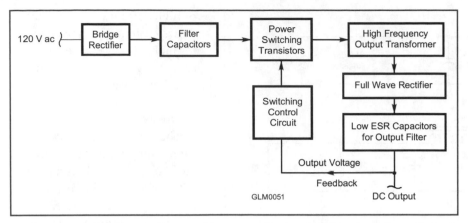

Figure 4-28 — This block diagram illustrates the basic operation of a switched-mode power supply. The power switching transistors are turned on and off at a very high rate (many kHz) so that smaller transformers and filter components can be used.

and filtered. A transistor switch then supplies current pulses to a small inductor or transformer at a very high frequency — 20 kHz or more, compared to 60 Hz for a linear supply — which transfers the energy into another filter capacitor that smoothes the pulses for a steady output voltage. The high frequency of the pulses means that the supply can react quickly to changing current demands. The high frequency also means that small, lightweight inductors and transformers can be used to smooth the pulses and filter the output. The filter capacitors can also be much smaller than in linear supplies because the rapid charging pulses mean that they do not need to store so much energy.

The high frequency of the current pulses places additional demands on the filter capacitors. Along with the need for low ESR, inductance becomes important. A capacitor's construction causes it to have some parasitic inductance, modeled as a single inductance called *equivalent series inductance* (ESL). Capacitors used in switching supplies must have both low ESR and low ESL.

Output Protection

At the very output of both linear and switch-mode supplies, a final protective circuit is employed to prevent applying excessive voltage to the connected equipment in case of a power supply failure. Overvoltage protection monitors the output voltage of the supply. The most common overvoltage protection circuit is called a *crowbar* circuit. When excessive voltage is detected, the crowbar circuit turns on a heavy duty transistor to place a short circuit across the output! The short circuit blows the input protection fuse and removes power from the supply.

Before you go on, study test questions G6B04, G7A01, G7A02, G7A03, G7A04, G7A14, G7A15, G7A16, G7A17 and G7A18. Review this section if you have difficulty.

BATTERIES AND CHARGERS

Battery power operation is important to amateurs. Everyday use of handheld and portable radios requires dependable, high-capacity batteries that can be easily recharged. Emergency and portable operation depends on battery power. Because of these important roles for batteries, the General class exam focuses on the different types of batteries and how to recharge them.

There are two basic types of batteries: *primary* and *secondary*. A primary, or disposable, battery is discarded after it is discharged. Examples of primary batteries include carbon-zinc, alkaline and silver-nickel. Each of these types describes the chemicals that store energy in the battery, called the *battery chemistry*. For emergency operation, disposable

Table 4-8

Battery Types and Characteristics

Battery Style	Chemistry	Type	Full-Charge Voltage (V)	Energy Rating (average, mAh)
AAA	Alkaline	Disposable	1.5	1100
AA	Alkaline	Disposable	1.5	2600-3200
AA	Carbon-Zinc	Disposable	1.5	600
AA	Nickel-Cadmium (NiCd)	Rechargeable	1.2	700
AA	Nickel-Metal Hydride (NiMH)	Rechargeable	1.2	1500 - 2200
AA	Lithium	Disposable	1.7	2100 - 2400
C	Alkaline	Disposable	1.5	7500
D	Alkaline	Disposable	1.5	14,000
9 V	Alkaline	Disposable	9	580
9 V	Nickel-Cadmium (NiCd)	Rechargeable	9	110
9 V	Nickel-Metal Hydride	Rechargeable	9	150
Coin Cells	Lithium	Disposable	3 - 3.3	25 - 1000

Battery Schematic Symbols

+ – Single Cell

+ – Multi Cell

batteries are preferred because battery chargers may not be available without ac power.

A secondary, or rechargeable, battery can be recharged and reused many times. Examples of secondary batteries include nickel-cadmium (NiCd), nickel-metal hydride (NiMH), lithium-ion (Li-ion) and lead-acid. **Table 4-8** lists several common types of batteries and their important characteristics. There is one schematic symbol for batteries with a single cell, and another for those with multiple cells. Note that these symbols are the same for all battery types (NiCd, NiMH, lead acid, and so on).

Larger secondary batteries are also known as *storage batteries*. Storage batteries, such as deep-cycle lead-acid marine or RV storage batteries are often used as an emergency power source to replace a power supply operating from ac power. These batteries are available with liquid electrolyte for vehicle use or with the electrolyte in gel form ("gel-cells"). These batteries are rated as "12 V" batteries, but should actually be maintained at a voltage of 13.8 V. Lead-acid storage batteries can produce useful power until their output voltage drops to approximately 10.5 V, after which the voltage will fall quickly and the battery should be recharged.

Energy Ratings

A battery's energy rating in ampere-hours (Ah) describes its ability to deliver current while still maintaining a steady output voltage. Power output is the product of a battery's voltage and current. When output power (V × A) in watts is multiplied by the time that power is supplied, the result is energy. Batteries are rated in Ah since their voltage is fixed. The Ah rating described how long a battery can supply a given current while maintaining a steady output voltage. "Deep discharge" storage batteries are available with energy capacities as high as 150 Ah.

To get the most energy from a battery, limit the amount of current drawn. A low discharge rate keeps the battery cool inside and minimizes losses from the battery's natural internal resistance. Some types of batteries, such as NiCds, are specially designed to have low internal resistance to supply high discharge currents. A battery will also slowly lose its charge when not in use, called *self-discharge*. The rate of self-discharge varies with battery type. In general, self-discharge can be minimized by keeping the battery cool and dry. Do not freeze batteries because expanding water inside might crack the case or damage the electrodes. If a battery is damp, the moisture on the outside of the battery will supply a path for leakage current to flow directly between the battery terminals, discharging it.

Charging Batteries

Recharging batteries must be done properly to ensure that the battery is returned to its maximum level of charge without damage. First, never attempt to recharge a primary battery such as carbon-zinc or silver-nickel. The chemical reaction that produces energy is not intended to be reversed and often produces gasses and corrosive chemicals that can damage the charging equipment.

There are battery chargers designed specifically for each type of rechargeable battery. Using the correct charger maximizes the life and usefulness of the battery. Heed any manufacturer's warnings about heating or venting of gasses during recharging. For example, lead-acid batteries that aren't sealed can give off explosive hydrogen gas during the recharging process and should always be recharged in a well-ventilated area.

> *Before you go on, study test questions G4E07, G6B13, G6B14, G6B15, G6B16 and G7A20. Review this section if you have difficulty.*

ALTERNATIVE POWER

Sometimes batteries just aren't sufficient to get the job done and a longer-term source of power is required. Generators are widely used, but if you are really "off the grid" and don't have your own personal nuclear power plant, then solar and wind power can be put to work.

Solar Power

What is most often meant by "solar power" is really *photovoltaic conversion* of sunlight directly to electricity. Solar panels and solar cells are made of silicon PN-junctions that are exposed to sunlight. As opposed to transistors and diodes that are quite small, solar cells can be inches across with the PN-junction sandwiched between layers of P- and N-type material. The photons of sunlight are absorbed by electrons that then have enough energy to travel across the PN-junction and create dc current flow. The forward voltage created as the electron crosses the junction is approximately 0.5 V and can be measured as the *open-circuit voltage* of the solar cell.

A solar cell made from silicon (the most common material for cells) can have a *conversion efficiency* of more than 20%. With almost 1 kW per square meter of solar power available, that's a hefty amount of energy for radios! Individual solar cells must be assembled in panel-shaped arrays and the resulting efficiency after losses from resistance and arrangement of the cells is from 10 to 15%. Even then, a large panel can generate well over 100 watts of power in full sunlight. In a 12 V solar panel, strings of 24 cells are connected together to create the necessary voltage. Multiple strings are connected in parallel to supply the desired amount of current. Several panels connected together form an array.

Wind Power

Wind power is really solar power, too, but generated by thermal energy that drives the wind. Wind generators use a dc generator connected to a propeller though a gearbox that keeps the generator spinning at a fast rate even in low wind speeds. Larger wind generators use an electronic controller to regulate the generator output electrically or by controlling propeller blade pitch.

Systems that create energy from wind and solar power require one more component that adds to the cost of using them — a substantial energy storage system. When the sun is down or the wind doesn't blow, no power is available. If excess energy has been stored during periods of peak generation, there can be enough power to supply the operating needs until the winds pick up or the sun rises again. Storage batteries are the usual means of energy storage, and most solar energy systems are designed with battery backup capabilities.

Before you go on, study test questions G4E08, G4E09, G4E10 and G4E11. Review this section if you have difficulty.

CONNECTORS

Connectors are a convenient way to make an electrical connection by using mating electrical contacts. There are quite a few connector styles, but common terms apply to all of them. Pins are contacts that extend out of the connector body, and connectors in which pins make the electrical contact are called "male" connectors. Sockets are hollow, recessed contacts, and connectors with sockets are called "female." Connectors designed to attach to each other are called "mating connectors." Connectors with specially shaped bodies or inserts that require a complementary shape on a mating connector are called *keyed connectors*. Keyed connectors ensure that the connectors can only go together one way, reducing the possibility of damage from incorrect mating.

Plugs are connectors installed on the end of cables and *jacks* are installed on equipment. *Adapters* make connections between two different styles of connector, such as between two different families of RF connectors. Other adapters join connectors of the same family, such as double-male, double-female and gender changers. *Splitters* divide a signal between two connectors.

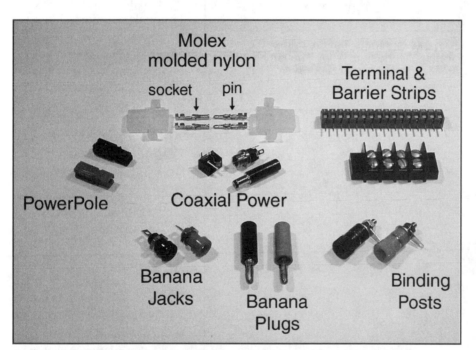

Figure 4-29 — These are the most common connectors used on amateur equipment to make power connections. (Courtesy of Wiley Publishing, *Ham Radio for Dummies*, or *Two-Way Radios & Scanners for Dummies*)

Power Connectors

Amateur Radio equipment uses a variety of power connectors. Some examples are shown in **Figure 4-29**. Most low power amateur equipment uses coaxial power connectors. These are the same type found on consumer electronic equipment that is supplied by a wall transformer or "wall wart" style of power supply. Transceivers and other equipment that requires high current in excess of a few amperes often use Molex connectors (**www.molex.com** — enter "MLX" in the search window) with a white, nylon body housing pins and sockets crimped on to the end of wires.

An emerging standard, particularly among ARES and other emergency communications groups, is the use of Anderson PowerPole connectors (**www.andersonpower.com** — click "Product Brands"). These connectors are "sexless" meaning that any two connectors of the same series can be mated — there are no male or female connectors. By standardizing on a single connector style, equipment can be shared and replaced easily in the field.

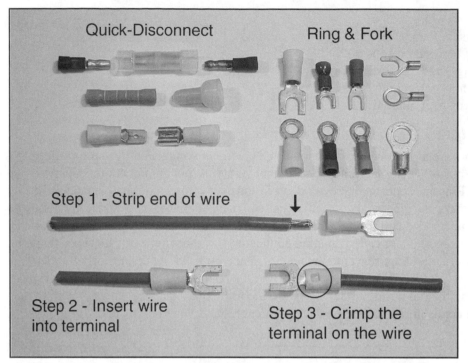

Figure 4-30 — Power connectors often use terminals that are crimped onto the end of wires with special crimping tools. (Courtesy of Wiley Publishing, *Ham Radio for Dummies*, or *Two-Way Radios & Scanners for Dummies*)

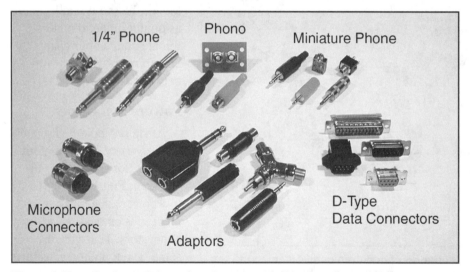

Figure 4-31 — Audio and data signals are carried by a variety of different connectors. Individual cable conductors are either crimped or soldered to the connector contacts.

Molex and PowerPole connectors use crimp terminals (both male and female) installed on the end of wires. A special crimping tool is used to attach the wire to the terminal and the terminal is then inserted into the body of the connector. Making a solid connection requires the use of an appropriate tool — do not use pliers or some other tool to make a crimp connection.

Some equipment uses terminal strips for direct connection to wires or crimp terminals, often with screws. Other equipment uses spring-loaded terminals or binding posts to connect to bare wire ends. **Figure 4-30** shows some common crimp terminals that are installed on the ends of wires using special tools.

Audio and Control Connectors

Consumer audio equipment and Amateur Radio equipment share many of the same connectors for the same uses. Phone plugs and jacks are used for mono and stereo audio circuits. These connectors, shown in **Figure 4-31** come in ¼ inch, ⅛ inch (miniature) and subminiature varieties. The contact at the end of the plug is called the tip and the connector at the base of the plug is the sleeve. If there is a third contact between the tip and sleeve, it is the ring (these are "stereo" phone connectors).

Phono plugs and jacks (sometimes called RCA connectors since they were first used on RCA brand equipment) are used for audio, video and other low-level RF signals. They are also widely used for control signals.

The most common microphone connector on mobile and base station equipment is an 8-pin round connector. On older transceivers you may see 4-pin round connectors used for microphones. RJ-45 modular connectors (see the section on telephone connectors below) are often used in mobile and smaller radios.

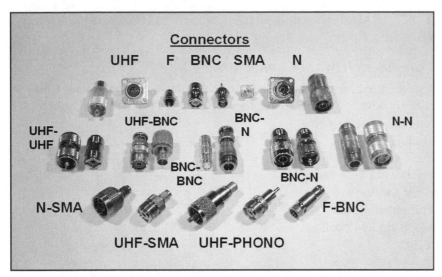

Figure 4-32 — Each type of RF connector is specially made to carry RF signals and preserve the shielding of coaxial cable. Adapters are available to connect one style of connector to another.

RF Connectors

Feed lines used for radio signals require special connectors for use at RF frequencies. The connectors must have approximately the same characteristic impedance as the feed line they are attached to or some of the RF signal will be reflected by the connector. Inexpensive audio and control connectors cannot meet that requirement, nor can they handle the high power levels often encountered in RF equipment. Occasionally, phono connectors are used for HF receiving and low-power transmitting equipment.

By far, the most common connector for RF in amateur equipment is the UHF family shown in **Figure 4-32**. (The UHF designator has nothing to do with frequency.) A PL-259 is the plug that goes on the end of feed lines, and the SO-239 is the jack mounted on equipment. A "barrel" (PL-258) is a double-female adapter that allows two feed lines to be connected together. UHF connectors are typically used up to 150 MHz and can handle legal-limit transmitter power at HF.

UHF connectors have several drawbacks including lack of weatherproofing, poor performance above the 2-meter band and limited power handling at higher frequencies. The Type-N series of RF connectors addresses all of those needs. Type-N connectors are somewhat more expensive than UHF connectors, but they require less soldering and perform better in outdoor use since they are moisture resistant. Type-N connectors can be used to 10 GHz.

For low-power, BNC connectors are often used. BNC connectors are the standard for laboratory equipment, as well, and they are often used for dc and audio connections. BNC connectors are common on handheld radios for antenna connections. The newest handheld transceivers often use small, screw-on SMA type connectors for their antennas, though.

Data Connectors

Digital data is exchanged between computers and pieces of radio equipment more than ever before in the amateur station. The connector styles follow those found on computer equipment.

D-type connectors are used for RS-232 (COM ports) and parallel (LPT port) interfaces. A typical D-type connector has a model number of "DB" followed by the number of connections and a "P" or "S" depending on whether the connector uses pins or sockets. For example, the DB-9P and DB-9S are used for PC COM1 and COM2 serial ports.

USB connectors are becoming more popular in amateur equipment as the computer industry moves to eliminate the bulkier and slower RS-232 interface. A number of manufacturers make devices for interfacing transceivers and station equipment through computer USB ports.

Null modem adapters or cables are used to connect data circuits when direct connections between the data interfaces would connect outputs to outputs and inputs to inputs.

DIN-style, multiple-pin connectors were the standard for computer accessories, such as keyboards and pointing devices like mice. The newest computers connect these devices through a USB port, though. Amateur equipment uses a variety of DIN connectors for accessory connections on transceivers.

Telephone and Computer Network Connectors

Modular connectors are used for telephone and computer network connections. Connector part numbers begin with "RJ." The connectors are crimped on to multiconductor cables with special tools. The RJ11 connector is used for single- and double-line telephone system connection with 4 or 6 contacts. The RJ10 is a 4-contact connector for telephone handset connections. Ethernet computer network connections are made using RJ45 connectors with 8 contacts.

Before you go on, study test questions G4D07, G4D08, G4D09, G4D10 and G4D11. Review this section if you have difficulty.

4.7 Basic Test Equipment

There's more to a radio than just operating it! As you gain experience with radios and accessories, you'll find yourself needing to make some simple checks and tests. You might try your hand at building some equipment and even repairing an ailing radio. To do so, you'll need some basic test equipment, and this section introduces you to some of the common items found on the radio workbench

ANALOG AND DIGITAL METERS

The *volt-ohm-meter* (VOM) is the simplest piece of test equipment and amazingly versatile. A garden-variety meter that can be purchased new for $20 or less can measure voltage, current and resistance, act as a continuity checker, and even test diodes and transistors! For a few more dollars, you can add frequency counting, component value (capacitance, inductance) measurement, and a data interface to your PC to record readings.

There are two types of VOMs: analog and digital, as shown in **Figure 4-33**. The analog meter has a moving needle with calibrated scales on the meter face. While this type of meter can't perform more advanced functions, it is perfectly okay for basic go/no-go testing, tuning and troubleshooting. In fact, experienced hams prefer the analog meter for tweaking a circuit for a peak or null since it's easier to just watch the meter needle move than a numeric display.

The digital meter or DMM (for digital multimeter) has a microprocessor inside that takes care of all the basic functions and adds the ability to count and perform calculations. The digital meter also offers significantly

Figure 4-33 — A digital voltmeter (DVM) shown at A (left) provides precise measurements of voltage, current and resistance. Many models can also act as a frequency counter or component tester. Analog meters (B, right) are often preferable for tuning and adjustments since the needle's movement makes adjusting for a maximum or minimum quite easy.

greater precision (ability to resolve small changes) than an analog meter. Many hams have both a digital and an analog meter to use as the situation demands.

For both meter types, the instrument should affect the circuit being measured to the smallest degree possible. When measuring voltage, the meter should have a high input impedance so that it places the minimum load on the circuit being measured. In a sensitive circuit, the small current required by a voltmeter can affect the circuit's operation. Other useful features include fused current inputs to prevent damage from a temporary overload, peak hold to capture a maximum value, and autoranging to automatically select the proper display range.

Before you go on, study test questions G4B07 and G4B16. Review this section if you have difficulty.

OSCILLOSCOPE

For working with fast-changing audio, data and RF signals, no instrument is more versatile or useful than the *oscilloscope*, often called a "scope." The oscilloscope provides a visual display of voltage against time as shown in **Figure 4-34**. The display can be updated thousands or even millions of times per second, giving the operator a real-time view of a signal's characteristics. This enables the technician to observe complex, fast-changing waveforms that are beyond the abilities of meters to measure. (For an on-line oscilloscope tutorial, see the ARRL's *Hands-On Radio* Web page, **www.arrl.org/tis/info/HTML/Hands-On-Radio**.)

The oscilloscope contains a *cathode-ray tube* (CRT) with a flat front surface. A beam of electrons is directed to the flat front surface, which is coated with a phosphor material that glows when struck by the electron beam. The electron beam is swept across the tube's surface by voltages applied to two sets of *deflection plates*. One set moves the beam horizontally and the other vertically.

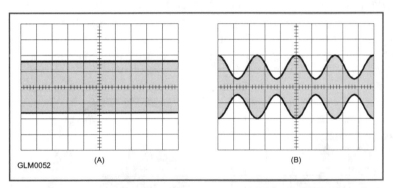

GLM0052   (A)   (B)

Figure 4-34 — Oscilloscope displays of RF signals. At A is an unmodulated carrier. The signal at B is from a full-carrier AM transmitter modulated with a single-frequency sine wave.

External signals from the circuits under test are connected to the scope through horizontal and vertical *channel amplifiers*. The gain of the amplifiers is variable to adjust the sensitivity of the oscilloscope's display. An internal *time base* usually sweeps the electron beam along the horizontal axis at a highly stable, calibrated rate so that the scope can make accurate measurements of time and frequency. The track of the electron beam across the surface of the tube is called a *trace*.

In the amateur station, a *monitoring oscilloscope* is very useful in monitoring transmitted signals by connecting the attenuated RF output of the transmitter to the vertical channel of the oscilloscope. Being able to monitor the transmitter output waveform in real time is of great assistance in adjusting keying waveforms, microphone gain and speech processing. Figure 4-34 shows an unmodulated carrier and an AM carrier modulated by a sine wave. **Figure 4-35** shows a typical keying waveform synchronized to the key closures that turn the transmitter on and off. The operator can clearly see the effects of any adjustments or conditions that might cause distortion or key clicks on the transmitted signal.

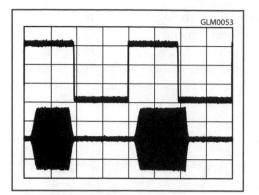

GLM0053

Figure 4-35 — It is easy to see the relationship between the key closure (top trace) and the transmitter output. If the transmitter turns on and off too abruptly or erratically, key clicks can result.

In recent years, oscilloscope manufacturers have begun replacing the bulky CRT with lightweight computer-type screens on digital oscilloscopes that simulate the CRT display. The input signals are converted to digital data and manipulated by a microprocessor to control how the signals are displayed. These digital scopes are becoming affordable for amateurs, both as new and used equipment. Some digital scopes do away with the separate display altogether and use a USB connection to display the signals on a computer.

Before you go on, study test questions G4B01, G4B02, G4B05 and G4B06. Review this section if you have difficulty.

SIGNAL GENERATORS AND TRACERS

Testing or adjusting receivers and transmitters often requires that a known signal be applied as a test. The equipment being tested is then monitored to see how the test signal is received or transmitted. A *signal generator* is the piece of equipment whose RF output signals are similar to those received over the air. The output of a signal generator is applied to the input of a receiver or signal processing circuit in order to test or troubleshoot it. **Figure 4-36** shows an RF signal generator.

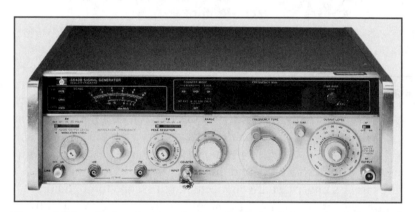 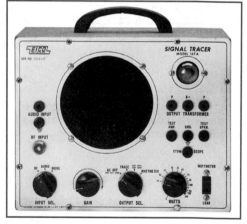

Figure 4-36 — A signal generator's output simulates actual signals that might be received on the air, including CW, AM or FM. Signal tracers are used to troubleshoot receivers by generating signals to test individual stages or by detecting the output of a stage for the technician.

The *signal tracer* shown in Figure 4-36 combines several features in one piece of equipment designed specifically for receiver testing. The signal tracer can act as a simple RF signal generator or function generator, as well as detect and demodulate signals found at various points inside a receiver. Signal tracers are used primarily to identify nonfunctional circuits or stages in receivers. Once the problem has been isolated to a specific stage, an oscilloscope and voltmeter are employed to identify the actual circuit problem.

Before you go on, study test question G4B03. Review this section if you have difficulty.

IMPEDANCE AND RESONANCE MEASUREMENTS

A *noise bridge* is a device that allows you to measure the impedance of antennas and other circuits at different frequencies. The noise bridge, shown in **Figure 4-37**, produces noise over a wide spectrum and applies it to the circuit or antenna being tested. A receiver is connected to the noise bridge and tuned to the frequency of interest. The noise bridge's calibrated resistance and reactance controls are then adjusted until minimum noise is received. The noise bridge is orders of magnitude less expensive and much easier to use than laboratory equipment.

It is often necessary to measure impedance when building or testing a new antenna or when performing maintenance on an existing antenna. A noise bridge can also be used to "pre-tune" an antenna impedance matcher or tuner by setting its resistance control to 50 Ω and the reactance control to 0 Ω. The receiver is set to the operating frequency and the tuner adjusted for minimum noise. All that is then required is a short test transmission at full power. That's a great way to reduce electrical stress on your transmitter and tuner and it also keeps annoying test signals off the air!

Figure 4-37 — A noise bridge works with a receiver to determine impedance at a particular frequency. The noise bridge is connected between the unknown impedance and the receiver. It generates noise that can be heard on the receiver. The bridge is then adjusted until the noise is minimized. The load impedance is then displayed on the bridge's controls.

An incredibly useful instrument that has made antenna testing much easier is the *antenna analyzer* shown in **Figure 4-38**. The analyzer contains a CW signal generator, a frequency counter, an SWR bridge and an impedance meter. Different models of analyzers can display both resistive and reactance values of antenna impedance as well as the precise frequency at which the measurement is being made. By connecting the analyzer directly to the antenna feed line, SWR can be checked without having to transmit a signal at high power. The battery-powered analyzers are also small enough to be part of a tool kit so that antennas can be tested at the point of adjustment without having to go back into the shack to make measurements.

Noise bridges and antenna analyzers can measure a lot of things, but they can't measure the resonant frequency of a circuit, such as an oscillator's resonant tank circuit or an antenna "trap" that isolates sections of antenna. That job falls to the *dip meter*. A dip meter consists of a tunable oscillator and a meter showing oscillator output voltage. The test circuit's resonant frequency is measured by coupling the dip meter oscillator to the circuit and adjusting the oscillator's frequency until a sharp dip in the meter level is seen at the resonant frequency.

A related device, the *wavemeter*, is an adjustable resonant LC circuit that is held near an operating oscillator or amplifier. The wavemeter is adjusted until the metering circuits of the circuit under test show a sharp change, indicating the wavemeter circuit has absorbed some of the energy.

Figure 4-38 — An SWR analyzer, such as the MFJ 269 shown here, is handy for testing transmission lines and antennas. It displays SWR and impedance at frequencies of 1.5 to 170 MHz and across the 70 cm band.

Before you go on, study test questions G4B04, G4B12, G4B13 and G4B14. Review this section if you have difficulty.

FIELD STRENGTH AND RF POWER METERS

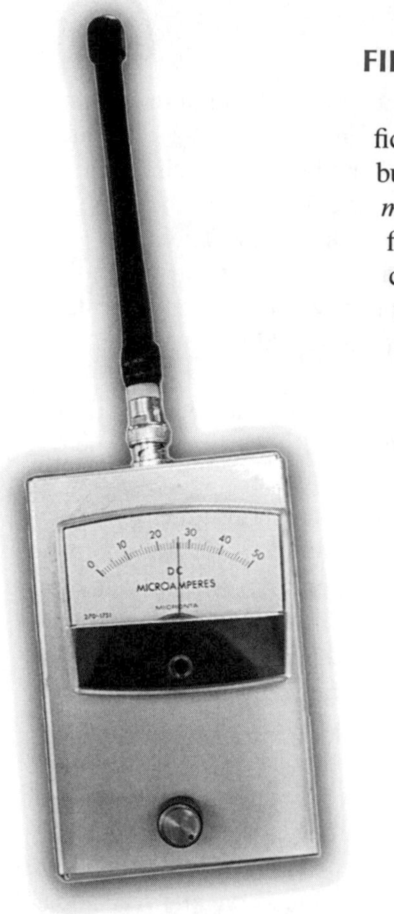

Another useful set of antenna tests and diagnostics concern the radiation efficiency and pattern of the antenna. A receiver can make these measurements, but it is often inconvenient to take a receiver into the field. A *field strength meter* is the better choice for that job, making calibrated readings of electric field strength. **Figure 4-39** shows a typical unit. While signal strength levels can be inferred from measurements of power and SWR, a field strength meter actually measures the transmitted signal level. It is often used to compare relative levels of RF output during antenna and transmitter adjustments.

By placing the field strength meter in one location and rotating the antenna, the radiation pattern of the antenna can be measured. Conversely, the meter can be carried to different locations to determine the radiation pattern of a fixed antenna, such as a wire beam or array. Finally, the field strength meter can even be used for radio direction finding or hidden transmitter hunting when close to the signal source.

Another power measurement tool is the *directional wattmeter* shown in **Figure 4-40**. Placed in a transmission line, usually at the transmitter output, the directional wattmeter can measure both forward and reflected power in the line. Some meters can measure both simultaneously with independent meters or by turning a switch or power sensing element. Power meters are used to adjust transmitter and amplifier output circuits and drive levels.

Standing wave ratio (SWR) can be calculated from forward and reflected power measurements made using a directional wattmeter. SWR is then calculated using the following formula:

$$SWR = \frac{1 + \sqrt{P_R / P_F}}{1 - \sqrt{P_R / P_F}}$$

Figure 4-39 — A field strength meter is used to check relative performance of an antenna by measuring the electric field intensity.

Figure 4-40 — The Bird Model 43 directional wattmeter uses sensing elements designed for a specific frequency range and power level. Forward and reflected power are read by rotating the sensing element. (One sensing element is plugged into the meter, and four other elements for different power levels and frequency ranges are shown below the meter.)

Before you go on, study test questions G4B08, G4B10, G4B11 and G4B15. Review this section if you have difficulty.

Chapter 5

Radio Signals and Equipment

After learning about the fundamentals of electronics and components, you're ready to "build" on that knowledge. In this section, we study real radios and investigate what's going on as adjustments are made. We'll start with the building blocks and then put them together into complete packages — transmitters, receivers and amplifiers. You'll be getting deeper into circuits and the structure of radio equipment, so you may need to brush up on your understanding of schematics and block diagrams. A helpful tutorial is available on the *General Class License Manual* Web site, **www.arrl.org/gclm**. This leads to the things you'll need to know about putting a station together and managing it. Set the power switch to ON and let's get busy!

5.1 Signal Review

Even though you studied the following terms and concepts for your Technician class license, it helps to start by reviewing the basics of radio signals. A radio signal at one frequency whose strength never changes is called a *continuous wave*, abbreviated CW. Adding information to a signal by modifying it in some way, such as changing its frequency, phase angle or amplitude, is called *modulation*. The method of modulation that carries the information is the signal's *mode*. The simplest mode is a continuous wave turned on and off in a coded pattern, such as CW.

Recovering the information from a modulated signal is called *demodulation*. A signal that doesn't carry any information is *unmodulated*. If speech is the information used to modulate a signal, the result is a *voice mode* or *phone* (short for *radiotelephone*) signal. If data is the information used to modulate a signal, the result is a *data mode* or *digital mode* signal. *Analog* modes carry information such as speech that can be understood directly by a human. Digital or data modes carry information as data characters between two computers.

Any characteristic of a signal can be varied to carry information if the variations are observable at the receiving end to recover the information. Three characteristics that can be modulated are the signal's *amplitude* or strength, its frequency and its phase. The term *instantaneous* when applied to amplitude, frequency or phase refers to the value of those characteristics at a specific instant in time.

AMPLITUDE MODULATED MODES

Varying the power or amplitude of a signal to add speech or data information is called *amplitude modulation* or AM. The information is contained in the signal's *envelope* — the maximum values of the instantaneous power for each cycle. The process of recovering speech or music by following the envelope of an AM signal is called *detection*. An AM signal is composed of a *carrier* and two *sidebands*. The total power of an AM signal is divided between the carrier and sidebands. The AM signal's carrier is a continuous wave whose amplitude does not change and contains no information.

An AM signal modulated by a tone has two sidebands that are present as steady, unchanging signals as long as the tone is transmitted. The *upper sideband* (USB) is higher in frequency than the carrier by the frequency of the tone. The *lower sideband* (LSB) is lower in frequency than the carrier. The information to recover the tone is contained in the amplitude of the sidebands and their differences in frequency from that of the carrier. Each sideband contains an exact copy of the modulating signal.

Before you go on, study test questions G8A01, G8A05, G8A06 and G8A07. Review this section if you have difficulty.

An AM signal with the carrier and one sideband removed by electronic circuitry is called a *single sideband* signal (SSB). SSB transmissions have a superior range compared to AM because all of the SSB signal's power is contained in the remaining sideband. SSB's smaller bandwidth also makes it possible to fit more signals in a fixed range of frequencies. The wider AM signals tend to have a fuller frequency response that sounds "warmer" on the air.

ANGLE MODULATED MODES

Modes that vary the frequency of a signal to add speech or data information are called *frequency modulation* or FM. The frequency is varied in proportion to the amplitude of the modulating signal. The amount that an FM signal's frequency varies when modulated is called *deviation*. *Phase modulation* (PM) is created by varying a signal's *phase angle*. Receivers can demodulate FM and PM with the same demodulator circuits.

FM and PM are called *angle modulation* because both techniques modulate the signal by varying the amount of time it takes for the signal to make a 360-degree cycle (FM) or the relative phase difference between the signal and some reference phase (PM). FM and PM signals have one carrier and many sidebands. These signals have a *constant power* signal, whether modulated or not.

BANDWIDTH DEFINITION

Composite signals are groups of individual signals that combine to create a complex

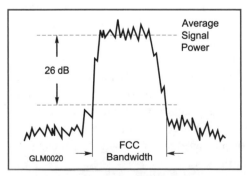

Figure 5-1 — The FCC defines bandwidth as "the width of a frequency band outside of which the mean [average] power of the transmitted signal is attenuated at least 26 dB below the mean power."

Table 5-1
Amateur Signal Bandwidths

Type of Signal	Typical Bandwidth
AM voice	6 kHz
Amateur television	6 MHz
SSB voice	2 to 3 kHz
Digital using SSB	500 to 3000 Hz (0.5 to 3 kHz)
CW	100 to 300 Hz (0.1 to 0.3 kHz)
FM voice	5 to 15 kHz

signal. Composite signals have *components* that may cover a range of frequencies. The difference in frequency between the lowest and highest component of a composite signal is the signal's *bandwidth*.

The FCC has a more specific definition of bandwidth in section §97.3(a)(8): "*Bandwidth*. The width of a frequency band outside of which the mean [average] power of the transmitted signal is attenuated at least 26 dB below the mean power within the band." **Figure 5-1** illustrates how this measurement is made.

The FCC limits signal bandwidth so that many stations and types of signals can share the limited amount of spectrum space. **Table 5-1** lists the bandwidth of the most common amateur signals.

Before you go on, study test questions G8A02, G8A03 and G8A11. Review this section if you have difficulty.

5.2 Digital Modes

Digital communications systems exchange data between two computing systems. A computing system is anything that is capable of exchanging digital data. That can mean a computer, a data terminal or a radio with a remote control interface, to name a few. Amateur Radio is home to experimenters trying new protocols and modes for digital communications. More and more hams are using digital modes such as radioteletype, PSK31 and packet every day. Even Morse code is rightfully considered a digital mode!

The fundamental unit of data is the bit — a 0 or 1 that represents all or part of a binary number. In some modes, such as RTTY or packet, bits are sent individually over the air one at a time. (The part of the communication system that involves radio transmission and reception of signals is called the *air link*.) The bits are transmitted as audio tones over a radio link. A *modem* (short for modulator-demodulator) translates the bits into tones (and back again). If you listen to an older fax machine or modem exchange data, you can hear the bits being exchanged as a sequence of two tones changing rapidly. (This is frequency-shift keying, discussed later.)

Advanced systems save transmission time by grouping the bits together in special coding systems, sending combinations of more than one tone at once and varying the phase relationships between the tones. Each unique combination is one *symbol* and the number of symbols sent each second is the symbol rate. Baud (after Baudot, the inventor of the radioteletype code) is the name for symbol (or signaling) rate. If one bit is sent in each symbol, then baud and bit rate are the same. As more and more bits are encoded in each symbol, the bit rate will be higher than the symbol rate.

It is also important to know the typical duty cycle for a digital mode because most Amateur Radio transmitters are not designed to operate at full power output for an extended time. When you are operating CW, for example, the transmitter is turned on and off to form the Morse code characters so that the transmitter is only operating at full power about 40 to 50% of the time. During the off times, the amplifier stage cools sufficiently to allow full power operation. When you are operating single-sideband voice, the trans-

Digital Mode Definitions

When diving into the details of the many amateur digital modes, it's helpful to define some useful terms.

✔ Bit rate — the number of digital bits sent from one computing system to the other per second.

✔ Baud or bauds — the number of symbols that are sent from one computing system to the other per second, also known as signaling rate and symbol rate.

✔ Duty cycle — the ratio of time that the transmitter is on to the total of on time and off time.

✔ Protocol — the rules that control the method used to exchange data between two systems.

✔ Mode — the combination of a protocol and modulation method.

✔ Stack — the set of software and hardware that implements a protocol in a computing system.

mitter is producing full power only when your voice reaches maximum amplitude. For a typical SSB conversation, the transmitter is operating at full power only about 20 to 25% of the time.

When you are operating some data modes, however, your transmitter may be operating at full power the entire time you are transmitting. For Baudot radioteletype the transmitter is producing full output power, switching between the mark and space tones of the code, so the duty cycle is 100%. For PSK31 and similar modes, the transmitter is producing full power for virtually the entire transmit time, so the duty cycle is nearly 100%. PACTOR, packet radio and a few other modes have slightly reduced duty cycles because the transmitter sends some data and then waits to receive an acknowledgement. If you are operating a high-duty-cycle mode you should reduce your transmit power to prevent overheating the amplifier. Reduce your transmitter power to about 50% of maximum output power for most data modes.

The following sections do not by any means cover all of the different digital modes used in Amateur Radio, just those that are part of the General class examination. More digital modes are being invented by hams all the time! If you'd like to know more about digital communications in Amateur Radio, check out some of the references at **www.arrl.org/gclm**.

> *Before you go on, study test questions G8B09 and G8B10. Review this section if you have difficulty.*

FREQUENCY SHIFT KEYING (FSK) MODES

Frequency shift keying (FSK) is a method of digital communications in which the individual bits of data are encoded as shifts in signal frequency. In true FSK, the frequency of the transmitter is shifted by a digital data signal from the computer representing the 1s and 0s of the code. More commonly, AFSK (audio frequency shift keying) is used. The transmitter's carrier frequency is kept constant while audio tones modulate the transmitter through the microphone input. AFSK is a convenient method, but the operator must be careful to manage the audio level to avoid noise and distortion that could adversely affect signal quality or cause interference to nearby stations.

Whether FSK or AFSK is used, the rate at which symbols are sent affects the amount of frequency shift required. The faster the symbol rate (or keying rate), the greater the frequency shift required. This is because the closer the tones are in frequency, the longer it takes the receiving system to discriminate between them. Tones must be spaced far enough apart in frequency for the receiver to be able to determine which tone is being sent during the time interval in which the tone is present.

RADIOTELETYPE (RTTY)

The oldest (and still very popular) form of ham radio digital communication is radioteletype, known as RTTY or "ritty." Originally, bulky military and commercial surplus teleprinters and terminal units (modems) were used by hams to communicate using RTTY. Today a sound card and modem software does the conversion between audio tones and characters simply and at low cost.

RTTY uses the Baudot code that represents (encodes) each text character as a sequence of 5 bits as shown in **Figure 5-2**. An initial bit (the *start bit*) and an inter-character pause (the *stop bit*) are used to synchronize the transmitting and receiving stations. With only 5 bits for encoding data, there can be only 2^5 or 32 different characters, not enough for all of the English alphabet, numerals and punctuation. Two special codes, LTRS and FIGS, are used to switch between two tables of characters, increasing the number of available characters to 62 (not including the LTRS and FIGS codes).

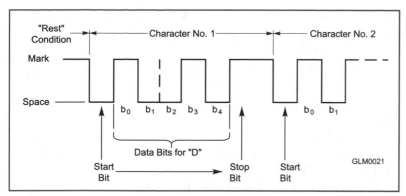

Figure 5-2 — The Baudot timing sequence for the bit pattern that encodes the letter "D." Start and Stop bits are required to allow the receiving and transmitting systems to synchronize. Mark and Space are represented as audio tones sent by the transmitter.

RTTY uses FSK to send each 5-bit code as a sequence of tones. The standard tone frequencies are 2125 Hz (the *mark* tone) and 2295 Hz (the *space* tone). The difference between them, 170 Hz, is called the signal's *shift*. Other tone pairs and shifts are used, as well. When using AFSK, LSB is the standard sideband to use.

MISCELLANEOUS FSK MODES

Amateurs also use other forms of FSK protocols. Two popular FSK protocols are MFSK16 and MT63. MFSK16 stands for Multiple Frequency Shift Keying and uses 16 separate tones, all 15.625 Hz apart, so that the entire set can be received through one HF CW 500 Hz filter. The protocol sends error correction information with the data. Error-free communications is possible at up to 40 WPM typing speeds. Even when operated without error correction, MFSK16 performs well in the weak-signal environment of HF.

Another popular FSK mode is MT63 (Multi Tone 63), which uses 64 different tones spread over a 1 kHz channel. By spreading the information across so many tones and using sophisticated digital signal processing, MT63 is effective even in the presence of severe noise. It has a wide bandwidth of up to 1 or 2 kHz, making it difficult to use in crowded band segments.

Before you go on, study test questions G2E01, G2E05, G2E06 and G8B08. Review this section if you have difficulty.

PHASE-SHIFT KEYING (PSK) MODES

If you listen to a modern dialup modem making a call, initially you'll hear the warbling whistle of frequency shift keying at the beginning of the "conversation," followed by faster tone variations and then what sounds like buzzing noise. That "training sequence" is the modems changing from frequency shift keying to an encoded sequence in which combinations of bits (symbols) are sent encoded as the phase relationship between tones.

The most common type of phase shift is to simply invert the tone waveform, shifting its phase by 180°. The difference in phase can be measured with respect to the phase of the same signal at an earlier time (see PSK31) or with respect to some other tone — advanced modem protocols use that method. The rapid changes in phase are heard by the human ear as a raspy noise or buzz — the sign of PSK signals on the air received by a CW or SSB receiver.

Saving Time with Varicode

An important innovation of PSK31 is its use of *Varicode.* Instead of using a fixed number of bits to represent each character, Varicode uses short codes for common characters (like "E") and longer codes for others. Just as in Morse code, this saves a great deal of time.

PSK31

The most popular PSK mode is PSK31. The "31" stands for the baud rate of the protocol, actually 31.25 baud. That may sound slow, but it is just right for keyboard-to-keyboard QSOs. PSK31 can support typing rates of up to 50 WPM under good conditions.

PSK31 sends a single tone, encoding each symbol as reversals of the tone's phase at regular intervals. Symbols are sent continually, with a reversal of phase from one interval to the next representing a "0" and no reversal a "1". (Two intervals of transmission are required to send one symbol.) If you listen to a PSK31 signal on the air, you'll hear a steady buzz with short variations as one station types characters. Zeroes are sent continuously when no other data is present so that the transmitter and receiver stay synchronized — you can hear the pauses as periods of consistent, unvarying buzz.

Before you go on, study test question G2E02. Review this section if you have difficulty.

PACKET MODES

Packet modes are derived from computer-to-computer network protocols. Packet protocols, developed in the early days of computing, are the basis of the modern protocols used for the Internet today. Hams adapted those protocols to be used over radio links, creating packet radio, PACTOR and other communications systems.

Packet Basics

Packet refers to the structure of the data transmitted over the air as shown in **Figure 5-3**. While there are many different packet protocols, all of them use the same basic structure.

• *Header* — contains bit patterns that allow the receiver to synchronize with the packet's structure, control and routing information, and sometimes error detection and correction information.

• *Data* — the data to be exchanged between computing systems, it is often compressed or packed for efficiency.

• *Trailer* — additional control or status information and data used for error detection.

The process of packaging data within a packet structure is called *encapsulation*. Packets from one protocol can be treated as data by another protocol, so that entire protocols can be encapsulated. In fact, that is the basis for the popular TCP/IP protocol pair used for Internet connections. The Internet Protocol (IP) encapsulates packets from the Transport Control Protocol (TCP) and carries them to the destination.

If the packets contain error detection data, it is possible for the protocol to provide *reliable transport*. The most common error detection mechanism is a Cyclic Redundancy Check or CRC. The CRC is a number calculated from the contents of the packet and transmitted with the data. The receiving system performs the same calculation and if the results match, accepts the data as transmitted without error. If a mismatch is detected, the protocol requests that the packet be retransmitted. The system will continue to retransmit a packet until it is received without errors or the time limit for retransmission is exceeded. In that way, corrupted data is never accepted.

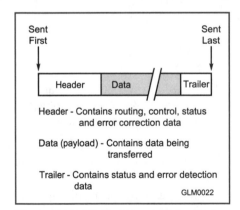

Figure 5-3 — Packet communication systems package data with control and routing information and add error detection information. Different packet protocols use different sets of information and methods of packaging.

Packet Radio

Packet radio, used almost exclusively on VHF and UHF bands, is based on the computer network protocol X.25. Amateurs adapted it to radio transmission instead of transmission over network cables and renamed the protocol AX.25. Packets are exchanged using VHF FM voice transceivers at 1200 or 9600 baud. Packet does not work well on HF because the data is easily disrupted by noise and fading, even at slow signaling rates of 300 baud.

Packet radio is used for keyboard-to-keyboard communications, bulletin board systems, data links for email systems such as *Winlink*, and DX spotting networks called *clusters*. The Automatic Position Reporting System (APRS) also uses packet radio for stations to report their locations. Relay stations that store and forward packets to other stations are called *digipeaters*.

PACTOR

The RTTY protocol is not designed to manage transmission errors. As a result, text is frequently garbled, particularly in the noisy, fading environment of HF radio. To improve communications reliability, Teletype Over Radio (TOR) systems were developed, such as AMTOR, G-TOR and others. These systems send short bursts of characters with error detection and correction data. TOR modes are definitely more reliable, but the original versions were still quite slow, particularly in the presence of interference or noise.

In response, the PACTOR protocol was developed to combine the best features of packet protocols (the packet structure) with the error management of TOR modes. PACTOR is used mostly on HF, where it gives excellent performance on HF channels. There are three flavors of PACTOR: PACTOR I, II and III. The performance of PACTOR I has been greatly exceeded by PACTOR II, but is still in use. PACTOR III is a sophisticated protocol capable of up to 5.2 kbps performance over HF channels under good conditions. It requires special signal processing equipment; PACTOR I and II can be used with regular computers.

Before you go on, study test question G2E03. Review this section if you have difficulty.

5.3 Radio's Building Blocks

Nearly all radios are made up of a few fundamental types of circuits. The way in which the circuit designers choose to build those circuits varies quite a bit, but the basic functions of the circuit are the same. In this section we cover four of those circuits; oscillators, mixers, multipliers and modulators. You'll learn the functions and important characteristics of each.

OSCILLATORS

The function of an oscillator is to produce a pure sine wave with no noise or distortion — as close to a single-frequency signal as possible. The block diagram symbol for an oscillator (a circle with a sine wave inside) is shown in **Figure 5-4** along with the fundamental circuit that makes an oscillator work.

An oscillator consists of an amplifier (the triangle is the amplifier's block diagram symbol) that increases signal amplitude (*gain*) and a *feedback* circuit to route some of the amplifier's output signal back to its input. If at any frequency, the product of the amplifier's gain and the amount of feedback is greater than unity, the circuit's output will be self-sustaining, called *oscillation*. To make an oscillator produce a single-frequency output, the feedback circuit must include a filter so that feedback is present at only the intended frequency.

An oscillator's output frequency can be fixed or variable. There are three basic types of fixed-frequency oscillators: RC, LC and crystal.

An RC oscillator's feedback circuit is made up of resistors (R) and capacitors (C). Because of the combination of reactance and resistance, the RC circuit shifts the phase of the feedback circuit

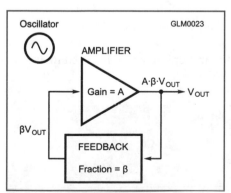

Figure 5-4 — An oscillator consists of an amplifier with feedback from the output to input. The product of gain and feedback ratio must be greater than 1 at the frequency of oscillation.

so that the resulting signal, when applied to the amplifier's input, reinforces the output signal, building up a steady output signal. The amount of phase shift is determined by the *time constants* of the resistors and capacitors in the RC feedback circuit. RC oscillators are used for audio and low-frequency radio oscillators.

The LC oscillator's feedback circuit consists of an inductor (L) and capacitor (C) connected in parallel or series to form a resonant circuit, often called a *tank circuit* because it stores electrical energy like a mechanical flywheel. The resonant frequency of the LC circuit, determined by the values of L and C, is the frequency of the oscillator. LC oscillators are more stable than RC oscillators and can be used throughout the radio frequency spectrum.

A quartz crystal is often substituted for the LC tank circuit, creating a *crystal oscillator*. The quartz crystal acts like a resonant LC circuit and is orders of magnitude more stable than an LC circuit. Crystal oscillators are used whenever an accurate, stable signal source is required.

A *variable-frequency oscillator* (VFO) whose output frequency can be adjusted is used to tune a radio to different frequencies. The frequency of the oscillator is adjusted by varying the value of one or more components in the feedback circuit. In radio circuits, VFOs are usually created by varying the capacitance of the LC feedback circuit, although some designs vary the inductance. Two other widely used VFO circuits are the *phase-locked loop* (PLL) and *direct digital synthesizer* (DDS).

Before you go on, study test questions G7B07, G7B08 and G7B09. Review this section if you have difficulty.

MIXERS

A key function in both receivers and transmitters is to be able to change the frequency of a signal as you will see in the following sections. The circuit that performs this job is called a *mixer*. The block diagram symbol for a mixer is shown in **Figure 5-5**. The most common application of a mixer is also shown in the figure.

A mixer circuit combines two input frequencies, f_1 and f_2, and produces their sum and difference at its output. This process is called *heterodyning*. For example, if $f_1 = 14.050$ MHz and $f_2 = 3.35$ MHz, the output of the mixer will contain signals at both 10.7 MHz ($f_1 - f_2$) and at 17.4 MHz ($f_1 + f_2$). It is up to the following circuits to select the desired signal from the pair and make use of it. A mixer can change a signal to any other frequency — the input and output frequencies do not have to be related in any way.

In radio circuits, the input f_1 to the mixer is usually referred to as the RF input because that signal is usually associated with a received or transmitted signal. Input f_2 is usually labeled the *local oscillator* (LO) because it represents a reference signal produced locally by an oscillator within the equipment. All of the mixer outputs are called *mixing products*.

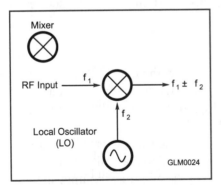

Figure 5-5 — The mixer combines signals of different frequencies, producing signals at the sum and difference frequency. Mixers are used to change or shift the frequency of signals.

Before you go on, study test questions G8B03 and G8B12. Review this section if you have difficulty.

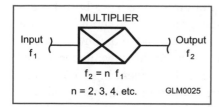

Figure 5-6 — A multiplier is a special type of tuned amplifier that creates harmonics of an input signal and then selects the desired harmonic at its output. The output of low frequency oscillators or modulators can be multiplied to frequencies at which it might be difficult to operate directly.

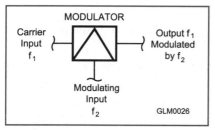

Figure 5-7 — The general symbol can be used for a modulator of any type — AM, FM or SSB.

MULTIPLIERS

A circuit that acts similarly to a mixer is the *multiplier*. Instead of creating the sum and difference of two input frequencies, a multiplier creates an integer multiple of an input frequency. The block diagram symbol for a multiplier circuit is shown in **Figure 5-6**. Multipliers are often used when a stable VHF or UHF signal is required, but constructing an oscillator at that frequency would be difficult. A low-frequency oscillator supplies the multiplier input and the output is tuned to the desired harmonic of the input signal. Multipliers are also used in FM transmitters as you will see in a following section.

MODULATORS

Modulators are the circuits that perform the neat trick of adding information to a carrier signal, either as amplitude, frequency or phase variations. The block diagram symbol for a modulator is shown in **Figure 5-7**. The input signal on the left-hand side is usually the unmodulated input, the input from below is the signal whose information is to be added to the unmodulated input, and the output is on the right. (You may have noticed that all four of the block diagram symbols support the left-to-right signal flow that is recommended for schematics and block diagrams.) The same symbol is used to represent demodulator circuits, as well.

Amplitude Modulators

Amplitude modulation was originally generated by varying the power supply voltage to the output circuit of a CW transmitter. You can easily imagine this process: As the voltage is varied, the amplitude of the output signal's envelope follows along. This is called *plate* or *collector (or drain) modulation* because the voltage that is varied is connected to a vacuum tube plate or a transistor's collector or drain. A modulation transformer was used to add and subtract an amplified version of the operator's voice to the power supply voltage, creating the modulation.

After SSB became popular, transmitters were required to generate both SSB and AM signals. SSB cannot be generated by amplitude modulating an output circuit — different techniques must be used at lower signal levels. However, AM and *double-sideband* (DSB) can be generated by a *balanced modulator*. DSB is the same as AM with the carrier removed, leaving the upper and lower sidebands as shown in **Figure 5-8**.

A balanced modulator is a special type of mixer where f_1 is the carrier signal and f_2 is the modulating signal. Take another look at Figure 5-5. The output signal, shown as $f_1 \pm f_2$, is exactly a DSB signal — a pair of

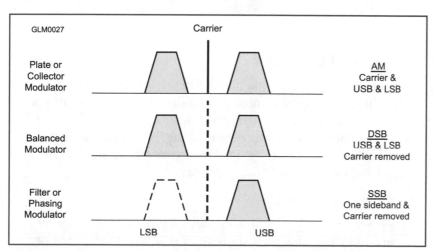

Figure 5-8 — The spectrum of three types of AM signals. AM has both sidebands and the carrier. DSB removes the carrier, but has the same bandwidth as AM. SSB removes one sideband and has the lowest bandwidth of the three.

frequencies without a carrier signal. The balanced modulator circuit produces DSB because it cancels the carrier signal internally. AM can be generated by a balanced modulator if the circuit is intentionally unbalanced, allowing the carrier to reappear in the output signal.

Starting with a DSB signal, SSB can be generated by filtering out the unwanted sideband. This is the filter method of generating SSB. The phasing method of generating SSB signals without filters uses a pair of balanced modulators fed by carrier and modulating signals that are 90° out of phase. The resulting DSB signals are then added together, with the result being an SSB signal.

Frequency and Phase Modulators

Frequency and phase modulation are examples of *angle modulation* in which the amplitude of the modulated signal is unchanged, but its frequency and phase are varied. Frequency modulation is the result when the frequency of the modulated signal deviates only in proportion to the modulating signal's amplitude. Phase modulation occurs if the deviation is proportional to both the modulating signal's amplitude and frequency. The design of the modulator circuit determines whether the output signal is FM or PM. It is important to note that except for very specific circumstances, FM and PM sound identical on the air and can both be demodulated by the same circuits.

The most common method of performing angle modulation is a *reactance modulator*, shown in **Figure 5-9**. The LC tank circuit determines the frequency of a fixed-frequency oscillator. Varactor diodes act as small capacitors that vary with the modulating input signal. The change in capacitance affects the capacitance of the tank circuit, changing the oscillator's frequency. A reactance modulator can be used to generate frequency or phase modulation. If the modulator is connected to the oscillator tuned circuit, then the frequency will change when the modulation is applied, creating frequency modulation. To make phase modulation, the reactance modulator is connected to the tuned amplifier following the oscillator. When modulation is applied, the phase of the carrier will be changed but the average frequency will not be changed.

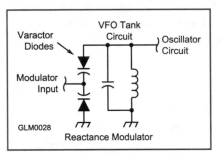

Figure 5-9 — The varactor diodes in a reactance modulator vary their capacitance in response to the modulating signal's amplitude. The variations in capacitance shift the frequency of the tank circuit, producing phase modulation.

Before you go on, study test questions G8A04 and G8A12. Review this section if you have difficulty.

5.4 Transmitter Structure

From the building blocks are assembled the equipment of radio — transmitters and receivers. In this section, you'll learn how the components produce the many signals you hear on the air — CW, SSB and FM. Armed with that understanding, you'll understand the effects of transmitter controls and how to keep your signal "clean." We'll take a close look at amplifiers — the business end of a transmitter — and how to use them properly. The goal is for you to transmit a signal you can be proud of, every time.

AM MODES

As you learned in previous sections, CW, AM and SSB are all types of amplitude modulation. They can all be generated by the same basic transmitter structure, the topic of this section.

CW Transmitters

The simplest transmitter is a two-stage CW rig, shown in **Figure 5-10**. It consists only

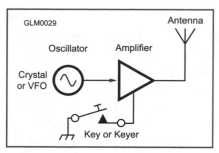

Figure 5-10 — The simplest transmitter consists of the oscillator and amplifier and a means of turning the output signal on and off — the key.

of an oscillator and an amplifier, with the amplifier turned on and off by a key or keyer. Many amateurs began their on-the-air operating careers with a simple transmitter just like this — one tube or transistor for a crystal-controlled oscillator and a larger tube or transistor for the amplifier! Using a crystal restricts the transmitter to one frequency per crystal, but the output frequency is quite stable. If the crystal oscillator is replaced with a variable-frequency oscillator, it becomes a VFO-controlled transmitter.

The oscillator frequently includes a *buffer* amplifier that isolates the oscillator from the output amplifier. This makes the signal cleaner and less prone to *chirp*, a rapid change in frequency during key-down periods caused by power supply or load changes. The output amplifier often includes two amplifiers, as well: a *driver* stage and a *power amplifier* (PA) stage. The driver amplifier brings the low-power oscillator output signal to a sufficient strength to drive the PA to full power.

In a VFO-controlled transmitter that operates on more than one band, mixers are used to change the transmitter output frequency band without changing the VFO frequency range. This keeps the VFO design simple and stable for good signal quality. **Figure 5-11** shows a simple scheme for a three band, VFO-controlled transmitter. The mixer input from the VFO always covers the same frequency range. The local oscillator (LO) outputs a signal on one of three frequencies determined by which crystal is switched in. A filter tuned to one of the three bands follows the mixer to eliminate the undesired sum or difference frequency.

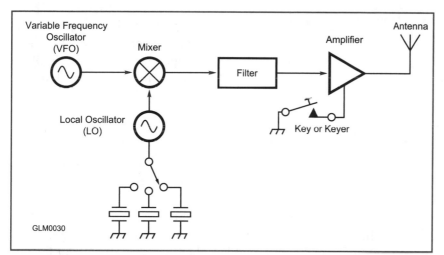

Figure 5-11 — By changing the frequency of the Local Oscillator (LO), the VFO's output can be shifted from band to band, creating a multiband transmitter.

Table 5-2
Three-Band VFO - LO Combinations

Band	VFO Frequency (MHz)	LO Frequency (MHz)	Transmit Frequency (MHz)
80 m	5.000-5.100	8.6	3.500-3.600
40 m	5.000-5.100	12.1	7.000-7.100
20 m	5.000-5.100	19.1	14.000-14.100

Table 5-2 shows one combination of oscillator frequencies that generate a signal in the 80, 40 and 20 meter amateur bands. The VFO always tunes a frequency range starting at 5 MHz. The difference of the LO and input frequencies results in a frequency on the desired band. An LO frequency lower than the VFO frequency could be used on the 40 meter and 20 meter bands, but not on 80 meters where the VFO frequency is already higher than the output frequency. A filter between the mixer and the output stages removes the undesired signal from the mixer output.

AM PHONE TRANSMITTERS

To change the CW transmitters to AM phone, a modulator stage is added between the oscillator and mixer. **Figure 5-12** takes the three-band CW transmitter and modifies it to become an SSB phone transmitter. Voice signals from a microphone (mic) are processed by a speech amplifier and input to the balanced modulator. The VFO, renamed the Carrier Oscillator, is the other input to the balanced modulator. The output is a DSB signal, so a filter is required to remove the undesired sideband. (USB signals are the standard on 20 meters and LSB on 80 and 40 meters.) A mixer then converts the signal to the correct frequency as before. This SSB transmitter can also produce AM signals by unbalancing the modulator so that the AM carrier is present in the modulator output. For SSB signals, the FCC requires that the carrier must be reduced or suppressed to at least 40 dB below the signal's peak power output on the air to prevent unnecessary interference.

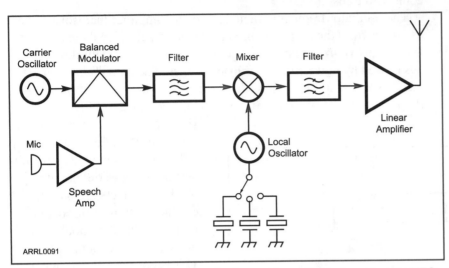

Figure 5-12 — Substituting the circuits to create an SSB signal for the VFO creates a multiband SSB transmitter.

Note that the output amplifier is now labeled a "Linear Amplifier." That change is necessary because the transmitter must accurately reproduce the rapidly changing speech waveform. In a CW transmitter, it is only necessary to turn a sine wave on and off. In an AM or SSB transmitter, however, all of the stages must be designed to accurately reproduce the input signal, whether they amplify, mix or filter it. Nonlinearities anywhere in the "transmit chain" (meaning the sequence of circuits that produce the transmitted signal) will generate unwanted spurious signals such as harmonics, mixing products or splatter.

The FCC does not specify bandwidth limits on any phone signal except to say that signals should not occupy more bandwidth than is dictated by "good amateur practice" [§97.307(a)] .Generally speaking, that means an SSB signal should have a bandwidth of no more than 3 kHz and an AM signal about 6 kHz. There is one exception. On 60 meters, the FCC specifies in §97.303(s) that the USB signals should occupy no more than 2.8 kHz of bandwidth as defined in §97.3(a)8.

> *Before you go on, study test questions G7A06, G7A07 and G7A10. Review this section if you have difficulty.*

FM TRANSMITTERS

Modulation and frequency changing are performed differently in FM transmitters. While it is possible to generate an FM signal and then use mixers, it is much less expensive and more practical to generate the FM signal at a low frequency and multiply it to reach the desired band. This technique is illustrated in **Figure 5-13**. In a 2 meter band FM transmitter, the modulated oscillator frequency is approximately 12 MHz and the multiplier selects the 12th harmonic for transmission. For example, for an output on 146.52 MHz,

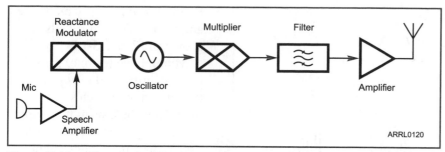

Figure 5-13 — The carrier and modulation are generated at relatively low frequencies in an FM transmitter. The modulated signal is then multiplied to the desired output frequency. The amount of signal deviation is also multiplied.

the oscillator must produce a $146.52 \div 12 = 12.21$ MHz signal.

It's important to realize that the deviation of the modulated oscillator output is also multiplied, increasing with each harmonic. The radio designer must compensate for that factor when designing the modulator circuit. For example, if that same 146.52 MHz signal is to have no more than the standard deviation of 5 kHz, the maximum deviation at the oscillator can only be $5 \div 12 = 416.7$ Hz.

Just as for AM signals, the FCC requires amateurs to limit the bandwidth of FM signals to that which represents good amateur practice. Any angle modulated signal has a theoretically infinite number of sidebands, so what is the bandwidth of an FM signal? While there may be a lot of sidebands, except for those close to the carrier they have vanishingly small amounts of power. Carson's Rule is a formula that gives a good approximation of an FM signal's bandwidth:

$$BW = 2 \times (\text{peak deviation} + \text{highest modulating frequency})$$

As an example, if an FM phone signal's peak deviation is limited to 5 kHz and the highest modulating frequency is 3 kHz, then $BW = 2 \times (5 + 3) = 16$ kHz. This signal will stay safely within the 20 kHz channels used by repeater coordinators. Thus, it is important to control both deviation (the swings in frequency from the amplitude of the modulating signal) and the frequency content of the modulating signal. This wide bandwidth is the reason FM phone is not used below 29.5 MHz — it is just too wide for the relatively narrow HF bands.

Another thing you might have noticed about Figure 5-13 is that the output amplifier is no longer required to be a linear amplifier. FM and PM signals have a constant power level, so it doesn't matter whether an amplifier can faithfully reproduce the input waveform or not. The only important characteristic of the FM signal is its frequency. Amplifiers in an FM transmitter can be highly nonlinear as long as harmonics are removed from the transmitted signal!

Before you go on, study test questions G8B04, G8B05, G8B06 and G8B07. Review this section if you have difficulty.

SIGNAL QUALITY

Operating a transmitter so that the on-the-air signal is intelligible and does not have excessive bandwidth is an important part of operating. This section discusses the causes of poor signal quality and what the operator should do about them.

Overmodulation — AM modes

If the amplitude of an AM or SSB signal is varied excessively in response to the modulating signal, this is called *overmodulation*. Overmodulation distorts the transmitted audio and increases the signal's bandwidth with unwanted spurious signals called *splatter*, transmitted on nearby frequencies and interfering with other communications. Ovemodulation is caused by speaking too loudly or by setting the microphone or audio gain too high.

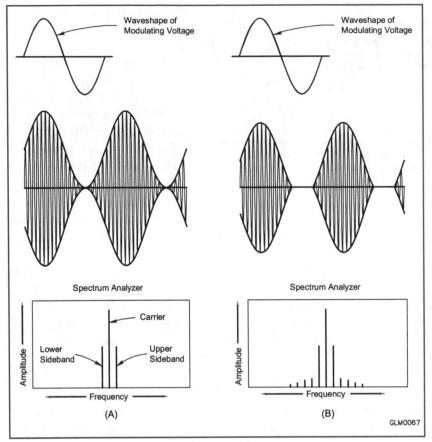

Figure 5-14 — A properly modulated signal at A. The results of over-modulation are visible at B. This distorted signal causes interference on nearby frequencies.

Examples of properly modulated and overmodulated signals are shown in **Figure 5-14**.

Microphone (or mic) gain is the control used to adjust the amount by which speech modulates the transmitter output signal. To prevent overmodulation, reduce microphone gain or speak more quietly. If you have a monitoring oscilloscope in your shack, you can watch the transmitter output on voice peaks to see if your signal appears "clean." It also helps to have a friend check your signal on the air to make sure you are not causing interference to other operators. Once your transmitter is operating properly, take note of the transmitter settings, meter behavior and oscilloscope images so that you can keep your signal properly adjusted in the future.

If the drive level to transmitter output stages or external amplifiers is increased beyond the point of maximum output power level, the result is *flat-topping* or *clipping*. The peaks of such a transmitted signal appear "flattened" on a monitoring oscilloscope. If the output signal is completely cut off between peaks, the result is *carrier cutoff*. Both cause interference to nearby channels by generating spurious signals beyond the normal signal bandwidth.

Harmonics and Spurs

Two other kinds of spurious outputs are harmonics and *spurs*. Harmonics are generated by nearly all circuits because of minor nonlinearities in their operation. Transmitters use filters to remove harmonics from their output signals. Nevertheless, you should be aware that a misadjusted or overdriven transmitter or defective equipment external to the transmitter can produce harmonics. Spurs are unwanted outputs that are not harmonically related to the desired output. They may even be low-level replicas of the desired output signal! Spurs are usually caused by excessive drive levels to the output stage of a transmitter or to an amplifier. The solution to reducing or eliminating harmonics and spurs is often to simply reduce the overall power level of the transmitted signal.

Audio level adjustment is somewhat different for each radio and style of signal monitoring equipment. The basics are similar, however. First, use normal speech or audio levels during both testing and on the air contacts. It's natural under difficult conditions to raise your voice, but that usually only reduces intelligibility. Next, make use of the monitor (or MON) function to listen to your own signal while you transmit. This is not an exact copy of your output signal, but is helpful in controlling your own speech volume and in catching any distortion in the audio circuits of the transmitter.

The automatic level control (ALC) circuits of your transmitter also help prevent overmodulation. ALC reduces output power during voice peaks. Your radio's manual will have some instructions on how to use ALC to properly set your transmit audio levels. In general, the microphone gain should be adjusted to cause the ALC to activate only on voice peaks.

Finally, the *two-tone test* for transmitter linearity is very helpful in keeping your signal clean. This test consists of modulating your transmitter with a pair of audio tones that are not harmonically related (700 and 1900 Hz are typical frequencies) while watching the transmitted signal with a monitoring oscilloscope. The transmitter and any external amplifier are then adjusted for an output free of distortion. This test needs only to be performed occasionally to note the appropriate settings of gain and level adjustments.

Speech Processing

Compared to modes like CW, the average power of an AM or SSB signal is quite low. Human speech spreads its energy out over a wide frequency range with only short periods of high sound levels. When transmitted over HF as an amplitude-modulated signal in the presence of noise, interference or fading, the received signal can be difficult to understand. *Speech processing* addresses this problem by increasing the average power of the speech signal without excessively distorting the signal. The result is improved intelligibility of the received signal. Speech processors are available that work on the audio input to the transmitter and on the low-level RF signal before amplification.

A common technique for speech processing is *compression*, which increases gain at low input levels while holding gain constant for louder speech components. The amount of compression is measured in dB as the difference in gain for different levels of input. For example, if low-level input signals are amplified with 10 dB more gain than for high-level signals, it is referred to as "10 dB of compression." Modest amounts of compression make a voice "sound louder" because the low-level speech components are easier to hear in the received signal.

Any kind of speech processing is, by definition, distortion. The proper use of processing balances the increase in average power against any reduction in intelligibility. Too much processing (called *overprocessing*) results in a signal with plenty of power, but that is harder to understand than the unprocessed signal! A processed signal also requires careful adjustment of transmitter modulation to avoid causing splatter on adjacent channels.

Overdeviation — FM and PM

FM signals can be overmodulated as well, but instead of distorting the carrier, the result is excessive deviation. This increases the strength of the extra FM signal sidebands that are usually too small to cause interference. The result of overdeviation is distortion of the received signal and interference to adjacent channels

Most FM rigs have limiting circuits that prevent overdeviation caused by speaking too loudly. Your voice may be distorted, but it won't cause interference. Multimode rigs with adjustable microphone gain may allow overmodulation, however. Read your owner's manual to learn the proper operating procedure for your radio.

Key Clicks

Key clicks are sharp transient clicking sounds generated as a transmitter turns on and off too rapidly during CW transmissions. Clicks can also be generated if the transmitter turns on and off erratically.

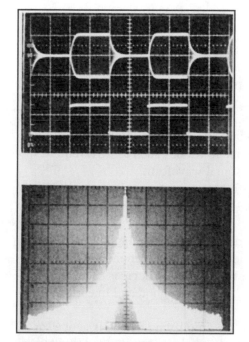

Figure 5-15 — CW waveforms can be inspected by using a monitoring oscilloscope. Key clicks that result from rising and falling edges that are too abrupt or not smooth cause interference on nearby frequencies.

These can be quite disruptive to nearby contacts. Key clicks can often be reduced by adjusting a transmitter configuration setting or by modifying the transmitter's keying control circuits. An oscilloscope can be used to monitor the CW waveform as shown in **Figure 5-15**. If the leading and trailing edges of the CW output are 4 to 8 ms long, clicks are not generated. Be sure to look closely at the keying waveform for transients or sharp steps.

Digital Mode Concerns

As long as we're on the subject of signal quality, digital mode operation has many of the same concerns about signal quality as phone and CW. Digital signals are just as capable of generating interference to nearby channels, plus the connection between the computer and radio can cause trouble.

For digital modes that use an SSB transmitter, the most common problem is supplying too much or too little audio from the computer to the radio's microphone input. A microphone input is very sensitive and it is easy to overdrive, resulting in splatter and spurious outputs. After adjusting the transmit audio level yourself, have a friend check your signal to confirm that your audio level is set properly.

Another common problem is having a ground loop that results in 60 or 120 Hz hum on transmit or receive audio. The solution is to use a transformer in both signal lines between the radio and the computer. These techniques also help prevent RF feedback from your transmitted signal. There are several built-and-tested digital signal interfaces on the market, or you can build one from a kit or project plans.

Some radios have direct digital inputs that can connect directly to a computer data interface. This eliminates audio interface and level setting problems entirely.

> **Before you go on, study test questions G4A02, G4A11, G4A12, G4D01, G4D02, G4D03, G8A08, G8A09 and G8A10. Review this section if you have difficulty.**

AMPLIFIERS

Many HF operators use an amplifier (sometimes called a *linear*) so that they can make contacts when conditions are poor, over difficult propagation paths, or for situations like running a net for which a strong signal is necessary. VHF and UHF amplifiers are most commonly available as solid-state "bricks" that require no tuning or adjustment — turn them on, hook up the rig and the antenna and go. On HF, high-power amplifiers usually use vacuum tube circuits that require operator adjustment. Modes such as SSB require linear amplifiers that accurately reproduce the input signal waveform.

An amplifier circuit can be operated in several different categories, called *classes*. Each different class is best suited for different radio uses. Hams use four common amplifier classes:

- *Class A* — The most linear (lowest signal distortion) of all classes and also the least efficient. The amplifying device in a Class A amplifiers is on all the time. Gain is limited.
- *Class B* — Also known as *push-pull* with a pair of amplifying devices each active during complementary halves of the signal's cycle. Efficiency is good and linearity can be good with careful design and adjustment.
- *Class AB* — Midway between Classes A and B, the amplifying device is active for more than one-half but less than an entire signal cycle. Linearity is not as good as Class A, but efficiency is improved.
- *Class C* — Amplifying devices are active for less than one-half of the signal's cycle. These amplifiers are quite efficient, but are only suitable for CW and FM because they have very poor linearity.

Most linear amplifiers can be operated in either Class AB for SSB operation or in Class C for CW. The efficiency of an amplifier is defined as the RF output power divided by the dc input power.

Tuning and Driving a Linear Amplifier

Amplifiers have three primary operator adjustments: Band, Tune and Load. No-tune or auto-tune amplifiers do not require these operator adjustments because of their circuit design or because a microprocessor makes the adjustments automatically. The Band switch configures the input and output impedance matching or filter circuits for the band on which signals will be applied to amplifier. Tune and Load adjust components in the output matching circuit, often a Pi network of the type introduced in Chapter 4.

With the band switch set properly, a small amount of drive power is applied to the amplifier while watching the amplifier's plate current meter and adjusting the Tune control for a minimum setting (or "dip"). This means the output matching circuit is resonant at the operating frequency. The Load control is adjusted to maximize (or "peak") output power and Tune readjusted for the dip in plate current. The adjustments interact, so the process is repeated until the desired amount of output power or plate current is obtained. Input power to the amplifier may also be adjusted during that process.

Drive power is important, particularly for *grid-driven* amplifier circuits in which the input power is applied to the tube's control grid. It is easy to destroy an expensive tube by applying too much drive, observed as excessive grid current on the amplifier's metering circuits. Some amplifiers even have protective circuits to prevent excessive grid drive. Excessive drive power or mistuning can also result in excessive plate current. This overheats the tube and can cause it to fail. Operate the amplifier according to the manufacturer's specifications and procedures to obtain the longest life from transmitting tubes.

Neutralization

In the section on oscillators, you learned that to make an amplifier oscillate, positive feedback must reinforce the input signal at some frequency for which the amplifier has gain greater than 1. HF amplifiers using triode tubes such as the popular 3-500Z are often capable of becoming an oscillator (called *self-oscillation*) at VHF frequencies because the physical construction of the tube and the circuit creates positive feedback. The main source of positive feedback is *inter-electrode capacitance* between the plate and control grid in a grid-driven circuit.

Self-oscillation creates spurious output signals and can even damage the tube or amplifier components. The technique of preventing self-oscillation is called *neutralization*. Neutralization is performed by creating negative feedback at VHF. Negative feedback consists of connecting some of the output signal back to the input, but out-of-phase with the input signal to cancel the unwanted positive feedback. For an HF amplifier, this is done by connecting a small variable capacitor between the amplifier's output and input circuits. The amplifier's operating manual will show the appropriate procedure for making the adjustments. Once an amplifier is neutralized, no further adjustment is needed unless the amplifier tubes are replaced or some other circuit changes are made.

> *Before you go on, study test questions G4A06, G4A07, G4A08, G4A09, G4A10, G7B10, G7B11, G7B12, G7B13 and G7B14. Review this section if you have difficulty.*

5.5 Receiver Structure

As the wise old radio saying goes, "You can't work 'em if you can't hear 'em!" That makes the receiver just about the most important part of the ham shack. HF receivers also have more adjustments than HF transmitters by far — why? This section explains how receivers are constructed — clean out your ears and tune in!

BASIC SUPERHETERODYNE RECEIVERS

Nearly all receivers in use today are some type of superheterodyne, a design invented in the 1920s by Edwin Armstrong. As you learned earlier, the mixing together of signals to obtain sum and difference frequencies is called heterodyning. The "superhet" is built around that process.

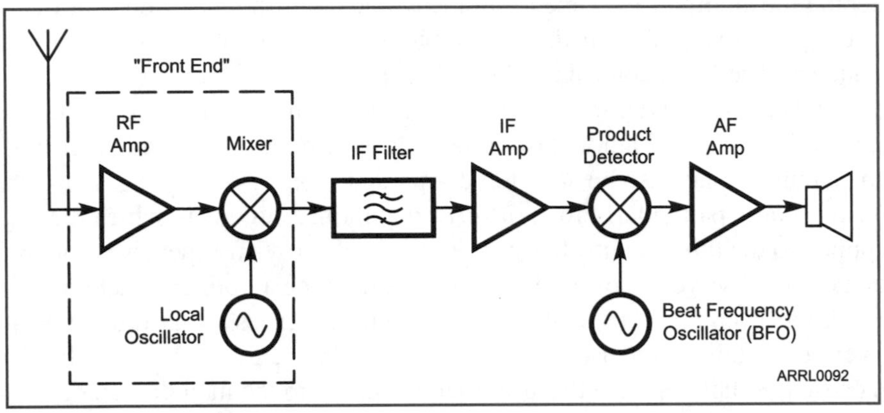

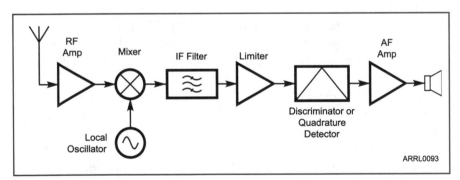

Figure 5-16 — A superheterodyne receiver converts signals to audio in two steps. The front end converts the frequency of a signal to the intermediate frequency (IF) where most of the gain of the receiver is provided. A second mixer — the product detector — converts the signal to audio frequencies.

Figure 5-17 — Once the FM signal is converted to the IF, high-gain amplifiers called limiters change the signal to a square wave that only varies in frequency (not amplitude). A discriminator converts the frequency variations to audio.

Received signals are incredibly weak — on the order of nano or picowatts. Thus, a receiver must be quite sensitive to make it possible for an operator to hear such a signal. Simultaneously, a single signal must be picked out of a crowded spectrum where nearby signals might be billions of times stronger. So the receiver must be very selective, as well. Both of these requirements are satisfied by the basic superheterodyne receiver structure shown in **Figure 5-16**. Let's trace the signal through the receiver from antenna to speaker.

Received signals are first strengthened by the RF amplifier, then applied to the RF input of a mixer. The local oscillator (LO) is adjusted so that the desired signal creates a mixing product at the *intermediate frequency* (IF). An IF filter removes all of the signals other than the desired signal, which is then amplified by the IF amplifier. A detector or demodulator stage follows the IF to recover the modulating information. The simplest possible superhet consists of a mixer connected to the antenna, an HF oscillator to act as an LO, and a detector.

An IF stage is used because it is much easier to create high quality filters and high gain amplifiers at a single frequency that does not need to be tuned to a signal's frequency. Only the LO needs to be tuned in a superhet receiver. For example, to convert an RF signal on 14.250 MHz to an IF of 455 kHz, the LO must be tuned to either 14.250 – 455 kHz = 13.795 MHz or to 14.250 + 455 kHz = 14.705 MHz.

To cover the entire 20 meter band, and assuming the difference mixing product is used, the LO would be tuned from 14.000 – 0.455 MHz = 13.545 MHz to 14.350 – 0.455 MHz = 13.845 MHz

Once amplified to a more usable level, SSB and CW signals are demodulated by a *product detector*, a special type of mixer. If an AM signal is being received, either a product detector or an *envelope detector* is used to recover the modulating signal. The output of the product or envelope detector is an audio signal that is amplified by an audio frequency (AF) amplifier and applied to a speaker or headphones or sound card.

The RF amplifier and mixer comprise the receiver's "front end." This section of the receiver processes weak signals at their original frequencies, so it must work over a wide frequency range and for both strong and weak signals. A tunable filter or *preselector* is sometimes used between the antenna and RF amplifier to reject strong *out-of-band* signals, such as those from broadcasters or commercial stations. These out-of-band signals are not in the desired frequency band, but they could overload the circuitry. If additional sensitivity is needed, an additional stage of RF amplification called a *preamplifier* (or *preamp*) is used.

FM receivers are very similar to an AM/SSB/CW superhet, but they have key differences as shown in **Figure 5-17**. The only information that matters in an FM signal is the frequency, so a *limiter* amplifier, a special, non-linear IF amplifier, replaces the linear IF amplifier in an AM receiver. A limiter amplifies the received signal until all of the amplitude modulated information, such as noise, is removed and only a square wave of varying frequency remains. The audio information is recovered by a *discriminator* or a *quadrature detector* that replaces the product detector. The audio is then amplified as before.

Like every design, the superheterodyne has some flaws. Because the mixers produce both sum and difference frequency signals (and to some degree, other combinations), undesired signals can also create their own mixing products at the IF. For example, if the IF is 455 kHz and the LO frequency is 13.800 MHz, signals at both 14.255 and 13.345 MHz will create a mixing product at 455 kHz. The first as 14.255 – 13.800 MHz = 455 kHz and the second as 13.800 – 13.345 MHz = 455 kHz. Assuming the receiver is supposed to receive the 14.255 MHz signal, the undesired signal at 13.345 MHz is called an *image*. Filters in the receiver front end are required to remove signals that might cause images. Another flaw is caused by the LO and other oscillator circuits inside the receiver. Leakage of these signals into the signal path can cause steady signals to appear. These signals are called *birdies*. Even if no signals are present at the receiver input, birdies will still be audible because they are caused by signals inside the receiver.

The receiver shown in Figures 5-16 and 5-17 is a *single-conversion* receiver, with only one mixer converting the signal from RF to IF. The IF stages provide most of the receiver's gain and almost all of its selectivity (the ability to reject unwanted signals). Depending on how many different frequency bands the receiver must cover and the demands for selectivity, superhet receivers may have one, two, or three IF stages, resulting in a single, double or triple-conversion receiver.

Another type of receiver related to the superhet is called a *direct-conversion* receiver. It is essentially a product detector connected directly to the antenna. In a direct-conversion design, an HF oscillator is tuned to the same frequency as the desired signal and the output of the product detector is the original modulating audio, so there is no mixer or IF amplifier. This makes for a very simple design, but achieving adequate selectivity without IF filters is a challenging design problem.

Before you go on, study test questions G7A08, G7A09, G7A11, G7A12, G7A13, G8B01 and G8B02. Review this section if you have difficulty.

DIGITAL SIGNAL PROCESSING

While the superheterodyne receiver design continues to be the most common type of receiver, microprocessor technology has begun to replace some of the analog circuits with digital. The general term for converting signals from analog to digital form, operating on them with a microprocessor and converting them back to analog is digital signal processing (DSP). **Figure 5-18** shows the basic structure of a digital signal processor in a communications receiver.

DSP technology requires an analog receiver front end to tune in a signal, convert it to the IF frequency and amplify it to suitable levels. Once prepared by the front end, the signal is converted to digital form by an *analog-to-digital converter* (ADC). In digital form, a specialized microprocessor called a digital signal processor performs filtering and other functions mathematically. The data is then converted back to analog form for the human operator by a *digital-to-analog converter* (DAC). If the receiver is intended to be used for digital modes, the data may be converted directly to characters instead of to analog form.

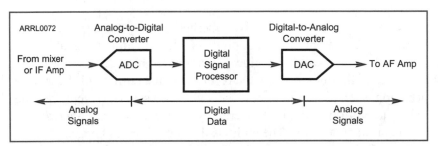

Figure 5-18 — DSP systems consist an analog-to-digital converter (ADC) to change the signal to digital data. A special type of microprocessor then performs the mathematical operations on the data to accomplish filtering, noise reduction, or other functions. A digital-to-analog converter (DAC) changes the processed data back to analog form for output as audio.

DSP technology has two major advantages over analog circuitry — performance and flexibility. Current DSP components can achieve performance as good or better than the best analog filters. Functions that would be prohibitively expensive in analog circuitry can be implemented in DSP as a program without any additional hardware cost. DSP is also much more flexible than analog circuitry, limited only by processor speed and available memory as to how many options, functions and adjustments can be implemented. DSP functions can even react automatically to the received signals and adjust the function's characteristics.

The most common DSP functions are:

● *Signal filtering* — Radios with DSP offer selectable preprogrammed filters and allow the operator to adjust the filter bandwidth and shape and even to define new filters.

● *Noise reduction* — It is possible for DSP to distinguish noise and remove a great deal of it, leaving only the desired speech or CW for the operator to copy.

● *Notch filtering* — Interfering signals, particularly carriers from broadcast stations, can be sensed and removed by DSP, including tracking them as they change frequency and even eliminating more than one at a time!

● *Audio frequency equalizing* — The operator can adjust receive or transmit audio frequency response to suit his or her preferences, compensating for hearing loss or optimizing microphone audio.

Before you go on, study test questions G4A01, G4A03, G4A04, G4A05 and G4A13. Review this section if you have difficulty.

MANAGING RECEIVER GAIN

Receivers need to have a lot of gain to bring those weak signals up to a level where their information can be recovered by ear or by computer. Just as too little gain can cause weak signals to be missed, too much gain can cause its own set of problems. There are several controls and displays that the operator can use to get the gain setting "just right."

RF Gain and Automatic Gain Control

The amount of receiver gain is set by the RF gain control. If you are tuning your receiver and looking for weak signals, you will likely set the RF gain to maximum so that receiver sensitivity is highest. Once you've tuned in a signal, unless it's very weak, maximum gain isn't required and so RF gain can be adjusted for the most comfortable listening. Lower values of RF gain also reduce the volume of the background noise heard in the output.

The automatic gain control (AGC) circuits vary the gain of the RF and IF amplifiers so that the output volume of a signal stays relatively constant for both weak and strong signals. The AGC control of the receiver can be set so that the circuit responds quickly or slowly (or not at all) to volume changes, depending on the operator's preference. Fast AGC response is usually used for CW and data signals, while slow response works best for phone.

The AGC circuit adjusts receiver gain by changing a voltage that controls the IF amplifier gain. This voltage is also read by the *S meter* of the receiver, which is used to measure received signal strength. ("S" stands for "signal.") The more the AGC circuit has to reduce gain to keep volume constant, the higher the reading on the S meter, since stronger signals require less gain to produce the same output volume. You'll notice that turning down the RF gain also increases the S meter reading because the RF gain control uses the same control voltage as the AGC circuit.

S meters are calibrated in *S units*, with a change of one S unit usually equal to a 6 dB (fourfold) change in signal strength, although this may vary with manufacturer. An AGC circuit may also respond differently at different signal strengths. Nevertheless, the S meter is a useful indicator of signal strength, with a signal strength of S9 being a strong signal. You'll notice that S9 is at the midpoint of the S meter display. To the right are additional markings of "20", "40" and "60." These correspond to "dB above S9," so a reading of "S9 + 20 dB" corresponds to a signal 20 dB (100 times) stronger than an S9 signal.

Receiver Linearity

It is important that a receiver respond linearly to received signals, just as it is important for a transmitter to amplify linearly. If the received signal is distorted, spurious signals will appear just as if the transmitting station was emitting them!

The most common form of receiver nonlinearity is *overload* or *gain compression*. (Overload is also called *front-end overload*.) This occurs when an input signal is simply too strong for the circuitry to handle and distortion results. The usual symptom is strong distortion of all signals when the overloading signal is present. The solution to overload is to either filter out the offending signal or reduce receiver gain using the *attenuator* circuit to reduce signal levels overall. Proper use of the attenuator and RF gain controls can dramatically reduce received noise and distortion caused by strong signals.

Intermodulation or "intermod" can occur when two strong signals combine in a mixer or amplifier, generating their own mixing products that are demodulated and heard along with regular signals. Intermodulation products can also be generated by poor contacts between conductors in a strong RF field, such as near a transmitting antenna. Signals that suddenly appear and disappear are one signature of intermod.

Accessory circuits in the receiver can also affect its linearity. Using a preamplifier makes it easier for strong signals to overload a receiver. Noise blankers that work by shutting off the receiver when a strong noise pulse is detected can confuse strong signals with the pulses, creating severe distortion as a result. Use these circuits only when necessary and to the minimum amount needed.

Before you go on, study test questions G4B09, G4D04, G4D05 and G4D06. Review this section if you have difficulty.

5.6 HF Station Installation

Along with understanding the structure of the equipment itself, assembling it into a working station at home or in a vehicle creates another set of concerns. HF operating, with longer wavelengths and typically higher field strengths, makes grounding and interference control much more important. The General class exam focuses on three related areas: mobile installations, RF grounding and RF interference.

MOBILE INSTALLATIONS

Once quite popular, mobile HF operation took a back seat, so to speak, during the 1980s and early 1990s as hams turned to VHF and UHF on the road and HF at home. Over the past decade however, the introduction of compact all-band, all-mode radios and a new generation of mobile antennas have accelerated HF mobiling dramatically. Not only is it an enjoyable change of pace from the home shack, but in this era of antenna restrictions, it offers an HF operating opportunity to many hams who might otherwise be off those bands. There are no restrictions on which modes may be used while mobile, so give operating-in-motion a try!

Power Connections

Unlike low power radios, a mobile rig capable of putting out 100 watts requires a solid power connection capable of supplying 20 A or more with a minimum amount of voltage drop. Solid-state radios perform unpredictably when input voltage drops below their specified minimum.

The power cable provided by the manufacturer should never be extended or replaced with smaller gauge wire. The best power connection is direct to the battery using heavy gauge wire with a fuse in both the positive and negative leads. Do not use the cigarette lighter socket, as that circuit is usually rated at only a few amperes and uses wire too small for a 100 W HF radio.

Do not assume that the vehicle's metal chassis is a suitable dc ground connection. Many vehicle bodies are made in segments, which leads to erratic ground connections over time. Some pieces may be made from plastic or other nonmetallic materials. Connect the radio power ground either directly to the battery or to the battery ground strap where it attaches to the engine block or vehicle chassis.

Tame That High-Pitched Whine

A good power connection also helps cut down on electrical noise from the vehicle's power system. Alternator whine, a high-pitched tone that changes with engine speed, is caused by current pulses from the alternator as it charges the battery. Connecting the rig's power cable directly to the battery uses the battery as a filter, greatly reducing alternator whine and all other electrical noise conducted to the radio through the power leads.

Antenna Connections

The most significant limitation of mobile operating is that antennas must be smaller in terms of a wavelength than at a home station. This is particularly true on the lower frequencies, such as 75 meters, a popular mobile band. When mobiling, the entire vehicle becomes part of the antenna system and attention to every detail can pay big benefits in signal strength. For example:

- Use the most efficient antenna you can.
- Make sure RF ground connections to the vehicle are solid.
- Mount the antenna where it is as clear as possible of metal surfaces.

Review some of the mobile operating references on the *General Class License Manual* Web site (**www.arrl.org/gclm**) before installing your mobile system. Don't hesitate to ask other mobile operators for advice — they're often glad to relate their own experiences and act as an Elmer.

Before you go on, study test questions G4E01, G4E02, G4E03, G4E04 and G4E05. Review this section if you have difficulty.

RF GROUNDING

Although a good station ground is important to prevent electrical shock, at HF and higher frequencies, ac safety ground wiring usually acts more like an antenna than a ground! In amateur stations, it's necessary to provide a separate RF ground from the ac safety ground. The goal of RF grounding is twofold. First, keep all equipment at as close to the same RF voltage as possible, and second, keep that RF voltage as close to ground potential as possible.

Keeping all of your equipment at the same RF voltage means there is no reason for RF current to flow between pieces of equipment on power and signal cabling. Such currents, called *ground loops*, can cause audio distortion or erratic operation of computer interfaces, introduce noise into sensitive receivers, and upset SWR measurements. If possible, connect all equipment enclosures or metal chassis to a common ground point, called a "star" ground, which is then connected to a ground rod. If you can't have a star ground, use a ground bus as shown in **Figure 5-19**. The basics for RF grounding in your shack are:

- Bond all metal equipment enclosures to a common ground bus.
- Keep all connections, straps and wires short.
- Connect the ground bus to a ground rod or grounded pipe with a short, wide conductor such as copper flashing or strip.
- In difficult situations, a piece of wide flashing or screen can be placed under the equipment and connected to the ground bus.

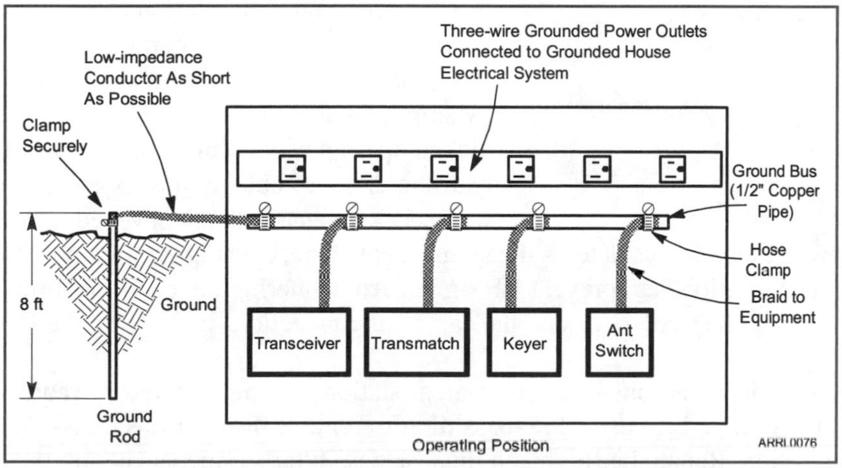

Such a ground system minimizes "hot spots" — conducting surfaces that have a high RF voltage.

Minimizing RF voltage with respect to ground is the more difficult goal. After all, any conductor more than $\frac{1}{10}$ of a wavelength long acts as an antenna, picking up RF. The antenna feed line, equipment enclosures and the connections between them act as antennas for your transmitted signal. Thus the ground connection to your ground rod should be as short as possible. If the ground

Figure 5-19 — A ground bus at the operating position helps keep all of the equipment at the same RF voltage. The ground rod and strap keep the voltage as low as possible. The connection between the bus and the ground rod should be as short as possible.

connection approaches ¼ wavelength at any frequency, it may begin to act as a resonant circuit, creating hot spots on the ground connection with the possibility of causing RF burns. For example, ¼ wavelength is only about 8 feet on the 10 meter band, so a resonant ground is hard to avoid, particularly for stations located above the ground floor! You may want to try two separate ground connections of different lengths to avoid ground connection resonance. A good RF ground also acts as a backup to your ac safety ground, reducing shock hazards, and helps to reduce interference.

The ARRL Technical Information Service (**www.arrl.org/ tis/tismenu.html**) dedicates an entire page to RF grounding with several *QST* magazine articles and Web references. Each station is a little different and you may have to experiment to get the results you expect.

> *Before you go on, study test questions G4C05, G4C06, G4C07, G4C09 and G4C13. Review this section if you have difficulty.*

RF INTERFERENCE

Radiating a good signal means that you'll probably discover some unintentional listeners in nearby receivers and consumer electronics. A license study manual cannot provide a thorough discussion of the causes and effects of RF interference (RFI), but the ARRL's Technical Information Service offers a lot of information. You can also learn more from the *ARRL RFI Book* and *The ARRL Handbook*.

Here are some common causes and solutions of RF interference to consumer electronics and broadcast receivers:

Common RFI Symptoms

The symptoms of RF interference are quite varied, but here are some common observations:

- CW, FM or data — The interference will consist of buzzes, humming or thumps corresponding to the on-and-off pattern of the signal.
- AM phone — Equipment experiencing overload or direct detection will often emit a replica of the speaker's voice.
- SSB voice — similar to AM phone, but the voice will be distorted or garbled.

- *Fundamental overload* — usually exhibited by radio or TV receivers unable to reject a strong signal that causes the internal circuits to act improperly, distorting or wiping out the intended signal. Prevent the offending signal from entering the equipment by using filters.
- *Direct detection* — any type of electronic equipment with internal electronics, including telephones, computers, music players and so on, can be affected by strong local signals. The signal is picked up on power connections, speaker leads, telephone cable, or any external wiring. The signal is then conveyed into the equipment, where the electronics detects the signal's envelope, causing erratic operation or audio noise. The solution is to prevent RF signals from entering the equipment by using RFI filters or RF suppression chokes on the cables or connections picking up the RF current.
- *Harmonics* — spurious emissions from an amateur station may be received by radio or TV equipment. The solution is to use a low-pass filter to remove the spurious emissions at the amateur station. Remember to match the low-pass filter's impedance with the characteristic impedance of the feed line into which it is inserted.
- *Rectification* — Poor contacts between conductors picking up RF signals can create a mixer and mixing products from the signals. If the mixing products are on the frequency

that the receivers are tuned to, they will cause interference to the desired signal. The solution is to find and repair the poor contact.

● *Arcing* — Any spark or sustained arc creates radio noise over a wide range of frequencies and will interfere with both amateur and consumer reception. When created by the ac power lines, the result will be a crackling buzz. If the arc is from a motor or welding equipment, the buzz will come and go when the equipment is energized. In general, poor contact between any current-carrying conductors will cause interference. The solution for power line noise is to isolate it to a single installation and then request that the power company make the necessary repairs. Noise from specific equipment may require filtering of that equipment.

Before you go on, study test questions G4C02, G4C03, G4C04, G4C11, G4C12 and G7A05. Review this section if you have difficulty.

RF INTERFERENCE SUPPRESSION

The best solution to many types of interference caused by proximity to an amateur station is to keep the RF signals from entering the equipment in the first place. If filters can be used, they are generally the most effective and least troublesome to install. The next approach is to prevent RF current flow by placing inductance or resistance in its path. This is done by forming the conductor carrying the RF current into a series inductor by winding it around a magnetic core or through a ferrite core.

Ferrite beads and cores can also be placed on cables to prevent RF current from flowing on the outside of cable braids or shields ("common mode" interference). The same beads and cores can be used to prevent signals from computers and computer accessories from causing interference to amateur communications. Audio equipment sometimes responds well to placing a small (100 pF to 1 nF) capacitor across balanced connections or from each connection to chassis ground.

Before you go on, study test questions G4C01 and G4C08. Review this section if you have difficulty.

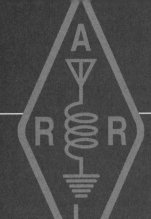

Chapter 6

Antennas

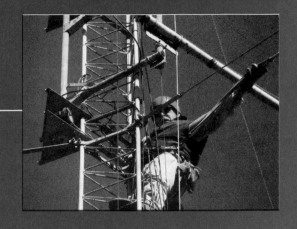

In this chapter, you'll learn about

- Antenna Basics

- Dipoles and ground planes

- Effects of antenna height and polarization

- How Yagis work

- Loop antennas

- Antennas with special characteristics

- Feed line basics

- SWR and impedance matching

Any conductor can act as an antenna for radio waves, but selecting an efficient and useful antenna takes a little bit of know-how. It's not necessary for General class licensees to be antenna designers, but you should understand the basic principles of antennas. You're going to learn more detail about how simple antennas and feed lines work, then extend your understanding of common directional antennas. Building on what you already know from your Technician studies, the things you learn for your General exam will help you make better choices about what sort of antenna to use and what sort of performance to expect.

6.1 Antenna Basics

Making a quick review of your existing knowledge of antennas and feed lines is a good way to be ready to learn. We'll start this section by refreshing definitions:

Elements are the conducting portions of an antenna that radiate or receive a signal. *Polarization* refers to the orientation of the electric field radiated by the antenna and is determined by the physical orientation of the elements with respect to the Earth's surface. If an element is horizontal, then that is the polarization of the signal it radiates.

Feed point impedance is the ratio of radio frequency voltage to current at an antenna's feed point. An antenna is *resonant* when its feed point impedance is completely resistive with no reactance.

An antenna's *radiation pattern* is a graph of signal strength in every direction or at every vertical angle. An *azimuthal* pattern shows the strength of the radiated energy in horizontal directions. An *elevation* pattern shows the strength of the radiated energy in vertical directions. An antenna transmits and receives with the same pattern. *Lobes* are regions in the radiation pattern where the antenna is radiating a signal. *Nulls* are the points between lobes at which radiation is at a minimum.

An *isotropic* antenna radiates equally in every possible direction, horizontal and vertical. Isotropic antennas do not exist in practice and are only used only as a reference. An *omnidirectional* antenna radiates a signal of equal strength in every horizontal direction. A *directional* antenna radiates preferentially in one or more directions.

The concentration of signal transmitted toward or received from a preferred direction is called *gain*. Signal strength is increased in the preferred direction for both receiving and transmitting. Antenna gain is specified in decibels (dB) with respect to an identified reference antenna. Gain with respect to an isotropic antenna is called dBi. Gain with respect to a dipole antenna's maximum radiation is called dBd. If no reference is specified, assume that the gain is in dBi.

The ratio of gain in the preferred or forward direction to the opposite direction is called *front-to-back ratio* (F/B). The ratio of gain in the preferred or forward direction to directions at right angles called the *front-to-side ratio* (F/S). Gain ratios are measured in dB.

6.2 Dipoles, Ground Planes and Random Wires

Simple antennas are by far the most popular antennas used by hams. They are inexpensive, easy to install and give good performance. The design of more sophisticated antennas is often based on these simple "skyhooks."

DIPOLES

The most fundamental antenna is a *dipole* (two parts) — a straight conductor ½ wavelength (λ/2) long with its feed point in the middle. (*Doublet* is another name for a dipole, but that term is generally applied to similar center-fed wire antennas that are not resonant.) A dipole radiates strongest broadside to its axis and weakest off the ends as shown in **Figure 6-1**. This "figure-eight" is the approximate shape of the azimuth pattern for a dipole installed ½ wavelength above ground.

Current in a half-wave dipole is highest in the middle and zero at the ends. Voltage along the dipole is highest at the ends and lowest in the middle. (See **Figure 6-2**.) The feed point impedance (the ratio of RF voltage to current) of a center-fed dipole in free-space is approximately 72 Ω, but it varies widely depending on its height above ground as we discuss later in this section. Impedance increases as the feed point is moved away from the center and is several thousand ohms at the ends.

To construct an HF dipole from wire, the formula for its length is:

$$\text{Length in feet} = \frac{468}{\text{frequency in MHz}} = \frac{468}{f}$$

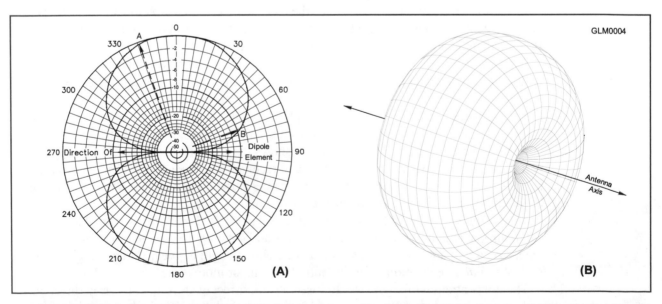

Figure 6-1 — Part A shows the radiation pattern in the plane of a dipole located in free space. The dipole element is shown on the line from 270 to 90 degrees in this figure. Part B show the three-dimensional radiation pattern in all directions around the dipole.

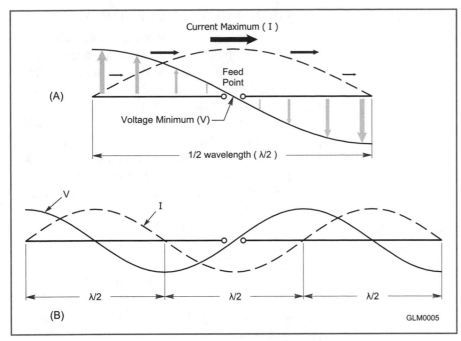

Figure 6-2 — The half-wave dipole at A has its maximum current in the middle and maximum voltage at each end. Feed point impedance is lowest in the middle. At odd harmonics of the fundamental frequency, the dipole's feed point impedance is low at the midpoint once again as shown at B.

If you do the math you'll discover that 468 is a few percent shorter than expected based on a direct conversion from the free-space wavelength of a radio wave with frequency, f. This is because the physical thickness of the wire makes the antenna look a bit longer electrically than it is physically. The value 468 was arrived at based on the customary *length-to-diameter* (*l/d*) ratio of wire antennas for the HF bands that varies from a few thousand to 20,000 or more. Making antennas out of thicker wire, cages of multiple wires, or tubing and rod all reduce the resonant frequency for a given length even further.

Example 1: What is the length of a dipole for 3.550 MHz?

$$L = \frac{468}{3.55} = 131.8 \text{ feet}$$

Example 2: What is the length of a dipole for 21.300 MHz?

$$L = \frac{468}{21.3} = 22 \text{ feet}$$

Center-fed dipoles are easiest to use on the band for which they are resonant. The feed point impedance of such an antenna is a good match for the 50 or 75 Ω coaxial cable used by most hams. The feed point impedance of a half-wave dipole is also a good match for coax on odd multiples of the fundamental frequency. For example, a dipole for the 40 meter band (7 MHz) can also be used on 15 meters (21 MHz). On its third harmonic, the dipole "looks like" the three half-wave dipoles in Figure 6-2 connected end to end. On even-numbered harmonics and non-resonant bands, the feed point impedance of the dipole can be high, just as it is near the antenna's end, requiring that a tuner be used.

> Before you go on, study test questions G9B04, G9B08, G9B10 and G9B11. Review this section if you have difficulty.

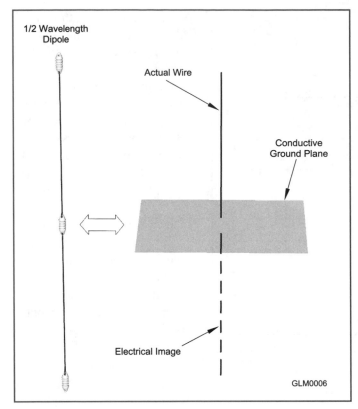

1/2 Wavelength Dipole

Actual Wire

Conductive Ground Plane

Electrical Image

GLM0006

Figure 6-3 — The ground plane, whether made of solid metal or radial wires, creates an electrical mirror image of the ¼ wavelength antenna. This creates the electrical equivalent of a dipole antenna.

GROUND PLANES (VERTICALS)

The ground-plane antenna is one-half of a dipole with the missing portion made up by an electrical mirror, called the *ground plane*. The ground plane can be made from sheet metal or a screen of *radial* wires. The basic ground plane antenna is ¼ wavelength (λ/4) long with the feed point at the junction of the antenna and the ground plane. Currents in the ground plane create an electrical image of the physical portion of the antenna as shown in **Figure 6-3**. For HF ground plane antennas mounted at ground level, the radial wires are laid on the surface of the ground or buried within a few inches of the surface.

Ground planes are often called simply "verticals" because that is the usual way of constructing and installing them. Full-length dipoles and Yagis can also be installed vertically, though. Like a dipole, the ground plane radiates best broadside to its axis. If installed vertically, this means the ground plane antenna is omnidirectional. This is a very useful characteristic for VHF and UHF communications while mobile or portable and for an HF antenna where signals may come from all directions.

The feed point impedance at the base of the ground plane is 35 Ω, half of a complete dipole's impedance, because only half of the antenna is physically there and able to radiate energy. Drooping or sloping the radials of an elevated ground plane antenna raises the feed point impedance. A droop angle between 30 and 45 degrees as shown in **Figure 6-4** results in the feed point impedance being raised to approximately 50 Ω, a perfect match for coaxial cable.

If the droop angle continues to increase, the antenna functions more and more like a physical dipole and the feed point impedance eventually reaches the 72 Ω of the dipole. As with the dipole, moving the feed point away from the base — the midpoint of the combined physical antenna and its image — raises the impedance.

The formula for the length of the λ/4 ground plane is:

$$\text{Length in feet} = \frac{234}{\text{frequency in MHz}} = \frac{234}{f}$$

Example 3: What is the length of a λ/4 ground-plane antenna for 50.1 MHz?

$$L = \frac{234}{50.1} = 4.7 \text{ feet}$$

Example 4: What is the length of a λ/4 ground-plane antenna for 21.05 MHz?

$$L = \frac{234}{21.05} = 11.1 \text{ feet}$$

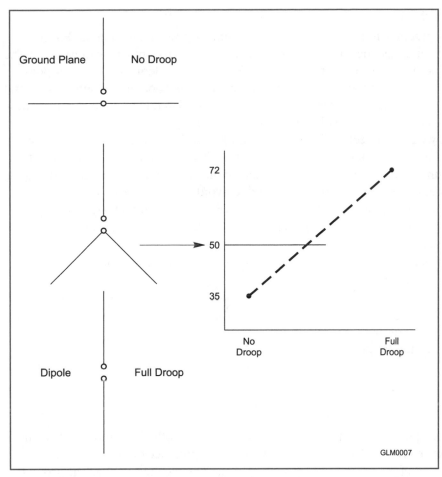

Figure 6-4 — The feed point impedance of a ground-plane antenna with radials perpendicular to the antenna is approximately 35 Ω, resulting in a 1.4:1 SWR with 50 Ω coaxial cable. Drooping or sloping the radials gradually raises the feed point impedance until, with the radials drooped so far as to become the other half of a dipole, feed point impedance becomes 72 Ω. A 50 Ω feed point is reached with radials drooping a bit less than 30 degrees.

In the previous section, we discussed why the physical thickness of the wire or tubing used for the elements changes an antenna's electrical length. The same effects occur for a vertical antenna if the length-to-diameter ratio of the antenna is substantially greater than that of wire. This is especially important at VHF and UHF frequencies where the antenna may only be several inches long. Be prepared to trim the antenna for resonance at the expected frequency if it is designed using this formula.

Mobile HF Antennas

Mobile HF antennas are often some form of ground plane antenna. The most popular mobile antenna by far is the vertically-oriented *whip* — a thin steel rod mounted over the conducting surface of the vehicle, giving omnidirectional coverage. Whips are common on the VHF and UHF bands. A full-sized λ/4 mobile whip is not feasible on the HF bands below 10 meters, so *loading* techniques are used to increase a physically small antenna's electrical size. See the sidebar, "Loading Techniques for Mobile Antennas."

While loading can cause an antenna to present reasonable feed point impedances, a loaded antenna is not as efficient as a full-sized straight whip. In recent years, an adjustable length whip with a loading coil at the base has gained popularity for HF mobile operation as a good compromise between performance and convenience.

Loading Techniques for Mobile Antennas

As a practical matter, mobile HF antennas must be physically small to be safe and manageable on a vehicle. Some common loading techniques are used to increase a mobile antenna's electrical size:

✔ *Loading coils* — a coil is added at the base or somewhere along the length of the antenna.

✔ *Capacitance hats* — spokes or a wheel-shaped structure is added near the top of the antenna.

✔ *Linear loading* — part of the antenna is folded back on itself.

Before you go on, study test questions G9B02, G9B03, G9B06 and G9B12. Review this section if you have difficulty.

RANDOM WIRES

It is not always practical to have a ½ or ¼ wavelength long resonant antenna. For portable operation and in other special circumstances, a *random wire* antenna can be used. The antenna is just what the name suggests, a random length of wire deployed however possible. Random wires, not intended to be resonant, are *multiband* antennas, useful on several of the ham bands. The radiation pattern of a random wire is also unpredictable, sometimes with several lobes at different vertical and horizontal angles.

A true random wire is connected directly to the output of the transmitter (more commonly to the output of an antenna tuner) without a feed line. The transmitter is also connected to the station ground, and so the antenna terminals are the antenna itself and ground. Using this type of an antenna requires a good RF ground to avoid significant RF currents and voltages on the shack equipment that could result in RF burns. Nevertheless, this simple antenna can give excellent results on any band for which the transmitter or tuner can accept the feed point impedance.

A variation of the random wire antenna is the *long-wire* antenna. This antenna is typically more than one wavelength (1 λ) long with a feed line attached at or near one end of the antenna. A long-wire antenna may or may not be resonant at the operating frequency.

Before you go on, study test question G9B01. Review this section if you have difficulty.

EFFECTS OF HEIGHT ABOVE GROUND AND POLARIZATION

An antenna's feed point impedance and radiation pattern are both affected by the antenna's physical height above ground. The effects are caused by the presence of the electrical image of the antenna created in the electrically conducting ground below the antenna. The ground may not be a very good conductor, but the image is still present and affects antenna performance.

Feed point impedance is affected because the electrical image, like all mirror images, is electrically reversed from the actual antenna. As the image and antenna get closer together, the actual antenna begins to be "shorted out" by the image. Below ½ wavelength in height, the antenna's feed point impedance steadily decreases until it is close to zero at ground level. Above ½ wavelength, the impedance varies as suggested by **Figure 6-5**, eventually reaching a stable value at a height of several wavelengths.

Height above ground also affects radiation patterns because of reflection of the antenna's radiated energy by the ground. The actual radiation pattern is composed of energy received directly from the antenna and energy that has been reflected by the ground. The direct and reflected signals take different amounts of time to travel to the receiving antenna, so they can be in phase (adding), out of phase (canceling) or anywhere in between. This creates a new pattern of lobes and nulls not present for an antenna in free space.

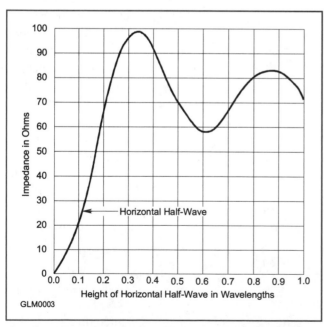

GLM0003

Figure 6-5 — The feed point impedance of a dipole over perfect ground varies dramatically with height. At ground level, the antenna is effectively "shorted out" by its electrical image. As the antenna is raised, the impedance gradually approaches the 72 Ω feed point impedance of a dipole in free space.

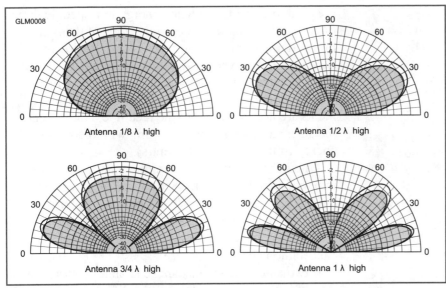

Figure 6-6 — As a low dipole starting at ⅛ wavelength above ground is raised, the effects of its electrical ground image cause the elevation to flatten out. At multiples of ½ wavelength in height, the pattern has a null in the vertical direction.

Figure 6-6 shows what happens when a dipole is slowly raised from a very low height to more than one wavelength above ground. At heights below ½ wavelength, the dipole's pattern is almost omnidirectional and is maximum straight up. As ½ wavelength in height is reached, the reflected and direct energy cancel in the vertical direction and add together at intermediate angles, creating a pattern of peaks and nulls in the radiation pattern for the antenna. Selecting the proper antenna height is important to achieving the desired goals for the antenna!

Polarization also affects the amount of signal that is lost from the resistance of the ground. Radio waves reflecting from the ground have lower losses when the polarization of the wave is parallel to the ground. That is, when the waves are horizontally polarized. Because the reflected waves combine with the direct waves (not reflected) to make up the antenna's radiation pattern, lower reflection loss results in stronger signal strength.

Ground-mounted vertical antennas, however, are able to generate stronger signals at low angles of radiation than horizontally polarized antennas at low heights. This means they are often preferred for DX contacts on the lower HF bands where it is impractical to raise horizontally polarized antennas to the height necessary for strong low-angle signals.

Before you go on, study test questions G9B05, G9B07 and G9B09. Review this section if you have difficulty.

6.3 Yagi Antennas

For the combination of economy, performance and simplicity it's hard to beat the Yagi antenna. More accurately called the Yagi-Uda antenna, the design was first described in 1927. With the end of World War II and the advent of television, coaxial cable, inexpensive aluminum, and steel towers placed the rotatable antenna within reach of amateurs.

HOW THEY WORK

The venerable Yagi remains the most popular of all directive antennas because of its simple construction and the ability to create gain and to reject interference. For example, a garden variety Yagi can reduce interfering signals and noise from unwanted directions to the rear and sides of the antenna by more than 20 dB — an important feature on a crowded band like 20 meters. A unidirectional antenna like the Yagi can increase your ability to hear and to be heard and that means you'll have more and better quality contacts.

While the dipole, ground plane and random wire use a single radiating element, the Yagi uses more than one. It is an example of an *array* antenna, in which several elements

There are two reasons you want to be able to aim an antenna: 1) to be heard better by a desired station, and 2) to hear better a desired station. The radiation pattern of a unidirectional antenna like a Yagi usually has one main lobe and at least three nulls — two side nulls and one rear null. If you know where each of those nulls is pointing, it's a simple matter to use the pattern to accomplish your goals.

The device that does the actual mechanical moving is called a *rotator* (not a "rotor"). The rotator's control box in your shack has a meter or digital readout that you can calibrate to provide the compass heading of where the boom of the antenna is pointing. From that heading, you know that the side nulls will be at 90 degrees from the boom to either side where the elements are aligned with their ends facing the signal. The rear null is usually aligned directly along the boom opposite to the direction of the main lobe. (The direction of the rear null may shift slightly from asymmetries in the antenna's installation or for signals arriving from different vertical angles.) To minimize noise or interference, try pointing one of these nulls at the source of the interference.

Being heard better by the station you're contacting means that you need to point the main lobe at the station. To aim the antenna accurately if that station is beyond your line of sight, you'll need a special kind of map called an *azimuthal projection* map. This map shows the world squashed into a circle centered on your location so that the direction shown on the map is the true *great circle* route across the globe. That's the shortest and most direct path between any two points on the globe. By aiming your antenna in the direction shown on the azimuthal projection map, you will be beaming your signal directly at the other station.

Once you have the antenna pointed in what you think is the right direction, don't hesitate to search or hunt for a slightly better signal somewhat off the direct path. It is not uncommon, particularly on HF, for the ionosphere to skew the signal path by up to 15 degrees. To minimize noise or interference, you rarely know the exact location, so you'll have to find the best location by using your ears and your radio's S meter to find the heading with the best reception.

are used to direct the radiated energy in a specific direction, called the *main lobe* or *major lobe* of the radiation pattern. There are two types of arrays: *driven* and *parasitic*. In a driven array, all of the antenna elements are connected to the feed line and are called *driven elements*. In a parasitic array, one or more of the elements are not connected to the feed line, but influence the antenna's pattern by interacting with the radiated energy from the driven element(s).

Whether an array is a driven or parasitic array, its radiation pattern is determined by *constructive* and *destructive interference*. When two waves interfere with each other, they can reinforce each other if they are in phase and cancel if they are out of phase. Partial cancellation occurs otherwise.

If two antenna elements are separated by more than a small fraction of a wavelength, the differences in travel time to a distant antenna from each is enough to result in cancellation that varies with the position of the distant antenna. **Figure 6-7** shows an example of cancellation for a pair of dipole antennas. The radiated fields from each antenna add and subtract at different angles around the antennas so that lobes and nulls are formed.

In a driven array, power is applied to all of the elements, such as in Figure 6-7. In a parasitic array, the antenna elements are so close together that energy is received by the parasitic elements and *reradiated*. The field from the driven element causes current to flow in the parasitic element. That current radiates a field — just as if it had been supplied by a feed line! By careful placement and tuning of the parasitic and driven elements, a directional antenna pattern can be created.

Before you go on, study test questions G2D04, G2D05, G2D11, G9C06 and G9C08. Review this section if you have difficulty.

YAGI STRUCTURE AND FUNCTION

The Yagi is a parasitic array with a single driven element and at least one parasitic element as shown in **Figure 6-8**. The elements are physically arranged to create gain along the axis of the antenna in a single primary region or *main lobe*. The parasitic elements placed in the direction of maximum gain are called *directors* and are slightly shorter than the driven element. Parasitic elements in the direction of minimum

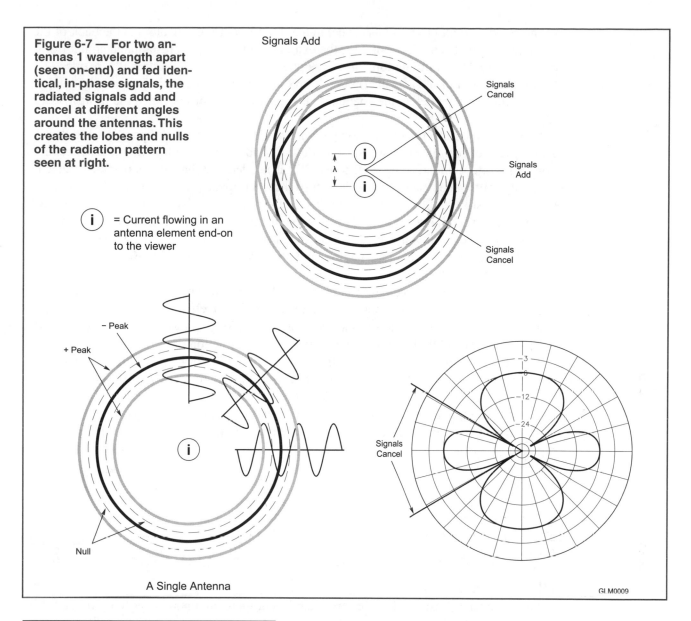

Figure 6-7 — For two antennas 1 wavelength apart (seen on-end) and fed identical, in-phase signals, the radiated signals add and cancel at different angles around the antennas. This creates the lobes and nulls of the radiation pattern seen at right.

(i) = Current flowing in an antenna element end-on to the viewer

Signals Add

Signals Cancel

Signals Add

Signals Cancel

− Peak

+ Peak

Null

A Single Antenna

Signals Cancel

GLM0009

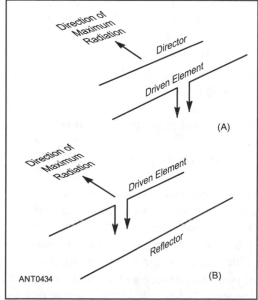

Direction of Maximum Radiation

Director

Driven Element

(A)

Direction of Maximum Radiation

Driven Element

Reflector

(B)

ANT0434

Figure 6-8 — Two-element Yagi antennas using a single parasitic element. At A the parasitic element acts as a director, and at B as a reflector. The arrows show the direction of maximum radiation.

gain are called *reflectors* and are slightly longer than the driven element.

The following description of how a Yagi works is somewhat oversimplified, but illustrates the general principles. The simplest two-element Yagi consists of a driven element and a reflector. The driven element (DE) is a resonant dipole, approximately ½ wavelength long. The reflector is slightly longer than ½ wavelength (by about 5%) and placed about 0.15 to 0.2 wavelength behind the DE, opposite the direction of maximum signal.

The original signal from the DE travels to the reflector where it causes current to flow, reradiating a signal. Reradiated signals are 180 degrees out of phase with the original signal, so the reradiated and DE signals cancel in the direction of the reflector (to the back of the antenna). To the front of the antenna, the extra travel time for the re-radiated signal from the reflector causes it to reinforce the DE signal. The ratio of signal strengths between those to the front of the antenna (in the desired direction) in the radiation pattern's major lobe to those to the back of the antenna (the opposite direction) is called the *front-to-back ratio*.

So why is the reflector slightly longer than the DE? The physical separation and the 180 degrees of reradiation phase shift don't quite add up to make for complete cancellation and reinforcement. Additional phase shift is needed and that comes from the reflector being slightly longer than a ½ wavelength so that its impedance is inductive. The additional phase shift to the current in the reflector from the inductive reactance is just enough to cause the original and reradiated signals to add and cancel in the desired directions. Neglecting the effects of height above ground, a two-element Yagi has a gain of approximately 7 dBi (over an isotropic antenna) and about 5 dBd (over a dipole). The front-to-back ratio is 10 to 15 dB.

A director element, placed in front of the DE by the same amount, increases forward gain. It works similarly but is somewhat shorter than ½ wavelength (by about 5%). The resulting capacitive reactance subtracts a small amount of phase shift, so that the DE and director signals add to the front of the antenna, in the direction of the director.

With the addition of a single director, a 3-element Yagi's forward gain improves to a theoretical maximum of 9.7 dBi and the front-to-back ratio to 30 to 35 dB. This is a very useful antenna!

Additional reflectors make little difference in either gain or front-to-back ratio. Therefore, most Yagi antennas have a single reflector. Adding more directors does not have a big effect on front-to-back ratio but does increase antenna gain, so it is not uncommon at HF to see Yagis with two to four directors. At VHF and UHF, there may be as many as a dozen or more directors, although each only adds a fraction of a dB in gain.

> *Before you go on, study test questions G9C02, G9C03, G9C04, G9C07, G9C09 and G9C18. Review this section if you have difficulty.*

DESIGN TRADEOFFS

Once the basic design principles are established, there are many ways to optimize the design of an actual antenna to fit a specific need. Is it more important to have the maximum gain or the best front-to-back ratio? How much variation of SWR is allowed across the entire band? Making a "one size fits all" antenna is quite difficult!

The primary design parameters for Yagi antennas are the length and diameter of each element and their placement along the boom of the antenna (the central support). These affect gain, SWR and front-to-back ratio in different ways:

● More directors increase gain.

● A longer boom for a given number of directors increases gain up to a maximum length beyond which gain is reduced.

● Larger diameter elements reduce SWR variation with frequency (increases SWR bandwidth).

● Placement and tuning of elements affects gain and feed point impedance (and SWR).

To be sure, there are other general rules of cause-and-effect, but these are typical of the decisions that antenna designers (and purchasers) should consider.

The process of modifying a design for a certain level of performance is called *optimizing*. Some antenna modeling programs can start with a basic design and then modify it so as to obtain the best gain, front-to-back ratio, feed point impedance and so on. For example, if you purchase a garden-variety commercial antenna, you could experiment with it to get more gain or better front-to-back ratio. Antenna design and modification is a very popular activity for hams.

Before you go on, study test questions G9C01, G9C05 and G9C10. Review this section if you have difficulty.

IMPEDANCE MATCHING

Most Yagi designs that have desirable radiation patterns also have a feed point imped-ance somewhat below the 50 Ω of regular coaxial cable; typically the feed point impedance is 20 to 25 Ω. This results in an undesirable SWR of greater than 2:1. To change the feed point impedance back to 50 Ω, various imped-ance matching techniques are used.

The most common tech-nique is the *gamma match* shown in **Figure 6-9**. The gamma match is actually a short section of parallel-conductor transmission line that uses the driven element as one of its conductors. The transmission line transforms the low impedance of the feed point to a higher value, creating some reactance in the process. An adjustable capacitor — either an actual variable capacitor or a short piece of insulated wire inside a hollow gamma rod — is used to eliminate the unde-sired reactance for an SWR of 1:1. A mechanical advan-tage of the gamma match over other techniques is that the driven element need not be insulated from the boom, simplifying construction.

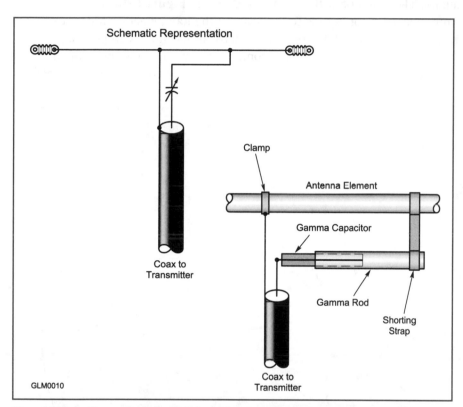

Figure 6-9 — The gamma match is a short section of transmission line that transforms a low impedance at the clamp to a higher impedance closer to that of coaxial cable. The gamma match is tuned with the gamma capacitor and by moving the shorting strap.

The are other techniques of impedance matching Yagi antennas, such as the beta match (or "hairpin"), the omega match, impedance transformers and transmission line stubs. These are described in references such as *The ARRL Antenna Book.* At VHF and UHF, it is also possible to use relatively large diameter ele-ments so that the feed point imped-ance is close to 50 Ω without any external matching devices.

Before you go on, study test questions G9C11 and G9C12. Review this section if you have difficulty.

6.4 Loop Antennas

Loop antennas completely enclose an area, usually one wavelength or more in circumference. Loop antennas can be oriented vertically or horizontally. On the HF bands, loops are made of wire because of their large size. At VHF and UHF, loops may be made of tubing or metal strap. The loop is cut to attach the feed line.

Loops can be circular, square, triangular or any simple open shape that is not too narrow. A square loop with each leg λ/4 long is called a *quad loop*. Triangular or *delta loops* are usually symmetrical, with each leg λ/3 long. Some delta loops shorten one leg and lengthen the other two equally. The radiation pattern of the 1 λ loop in **Figure 6-10** shows that the direction of maximum signal is broadside to the plane of the loop, whether round, quad or delta. If the loop is oriented horizontally, that means most of its signal will go straight up, making it a good antenna for local and regional contacts. Orienting the loop vertically aims the maximum signal toward the horizon, where it would be better for making DX contacts.

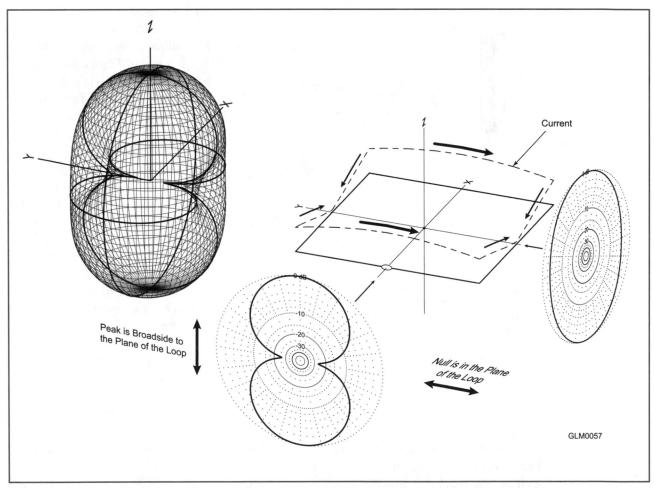

Figure 6-10 — The 1-wavelength loop can be envisioned as two ½-wavelength dipoles connected together and stretched into a square, circle, or triangle. Radiation is highest perpendicular to the plane of the loop.

A one wavelength loop is electrically like two dipoles connected end-to-end with the open ends brought together. The location where a loop's feed line is attached becomes a high current point, just like at the middle of a dipole. No matter where the feed point is attached, a mirror image of the high current point then appears ½ wavelength from the feed point across the loop as shown in Figure 6-10. Shorter and longer loops (not integer multiples of 1 λ) can't form the same pattern of current and have a higher feed point impedance.

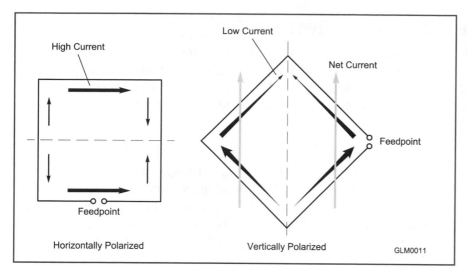

Figure 6-11 — The polarization of a vertical loop depends on the location of the feed point. Feeding the loop in the middle of a horizontal section forces maximum current to flow horizontally and the fields from vertical currents to cancel for a net horizontal polarization. Rotating the antenna 90 degrees also rotates the resulting polarization.

Loops can be used in arrays, just as dipoles can. In fact, a popular variation of the Yagi beam uses quad loops for elements. Not surprisingly, this beam antenna is called a *quad*! The quad has two or more full-sized loops mounted on a boom just like a Yagi's elements: reflector, driven element and director(s). The quad or delta loop beam driven elements are approximately 1 λ in circumference and operate on the same principles of re-radiation and phase shift as does the Yagi. Quad reflectors are about 5% longer in circumference than a quad driven element and the quad directors about 3% shorter.

A two-element quad or delta loop with a driven element and a reflector has approximately the same forward gain as a three-element Yagi. Front-to-back ratio is generally better for the Yagi. A two-element quad with the elements spaced about 0.2 λ apart appears almost to be a cube and is called a *cubical quad*.

The quad is mechanically more complex than the Yagi, requiring cross-arms to hold the loop. A quad has more surface area and wind loading than a Yagi with the same number of elements, which can be a drawback in environments with severe weather. Quad and delta loop beams with the same number of elements have about the same gain.

Interestingly, the polarization of a vertical loop antenna depends on where the feed point is attached as shown in **Figure 6-11**. Taking the quad loop as an example, attaching the feed point in the middle of the bottom or top leg of the loop results in horizontal polarization. Moving the feed point of the very same loop to one of the vertical sides results in vertical polarization. It doesn't matter either whether the loop is constructed with the top and bottom legs parallel to or at 45 degrees to the ground. The polarization of a horizontal loop is always horizontal, no matter where the feed point is located.

Before you go on, study test questions G9C13, G9C14, G9C15, G9C16, G9C17, G9C19, G9C20 and G9C21. Review this section if you have difficulty.

6.5 Specialized Antennas

This section covers several interesting topics associated with specific types of antennas or special ways of using them. There are literally hundreds of different types of specialty antennas, but these are common on the HF bands. You will also find that an ordinary antenna can be made to give unexpected results if constructed and installed in the just the right way!

NVIS

NVIS stands for *Near-Vertical Incidence Sky-wave*, a fancy way of saying, "Signals that go straight up!" When most hams think of an optimum antenna, they imagine one that sends a signal out at a low vertical angle so that it will be heard at the maximum distance for those great DX contacts. But it is not always desirable to work someone far away. Sometimes it's more important to make local and regional contacts, such as for emergency communications or nets.

Ground wave will work on the lower HF bands out to several tens of miles or more, but it's often necessary to cover an area several hundred miles across. If the signal is low enough in frequency that the ionosphere can reflect a signal at any angle, this sort of coverage can be achieved by beaming the signal straight up! If you've ever seen a searchlight sweeping across the clouds at night, you've observed NVIS. The beam of light is reflected down and visible over a much wider range than if the beam had been pointed toward the horizon.

Radio NVIS works the same way. An antenna that sends most of its signal at a high angle or straight up is used and the ionosphere reflects the signal back to Earth over a wide area as "short skip." On 75-meters, NVIS can cover an area 300 to 400 miles across. Therefore it is recommended for emergency communications. This works even during the day when low-angle signals would likely be absorbed by the ionosphere.

What kind of an antenna is used for NVIS signals? You may be surprised to find out that a simple dipole mounted a dozen or so feet above the ground is all that's required! You'll recall from earlier in this section that a dipole antenna mounted lower than $\lambda/4$ has a more-or-less omnidirectional pattern with the peak signal at 90 degrees — straight up. The best heights for NVIS communications are between $\lambda/10$ and $\lambda/4$. Lower than that and the feed point impedance becomes too low to provide a good match to coaxial cable. Higher than that and the main lobe starts to send more signal at lower angles than the desired 90 degrees.

> *Before you go on, study test questions G9D01, G9D02 and G9D03. Review this section if you have difficulty.*

STACKED ANTENNAS

You may have seen an installation with a pair (or more!) of identical Yagi antennas with their elements parallel mounted one above the other or side-by-side. *Stacking* antennas in the manner of **Figure 6-12** results in more gain.

There is an additional benefit to stacking antennas. If you study the azimuthal radiation patterns of Yagis, you notice that as more and more directors are added, the *beamwidth* of the main lobe (the angle between the points on the main lobe at which gain is 3 dB less than maximum) narrows. If you look at the elevation pattern, however, adding more directors doesn't have as great an effect. Vertically stacking antennas increases gain and controls the elevation beamwidth. Just adding directors to a single Yagi narrows the azimuthal beamwidth. Switching the feed line between one or both of the antennas in a stack varies the elevation pattern.

Most *vertical stacks*, with the antennas one directly above the other, space the antennas

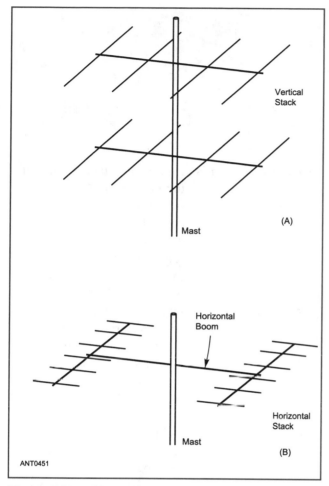

Figure 6-12 — Stacking antennas produces more gain in a main lobe that is carefully controlled. At A, two Yagis are stacked vertically on the same mast. At B, two Yagis are stacked horizontally side-by-side.

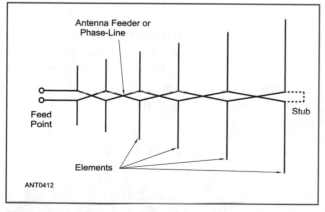

Figure 6-13 — The log periodic dipole array (LPDA) consists of dipoles fed by a common feed line that alternates polarity between elements. TV antennas sweep the elements slightly forward — there are many variations on the basic design.

about λ/2 apart, although spacings of up to more than 1 λ are sometimes used. Spaced λ/2 apart, the additional gain for a vertical stack of two beams is about 3 dB. For another 3 dB of gain, the number of antennas must be doubled to four.

Sometimes the antennas are aligned such that the elements are parallel, but end-on to each other, in a *horizontal stack*. In this arrangement, the spacing is larger to keep the antennas from interacting too strongly.

> **Before you go on, study test questions G9D04 and G9D05. Review this section if you have difficulty.**

LOG PERIODICS

If you don't look too closely at a TV antenna, you might think it is just another Yagi. Take a closer look and you'll be surprised — that's a *log periodic* antenna! Usually referred to as "logs," the log periodic antenna in **Figure 6-13** is designed to have a consistent radiation pattern and low SWR over a wide frequency bandwidth — as much as 10:1 — meaning the log periodic can be used over several bands. A log periodic will not have as much gain or front-to-back ratio as a Yagi antenna, however.

The "log" in log periodic refers to "logarithmic," and "periodic" means the spacing of the elements along the boom. The length and the spacing of the elements increases logarithmically from one end to the other. The result is that the part of the antenna doing the radiating and receiving shifts with frequency — the short elements are active at the high frequencies and the long elements at low frequencies. The elements are approximately the length of λ/2 dipoles at the frequency on which they are active. A log periodic antenna can be a good choice if only one rotatable antenna can be installed for several bands.

The log periodic is one member of an entire family of *frequency independent* antennas whose characteristics are consistent over wide frequency ranges. There are spirals and conicals and discones and many other interesting designs. They are designed so that the shape of the antenna is consistent from very small to very large scales. In that way, the radio waves will always find some area of the antenna to their liking!

Before you go on, study test questions G9D06 and G9D07. Review this section if you have difficulty.

BEVERAGE ANTENNAS

Invented in 1922 by Harold Beverage, this antenna was designed not to have terrific gain (it's actually quite inefficient) but to reject noise. At the low frequencies used in the early days of radio, atmospheric noise was intense. Rejecting it meant big improvements in receiving range, so Beverage designed a simple antenna that would reject noise and interfering signals in all but the desired direction. It consists of a long, low (less than 20 feet high) wire aligned with the preferred signal direction. One end is usually terminated in a resistor, and the antenna receives best toward the termination.

The Beverage of **Figure 6-14** is a *traveling wave antenna*. As the incoming wave moves along the antenna wire, it builds up a voltage wave just as wind blowing across water builds up a water wave. When the wave reaches the end of the antenna, the energy is transferred to the feed line. Voltage waves from signals arriving from the opposite

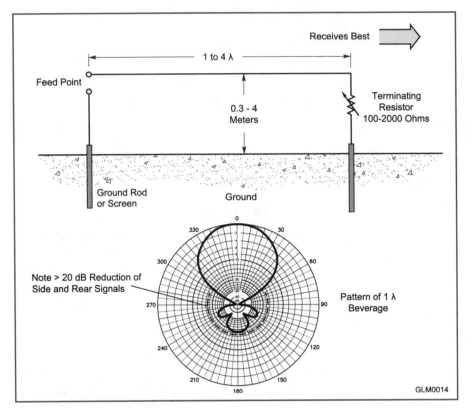

Figure 6-14 — Signals arriving from the direction of the terminating resistor induce a traveling voltage wave along the wire transferred to the feed line at the feed point. Signals arriving from other directions are either absorbed by the terminating resistor or do not induce voltage waves in the antenna.

end of the antenna are absorbed by the terminating resistor. Signals arriving from the side can not create voltage waves. So the Beverage favors signals only in the desired direction, dramatically improving the ratio of received signal to noise.

Used exclusively for directional receiving on the lower HF bands (40 meters and longer wavelength), the Beverage has high ground losses and is too inefficient for use as a transmitting antenna. The Beverage works by throwing away more noise than it does signal, not by acquiring more signal.

Before you go on, study test questions G9D08, G9D09 and G9D10. Review this section if you have difficulty.

MULTIBAND ANTENNAS

So far, the discussion has been mainly about antennas that are designed for a single band. It is terrific to be able to put up a separate antenna for each band, but that's rarely practical. The solution is *multiband* antennas that have good performance on more than one band, often several.

As discussed before, a half-wave dipole can be used on its odd harmonics without a tuner and gives good performance. A random wire or nonresonant antenna can also be used on multiple bands with a tuner. What hams generally mean by multiband antenna, however, is a design that reconfigures itself electrically for each band of operation.

The most basic multiband antenna, the trap dipole, is shown in **Figure 6-15**. Each trap is a parallel LC circuit. At resonance it acts like an open circuit, below resonance like an inductor, and above resonance like a capacitor. At their resonant frequencies, traps act like electrical switches, effectively cutting off the rest of the antenna beyond their location. At lower frequencies, the traps add inductance to the antenna, making the antenna look electrically longer. At higher frequencies, the capacitance electrically shortens the antenna.

For the trap dipole in Figure 6-15, at the lowest frequency of operation the antenna acts like a regular dipole, shortened by the inductance of the trap. On the band where the trap is resonant, the outer segments of the antenna are electrically disconnected and only the inner segment is active. Some trap antenna designs are useful on higher frequencies as well.

Yagis can also use traps to work on several bands. The three-element triband Yagi with traps in the elements is a time-proven performer on 20, 15 and 10 meters.

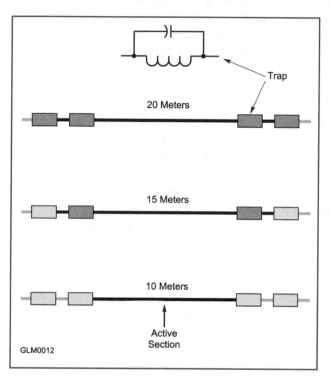

Figure 6-15 — Traps are parallel LC circuits. They may be made from discrete inductors and capacitors or may use coaxial cable or metal sleeves. The traps act like open circuits on different bands, causing different sections of the antenna to be active on different bands.

There are a few drawbacks of using techniques such as traps to make antennas work on multiple bands. First, because the antenna does work on multiple bands, it will happily radiate harmonics and spurious signals just as if they were intentional. It is up to the transmitter operator to be sure those signals are not generated. Second, the traps have losses and do reduce the efficiency of the antenna to some degree. Third, because the antenna is shortened on the lowest or lower frequencies of operation, it will not radiate quite as well as a full-sized antenna. Nevertheless, using trap antennas is often an excellent compromise between performance and available space and budget for antennas.

Before you go on, study test questions G9D11 and G9D12. Review this section if you have difficulty.

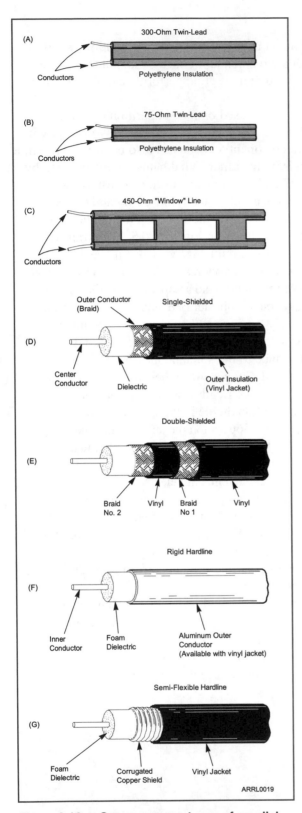

Figure 6-16 — Some common types of parallel conductor and coaxial cables used by amateurs. Parallel conductor line has two parallel conductors separated by insulation (dielectric). "Coax" has a center conductor surrounded by insulation. The second conductor, called the shield, covers the insulation and is, in turn, covered by he plastic outer jacket.

6.6 Feed Lines

As a General class licensee, you'll be assembling more sophisticated collections of equipment, trying bigger and better antennas and using more and more feed lines — more accurately, transmission lines — to connect everything together. Getting the best performance out of your equipment requires a basic understanding of how feed lines work, the goal of this section. Let's start by reviewing what you learned for the Technician class exam.

CHARACTERISTIC IMPEDANCE

All feed lines have two conductors. Coaxial cable has an inner or center conductor and an outer shield or braid. The inner conductor is insulated from the outer conductor by air or by foamed or solid plastic. Parallel or *balanced* feed lines consist of two parallel conductors separated by insulating material in the form of strips or spacers. **Figure 6-16** shows some examples of common feed lines used by hams.

Just as pipes and tubes have different "acoustic impedances" to the flow of sound or air through them, feed lines have different *characteristic impedances* (Z_0) that characterize how electromagnetic energy is carried by the feed line. This is not the same as the resistance of the feed line's conductors.

The geometry of the feed line conductors determines the characteristic impedance. For parallel feed lines, the radius of the conductors and the spacing between them are the parameters that determine Z_0. Flat ribbon TV-type twin lead has a characteristic impedance of 300 Ω. Amateurs also use parallel-conductor feed lines (also called *open-wire* and *ladder* or *window line*) that have impedances of 300 to 600 Ω.

In a coaxial feed line, Z_0 is determined by the diameters of the inner and outer conductors and the spacing between them. The characteristics of the insulating material has some effect on characteristic impedance, but has a larger effect on *feed line loss* and the *velocity of propagation*. The most common characteristic impedance for coaxial feed lines is 50 Ω (most common in radio applications) and 75 Ω (most common in video applications).

Before you go on, study test questions G9A01, G9A02 and G9A03. Review this section if you have difficulty.

FORWARD AND REFLECTED POWER AND SWR

A feed line transfers all of its power to an antenna when the antenna and feed line impedances are *matched*. If the feed line and antenna impedances do not match, some of the power is *reflected* by the antenna. Power traveling toward the antenna is called *forward power*. Power reflected by the antenna is called *reflected power*.

The waves carrying forward power and reflected power form stationary interference patterns inside the feed line. These are *standing waves*. The ratio of the peak voltage in the standing wave to the minimum voltage is called the *standing wave ratio* (SWR) and is used to measure how well the antenna and feed line impedances are matched. SWR of 1:1, a "perfect match," indicates that none of the power is reflected, all of it transferred to the antenna. An SWR of infinity indicates that all of the power was reflected.

SWR is always greater than 1:1 (for example, 3:1 and not 1:3). SWR is equal to the ratio of the higher of antenna feed point impedance or feed line characteristic impedance to the lower. That means the ratio is always greater than or equal to 1:1.

Example 5: What is the SWR in a 50 Ω feed line connected to a 25 Ω load?

$$SWR = \frac{50}{25} = 2:1$$

Example 6: What is the SWR in a 50 Ω feed line connected to a 225 Ω load?

$$SWR = \frac{225}{50} = 4.5:1$$

Example 7: If the feed line Z_0 = 50 Ω and SWR is 3:1, what is the impedance of the antenna? There are many combinations of load resistance and reactance that will create a 3:1 SWR, but the nonreactive antenna impedance could be:

16.6 Ω (50 / 3) or 150 Ω (50 × 3)

SWR can be measured anywhere along a feed line. It is most commonly measured at the transmitter where the feed line is connected. SWR meters (also called SWR bridges) are used to measure the SWR present in the feed line between the transmitter and the antenna.

Most amateur transmitting equipment is designed to work at full power with an SWR of 2:1 or lower. SWR greater than 2:1 may cause the transmitter to reduce power. The higher the SWR, the harder it is for a transmitter to transfer power to a feed line. High SWR may damage a transmitter. Antennas that are much too short or too long will not work well and will have extreme feed point impedances, causing high SWR. High SWR can be caused by a mismatch of the feed line and transmitter impedances, a mismatch of the antenna and feed line impedances, or by a faulty feed line.

Before you go on, study test questions G9A04, G9A05, G9A09, G9A10, G9A11, G9A12 and G9A13. Review this section if you have difficulty.

IMPEDANCE MATCHING AND TUNERS

Matching feed line and load (antenna) impedances eliminates standing waves from reflected power and maximizes power delivered to the load. This is not always practical, however, and the impedance matching is more conveniently done at the transmitter end of the feed line as shown in **Figure 6-17**. A device used to minimize SWR at the transmitter connection to the feed line is called an *impedance matcher*, a *transmatch* or an *antenna tuner*. It is common for a single piece of equipment to combine an impedance matcher, directional wattmeter and antenna switch.

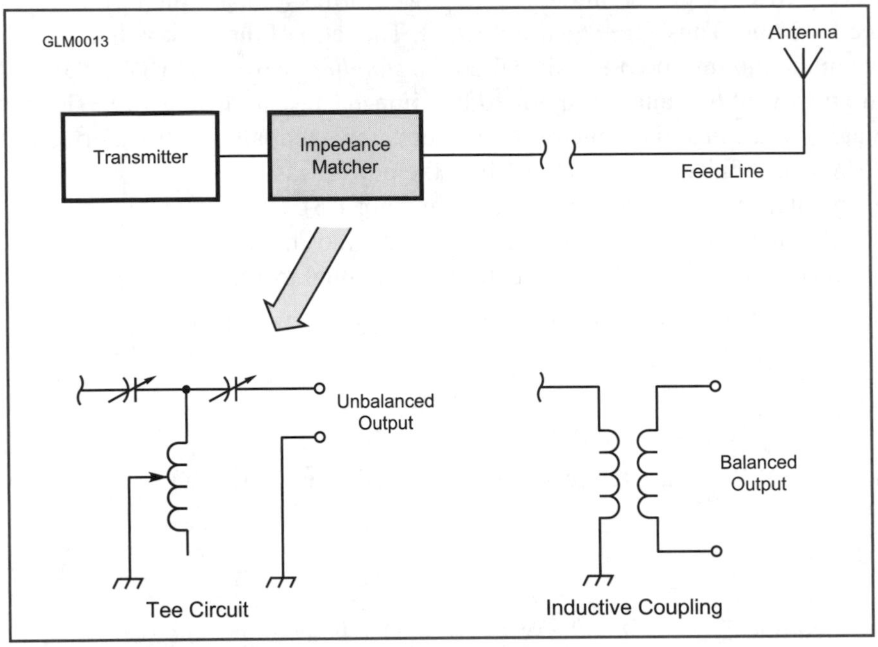

Impedance matching devices are constructed from inductors and capacitors. All of the inductors and capacitors are adjustable by the operator. The most common circuit configuration is the Tee shown in Figure 6-17. This circuit can match a wide range of impedances at the feed line connection to the 50 Ω that transmitters prefer.

Matching a balanced feed line requires that output of the impedance matcher also be balanced, meaning neither conductor of the feed line may be connected to ground. In this case, the impedance matching circuit's output is often inductively coupled to the feed line as shown in the figure.

Figure 6-17 — The Tee circuit is a popular impedance matching circuit for HF antennas. Installed at the transmitter end of the feed line, the Tee circuit is designed to be used with unbalanced, coaxial feed lines. To use balanced feed lines, such as open-wire lines, the output of a Tee circuit can be inductively coupled to the output so that neither feed line conductor is connected to ground.

It is also possible to use sections of transmission line called *stubs* to transform impedances from one value to another. These are used when the transmitter and antenna operate at a single frequency and the impedance levels will not change. Stubs are connected in parallel with the existing feed line near the transmitter or antenna.

Another type of impedance matching device that uses transmission line is the *quarter-wave matching transformer*. The quarter-wavelength section of feed line with a special value of Z_0 sets up a pattern of reflections that causes energy reflected from the load or antenna to be cancelled. Z_0 of the quarter-wave section must be equal to $\sqrt{Z_1 Z_2}$, where Z_1 and Z_2 are the impedances to be matched. The quarter-wave transformer is a single-frequency matching device and can only be used on one band.

Regardless of what technique is used to transform impedances, it is important to remember that the SWR in the feed line between the impedance matching device and the antenna does not change! If the SWR in the feed line is 5:1 and an impedance matching device causes a 50 Ω load to be presented to the transmitter, the SWR is still 5:1 in the feed line.

Before you go on, study test questions G9A06 and G9A14. Review this section if you have difficulty.

LOSSES

All feed lines dissipate as heat a little of the energy they carry — this is *attenuation* or *loss*. Loss occurs because of the resistance of the conductors and because the insulating material between the conductors absorbs some of the energy. Air insulated cables such as parallel feed lines and certain types of hardline have the lowest loss. Teflon insulation also has extremely low loss. Polyethylene, both solid and foamed, is used in most cables and has the highest loss, although it is still a very good insulating material.

Loss is measured in dB per unit of length, usually dB/100 feet of cable. Typical values for loss of different types of cable are given in **Table 6-1**. Loss increases with frequency for all types of feed lines. Small coaxial cables generally have higher loss at a given frequency than larger diameter cables.

Loss also increases as coaxial cables age. The outside jacket weathers so that small amounts of moisture can enter the braided outer shield. This degrades the connections between the strands of wire in the shield, increasing loss.

Table 6-1

Feed line Characteristics

Type	Impedance (Ω)	Loss per 100 ft (dB) at 30 MHz	Loss per 100 feet (dB) at 150 MHz
RG-8U	50	1.8	6.9
RG-8X	50	3.7	12.8
RG-58U	50	3.2	4
RG-174U	50	8.9	28.2
RG-213U	50	2.2	8
9913	50	1	4.5

Before you go on, study test questions G9A07 and G9A08. Review this section if you have difficulty.

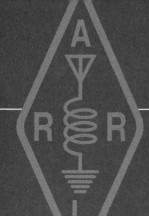

Chapter 7

Propagation

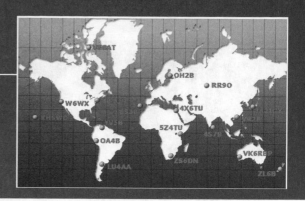

You've now studied electronics, signals, transmitters, receivers and antennas. Only one thing is missing — how the signals get from point A to point B! That's propagation and it's the subject of this section. On the HF bands, propagation is strongly affected by what's happening on the surface of the Sun so you'll need to learn a few things about solar phenomena. The effects of those events on the ionosphere are also important to HF operators. By learning some basic terms and relationships, HF propagation will be much easier to understand and use.

7.1 The Ionosphere

The upper reaches of the Earth's atmosphere are made up mainly of oxygen and nitrogen gas that gets thinner and thinner with distance from the Earth. Beginning at about 30 miles in height, the gas is thin enough that solar ultraviolet (UV) radiation can break the molecules of gas into individual atoms and then knock electrons away from them. The gas becomes *ionized*. The lack of an electron causes an atom to become a positively charged *ion* and the electron a *free electron*. These charged particles, the ions and the electrons, can respond to voltages just as electrons in a conductor and so this region of the atmosphere becomes a very weak conductor and is called the *ionosphere*.

REGIONS

The ionosphere extends to 300 miles above the Earth where the gas molecules, atoms, ions and electrons are so far apart that this is essentially the vacuum of space. The International Space Station, orbiting at 200 miles, is actually inside the ionosphere! Because of various physical processes, the ionosphere organizes itself naturally into several regions in which the density of the free electrons is higher than at adjacent altitudes. The main regions of the ionosphere are the D, E and F layers as shown in **Figure 7-1**.

- The *D region* (30 to 60 miles in altitude) is only present when illuminated by the Sun. It disappears at night because the ions and free electrons are close enough together to recombine quickly when no UV is present and the gas returns to a neutral condition.
- The *E region* (60 to 70 miles in altitude) acts similarly to the D region. Because it is higher and less dense than the D region, it lasts longer after sunset but still disappears at night, returning to its neutral state.
- The *F region* (100 to 300 miles in altitude) is the least dense of the three and can remain partially ionized at night. During the day, the F region splits into the F_1 and

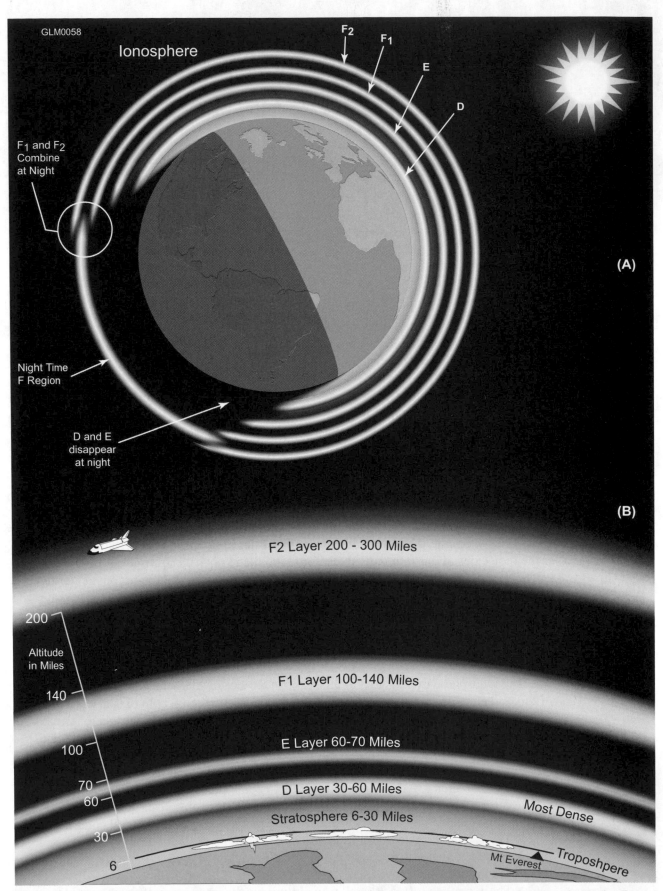

Figure 7-1 — The ionosphere consists of several regions of ionized particles at different heights above the Earth. At night, the D and E regions disappear and the F_1 and F_2 regions combine to form a single F region.

F_2 layers, which disappear back into the single F region at night. The height of the F region and the F_1 and F_2 layers varies quite a bit with local time, season, latitude and solar activity. At any particular location, the stronger the illumination from the Sun, the higher the F_2 layer will be, so the maximum height is reached at noon in the summer.

As the Earth turns, the ionosphere moves into and out of the sunlight, just as at the surface. The line between night and day is called the *terminator*. Because the ionosphere extends high above the Earth's surface, and because its regions appear and disappear with different speeds, different groupings of regions and layers are present at points near the terminator. Points at which only the upper F_1 and F_2 layers are present form a band near the terminator called the *gray line*.

Before you go on, study test questions G3C01 and G3C02. Review this section if you have difficulty.

REFLECTION AND ABSORPTION

That the ionosphere is a weak conductor enables it to respond to and affect radio waves passing through it, just as the electrons in a wire do. In the thick ionosphere regions and layers, the wave is gradually bent or *refracted* as shown in **Figure 7-2**. The ability of the ionosphere to bend radio waves depends on how strongly the region's gases are ionized and the frequency of the wave. The higher the region's ionization, the more the wave will be bent. The higher the frequency of the wave however, the less it is bent. In fact, at VHF and UHF, the waves are hardly bent at all and are usually lost to space. (There are exceptions, discussed later.) The continually shifting combination of ionization and frequency makes ionospheric propagation an exciting phenomenon!

At HF, the waves can often be bent enough to return to Earth as if they were reflected from a mirror high in the ionosphere. In fact, signals are always gradually bent and are never sharply reflected. Figure 7-2 illustrates how the height of this "mirror" is determined, called the region's *virtual height*.

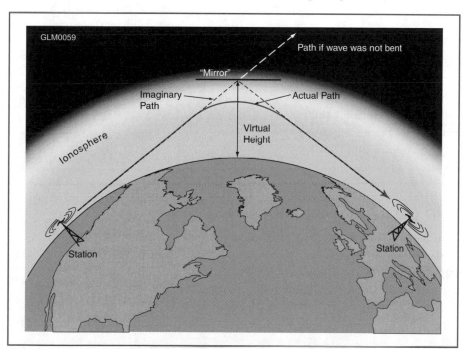

Figure 7-2 — Radio waves are refracted (bent) in the ionosphere, so they return to Earth far from the transmitting station. Without refraction in the ionosphere, radio waves would pass into space.

Some combinations of frequency and ionization level result in weak bending. In these cases, the signal must leave the Earth's surface at a low enough angle for the bending of the wave to send it back. The highest takeoff angle at which a wave can be returned to Earth is the *critical angle*. If the wave enters the ionosphere at a steeper angle, it might be diffracted, but not enough and it is lost to space, as shown in **Figure 7-3**. The critical angle depends on ionospheric conditions and frequency.

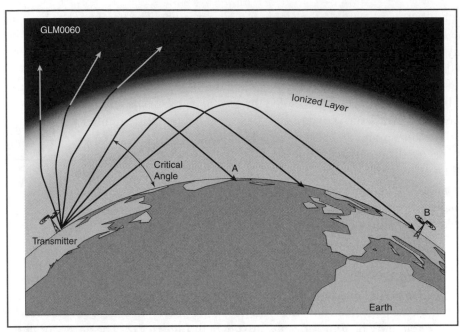

Figure 7-3 — Waves that leave the transmitter above the critical angle are refracted in the ionosphere, but not enough to return to Earth. Waves at and below the critical angle will return to Earth. The lowest angle waves return to Earth at the greatest distance, which is why low angles of radiation are often best for contacting DX stations.

The companion to critical angle is *critical frequency*, the highest frequency on which a signal transmitted straight up will be returned to Earth. Measuring the critical frequency by using radiosonde equipment gives the height of all the ionosphere's regions and helps provide a day-to-day picture of the ionosphere's status and activity.

The enemy of reflection is *absorption*. In the D and E regions, signals passing through the denser gas are partially absorbed, even as they are diffracted. In fact, the D region is not very good at diffraction at all. In the HF bands below 10 MHz, the AM broadcast bands, and at lower frequencies, the D region absorbs radio waves completely during the day, preventing those signals from returning to Earth until after dark. In general, absorption increases in the daytime and when solar UV is more intense. Lower frequency signals are most susceptible to ionospheric absorption.

Before you go on, study test questions G3C04, G3C05 and G3C12. Review this section if you have difficulty.

SKY-WAVE AND GROUND-WAVE PROPAGATION

Each reflection from the ionosphere is called a *hop* and allows radio waves to be received hundreds or thousands of miles away. Signals received in this way are called *sky-wave* and propagation via the ionosphere is called *skip*.

The higher the region from which the reflection takes place, the longer the hop. Signals reflected from the uppermost F_2 layer can travel up to 2500 miles before returning to the ground! Hops that use the E layer are shorter, up to 1200 miles, because of the lower reflecting height.

Sky-wave propagation can consist of multiple reflections because the Earth's surface also reflects radio waves. The highly conductive saltwater ocean is a particularly good reflector of radio waves. Propagation between Europe and the United States, for example, requires up to seven hops depending on location and time of day!

Hops can also be considerably shorter than those maximum figures if the ionosphere is sufficiently ionized so that the critical angle is high. Signals received via sky wave at much shorter than the maximum hop distance are called *short skip*. Short skip is also a good indicator that there is sufficient ionization to support longer skip distances on higher frequency bands. For example, short skip on the 10 meter band is a good indication that sky-wave propagation may be available on the 6 meter band at low takeoff angles.

Sky-wave signals also have a characteristic sound caused by the variations in density and height they encounter in the ionosphere. The ionosphere is not a smooth, stable medium through which the waves travel. The ionosphere is in motion itself and there are large variations in density and ionization at different heights and locations. This allows a sky-wave signal to take multiple paths before returning to Earth. Receiving several of these *multipath* signals at once gives the signal a characteristic echo or flutter as the quality of reflection changes or as signals combine from different paths.

Ground-wave signals travel along the surface of the Earth between stations. Rock and soil and concrete are not very good conductors and so a ground-wave signal loses strength much more rapidly than if it were traveling through air. The higher the frequency of the signal, the greater the loss as it travels. Ground-wave propagation on 40 meters, for example, may be up to 100 miles, but on 10 meters, only a few miles at best.

Depending on the critical angle for a particular frequency, a ring-shaped region around the transmitting station can occur between maximum ground-wave and minimum sky-wave range. This region is called the *skip zone* and stations located in the skip zone of a particular station can't be contacted on that particular frequency.

Before you go on, study test questions G3B09, G3B10, G3B14 and G3C03. Review this section if you have difficulty.

LONG PATH AND SHORT PATH

As you become more skilled in observing and understanding propagation, you'll begin to take advantage of unusual and short-term propagation effects. One of the most exciting is *long path* in which stations are contacted over a path that takes "the long way 'round." Most contacts are made via the *short path*, which is the shorter of the two great circle paths between stations. When the ionosphere along the short path does not support propagation, sometimes the long path will. The bearing of the long path is 180 degrees away from the short path bearing as illustrated by **Figure 7-4**.

Occasionally, propagation over both the long and short paths will be supported. Unless the long and short paths are almost equal (such as between stations located at each other's *antipode*) there will be an echo as the more delayed signal arrives a fraction of a second later. Occasionally, *round-the-world* propagation is supported and you can hear your own signal coming back around about $\frac{1}{7}$ of a second later!

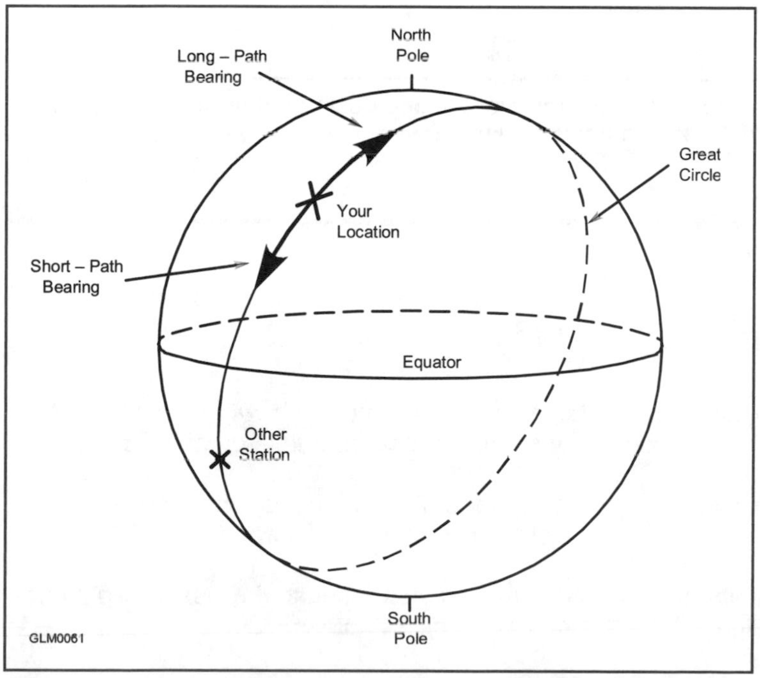

Figure 7-4 — This sketch of the Earth shows both great circle paths drawn between two stations. The bearings for the short path and the long path are shown from the Northern Hemisphere station.

Before you go on, study test questions G2D06 and G3B13. Review this section if you have difficulty.

7.2 The Sun

SUNSPOTS AND CYCLES

In the previous discussion, you learned that the ionosphere is dependent on solar UV to separate the electrons from their host atoms. The Sun is always generating UV radiation (even at night!) but there is a considerable amount of variation over time. A lot of this variation has been shown to be caused by sunspots, the slightly cooler (and comparatively darker) regions of the Sun's surface.

Sunspots vary in number over an approximately 11 year period known as the *sunspot cycle* or *solar cycle*. The number of sunspots and sunspot groups present on the solar disk at a particular time is the *sunspot number*. Sunspot number is used as an important parameter in assessing overall solar activity which rises and falls along with the presence of sunspots. As this book is written in late 2006, the solar cycle is at its minimum. Solar activity is expected to begin rising again as early as late 2007. The chart in **Figure 7-5** shows how the sunspot number has varied during the past several solar cycles.

The more sunspots are observed on the face of the Sun, the more UV is generated, creating more intense ionization in the ionosphere and improving propagation on the HF bands above 10 MHz and even into the lower VHF range. At the peak of the solar cycle, there may be sufficient solar UV to cause higher frequency bands such as 10 meters to stay open for long-distance contacts even at night. The high ionization takes a toll on the low frequency bands such as 80 and 160 meters as it increases absorption. Conversely, at

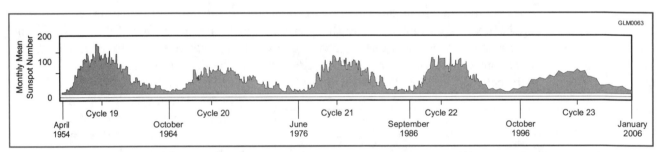

Figure 7-5 — One complete sunspot cycle lasts about 11 years, ramping up and down gradually. This graph shows the monthly sunspot numbers for the past five cycles.

Table 7-1
Daytime/Nighttime HF Propagation

HF Band (meters)	Daytime	Nighttime
160, 80, 60	Local and regional to 100-200 miles	Local to long distance with DX best near sunset or sunrise at one or both ends of the contact
40, 30	Local and regional to 300-400 miles	Short-range (20 or 30 miles) and medium distances (150 miles) to worldwide
20, 17	Regional to long distance, opening at or near sunrise and closing at night	20 meters is often open to the west at night and may be open 24 hours a day
15, 12, 10	Primarily long distance (1000 miles and more), opening to the east after sunrise and to the west in the afternoon	10 meters is often used for local communications 24 hours a day

the bottom of the solar cycle, the lower HF bands have good propagation and the higher HF bands above 20 MHz (15 meters and up) are often closed. One band that seems to do well at all times in the solar cycle is 20 meters (14 MHz), supporting daytime communications worldwide nearly every day!

Sunspots also seem to move across the Sun's surface because the Sun rotates once every 28 days. That is why propagation conditions (good and bad) on the higher HF bands such as 12 meters (24 MHz) and 10 meters (28 MHz) often repeat themselves in 28-day cycles as sunspots rotate back into view from Earth.

There are strong daily and seasonal variations in HF propagation at any point in the solar cycle. **Table 7-1** shows the typical variations in propagation on a daily basis across the HF bands for average solar activity. The seasons also affect propagation as the hemispheres receive more or less solar illumination. In the summer, the higher illumination and absorption make daytime HF propagation more difficult, shifting activity toward the evenings. The converse happens in the winter. Propagation around the equinoxes in March and September can be very interesting at any time of the solar cycle.

Before you go on, study test questions G3A09, G3A10, G3A11, G3A17, G3A18 and G3A19. Review this section if you have difficulty.

MEASURING SOLAR ACTIVITY

Solar activity is so important to propagation and communications that it is monitored around the clock by solar observatories all over the world. The results are available from Web sites, email distribution and radio broadcast announcements. By using this information, along with their experience and software tools to predict propagation, amateurs can confidently plan their on-the-air activity and be alerted of sudden changes in conditions.

Along with the sunspot number, there are three primary *indices* that are used to measure solar activity:

• *Solar Flux Index (SFI)* — describes the amount of 2800 MHz (10.7 cm wavelength) radio energy coming from the Sun. This index corresponds well to the amount of solar UV that is hard to measure at ground level. SFI starts at a minimum of 65 and has no maximum value. Higher levels indicate higher solar activity and generally better HF propagation above 10 MHz. **Figure 7-6** shows the correlation between SFI and sunspot number.

• *K index* — K values, from 0 to 9, represent the short-term stability of the Earth's geomagnetic field, updated every three hours at the National Institute of Science and Technology (NIST) in Boulder, Colorado. Steady values indicate a stable geomagnetic field. Higher values indicate that the geomagnetic

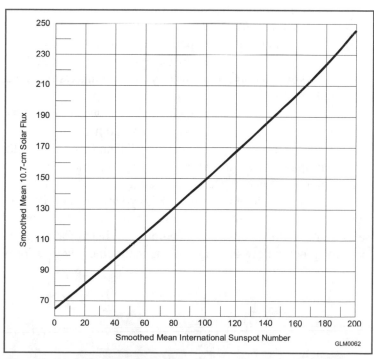

Figure 7-6 — This graph shows the approximate correlation between solar flux and sunspot number. Note that the minimum solar flux is 65, corresponding to a sunspot number of 0.

field is disturbed, which disrupts HF communications.

● *A index* — based on the previous 8 values of the K-index from around the world, the A index gives a good picture of long-term geomagnetic field stability. The A index can have values from 0 (stable) to 400 (greatly disturbed).

An announcement of the values of SFI, K, and A indices can be heard on the air by tuning in WWV or WWVH (**tf.nist.gov/stations/wwv.html**) at 18 or 45 minutes past the hour, respectively.

Before you go on, study test questions G3A04, G3A05, G3A12 and G3A13. Review this section if you have difficulty.

ASSESSING PROPAGATION

Given the solar activity indices and a reasonably good model of the Earth's magnetic field, scientists and communications engineers have developed fairly effective tools for predicting propagation. Amateurs make extensive use of these programs and as a General class ham operating on HF, you'll want to give them a try. Two key terms used by prediction programs are of particular importance to hams: *MUF — maximum usable frequency* and *LUF — lowest usable frequency*. Both the MUF and LUF depend on the specific path between two points — their location and distance apart. MUF and LUF also vary with time of day, season, the amount of solar radiation and ionospheric stability.

Use the MUF to Pick the Best Band

Operating near the MUF often gives excellent results because absorption is lowest just below the MUF. Low takeoff angles also raise the MUF because the signals will need less bending to complete a hop. Here are a couple of examples:

✔ If the MUF over a certain path is 19 MHz, the best band for that path is 17 meters (18 MHz).

✔ If the MUF over a certain path is 25 MHz, the best band for that path is 12 meters (24 MHz)

The MUF represents the highest frequency at which propagation exists between two points. Signals at or below the MUF will be refracted back toward the Earth. Note that MUF must include propagation at *all* points along the path between the two stations. The MUF will be different on every path between your station and any other station. It must account for variations in the ionosphere at every likely reflection as the signal hops its way from place to place. Signals above the MUF will at some point in the journey penetrate the ionosphere and be lost to space. MUF must also take into account the likely takeoff angles from your antenna system, since this affects the ability of the ionosphere to reflect your signal.

The LUF specifies the lowest frequency for which propagation exists between two points. Signals below the LUF will be completely absorbed by the ionosphere. To make contact with a distant station, you will have to use a frequency between the LUF and the MUF. If the MUF drops below the LUF, then no propagation exists between those two points.

Short-term variations in solar activity or the geomagnetic field can make predictions useless. There is no substitute for turning on the radio and listening with your own ears! Predictions do not take into account unusual propagation modes or paths, so you might be surprised.

One way to check the actual band conditions between two points is to listen for propagation *beacons*. There is an international network of beacon stations maintained by the Northern California DX Foundation (**www.ncdxf.org**) that transmit continuously. In addition, there are many beacon stations between 28.190 and 28.225 MHz that are excellent sources of information about 10 meter propagation.

Before you go on, study test questions G3B01, G3B02, G3B03, G3B04, G3B05, G3B06, G3B07, G3B08, G3B11, G3B12 and G3C11. Review this section if you have difficulty.

SOLAR DISTURBANCES

It would be wonderful if the Sun just beamed steadily, pumping up the ionosphere and never causing any trouble up there. That's not the case, unfortunately. The Sun is very turbulent, particularly during the years of peak activity during the solar cycle. There are several common events on the Sun that affect HF propagation. Their characteristics are measured by solar observatories and included in regular bulletins and broadcasts to alert users of the HF spectrum.

- *Solar flare* — a large eruption of energy and solar material when magnetic field disruptions occur on the surface of the Sun.
- *Coronal hole* — a weak area in the Sun's corona (the outer layer) through which plasma (ionized gas and charged particles) escapes the Sun's magnetic field and streams away into space at high velocities.
- *Coronal mass ejection (CME)* — an ejection of large amounts of material from the corona. A CME may direct the material in a relatively narrow stream or in a wide spray.

Sudden Ionospheric Disturbances

UV and X-ray radiation from a solar flare travels at the speed of light to impact the ionosphere about 8 minutes later. When the radiation hits the ionosphere, the level of ionization increases rapidly, particularly in the D region (see **Figure 7-7**). This increases

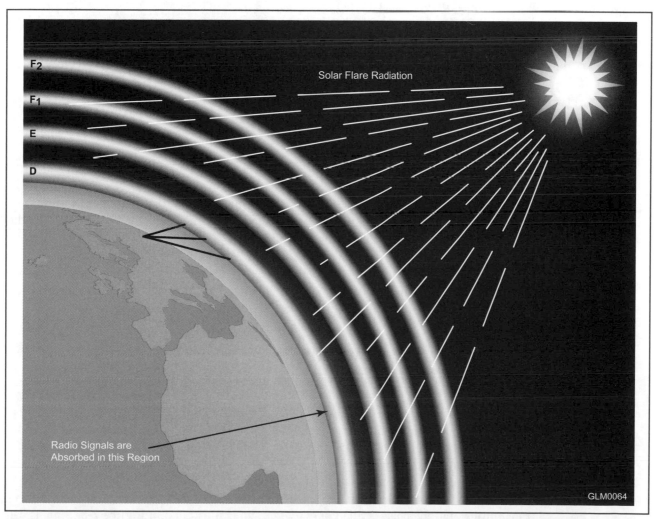

Figure 7-7 — Approximately 8 minutes after a solar flare occurs on the Sun, the ultraviolet and X-ray radiation released by the flare reaches the Earth. This radiation causes increased ionization and radio wave absorption in the D region.

absorption dramatically, causing a *sudden ionospheric disturbance* (SID) also known as a *radio blackout*. After a large flare, the HF bands can be completely devoid of sky-wave signals for a period of many seconds to hours, returning gradually to normal. The lower bands are affected first, so communication may still be possible on a higher band. SIDs only affect the sunlit side of the Earth so dark-side communications may be relatively unaffected.

Geomagnetic Disturbances

Following the UV and X-rays, charged particles and other material from coronal holes and coronal mass ejections travel considerably slower and take longer to reach Earth, up to 20 to 40 hours. When the charged particles arrive, they can be trapped in the Earth's magnetic field near the north and south magnetic poles. They then deposit their energy into the Earth's geomagnetic field and cause higher ionization in the E region of the ionosphere, causing auroral displays.

The sudden change in the geomagnetic field disrupts the upper layers of the ionosphere, causing propagation on the higher HF bands to be affected first. Long-distance paths that travel at high latitudes, particularly those that pass near the magnetic poles, may be completely wiped out for a period of hours to days.

Auroras are actually the glow of gases ionized by the incoming charged particles as they flow vertically down into the atmosphere, guided by the magnetic field. The resulting conductive sheets that light up the night sky also reflect radio signals above 20 MHz. In particular, auroral propagation is strongest on 6 and 2 meters, modulating the signals with a characteristic hiss or buzz.

> *Before you go on, study test questions G3A01, G3A02, G3A03, G3A06, G3A07, G3A08, G3A14, G3A15 and G3A16. Review this section if you have difficulty.*

7.3 Scatter Modes

As you may have experienced on VHF, radio waves often propagate by reflections from terrestrial objects and disturbances in the atmosphere. The same is true for HF radio waves on a larger scale. In particular, the ionosphere is not nearly so neatly organized into horizontal layers and regions as we imagine. There are regions that are tilted at significant angles and that reflect signals somewhat horizontally. Other regions may have significant variations in density that support localized reflections, such as the sporadic-E propagation common on 6 meters. These are *scatter* modes of propagation and can be quite useful when regular sky-wave is unavailable.

SCATTER SIGNAL CHARACTERISTICS

HF scatter signals are usually weaker than those received by normal sky-wave propagation because the reflection is not very efficient and tends to spread out the signal, delivering only a small fraction of the signal to the receiving station. Scatter signals often sound distorted because the signal may arrive at the receiver from many different directions, resulting in multipath interference, just as on VHF and UHF. The usual effect is a fluttering or wavering characteristic.

If the signal is very close to the MUF, reflections from features on the Earth's surface such as the ocean or a mountain range may return some of the signal back toward the transmitting station. This is called *backscatter* and is illustrated in **Figure 7-8**. Signals can

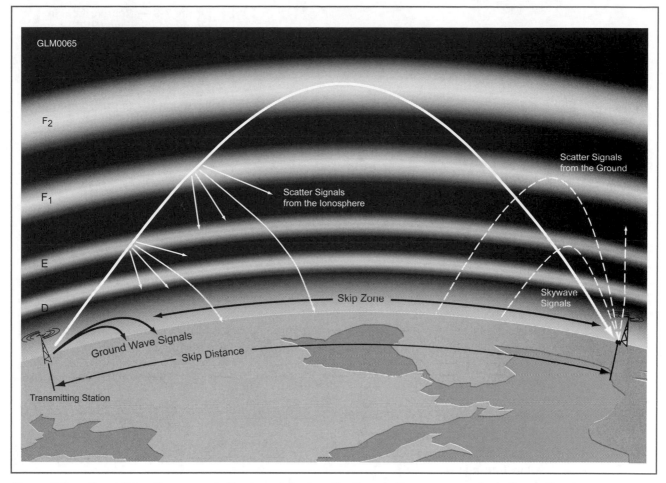

Figure 7-8 — On striking the ground after ionospheric reflection, radio waves may be reflected back toward the transmitting station. Some of this energy may be scattered back into the skip zone as a weak, highly variable signal.

also be scattered from within the ionosphere. These signals are heard from stations too distant to be heard by ground wave and on frequencies above the MUF for a short hop. Scatter and backscatter help fill in the skip zone where signals would otherwise not be heard.

Before you go on, study test questions G3C06, G3C07, G3C08, G3C09 and G3C10. Review this section if you have difficulty.

NVIS

You will recall that for signals below the critical frequency, the ionosphere reflects signals at any angle, even vertical. At most locations, the critical frequency is always above 5 MHz and frequently rises above the 40 meter band. By concentrating a signal so that it is radiated vertically, the reflection scatters the signal back to Earth over a wide area around the transmitter. Communication using this special scatter mode is called *Near Vertical Incidence Sky-wave* (*NVIS*).

To make use of NVIS as shown in **Figure 7-9**, horizontally polarized dipoles are

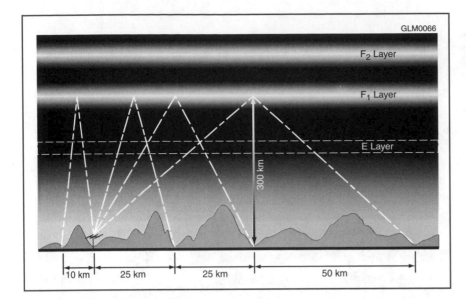

Figure 7-9 — Near Vertical Incidence Sky-wave (NVIS) communications relies on signals below the critical frequency transmitted at high vertical angles. The signals are reflected by the ionosphere back to Earth in the region around the transmitter.

placed low to the ground so that their radiation pattern is almost omnidirectional and concentrated at high elevation angles. Best results are obtained with the antenna ⅛ to ¼ wavelength high. The resulting skip will provide good signals throughout a region of up to 200 to 300 miles centered on the transmitter. Higher frequencies can be used during the day as the critical frequency rises due to solar illumination.

Before you go on, study test questions G3C13 and G3C14. Review this section if you have difficulty.

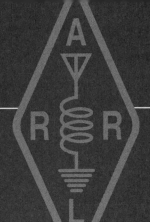

Chapter 8

Electrical and RF Safety

In this chapter, you'll learn about:
- **Basic electrical safety practices**
- **Electrical shock hazards**
- **Safety grounding and protective components**
- **RF exposure fundamentals**
- **Evaluating RF exposure**
- **Antenna installation practices**
- **Towers and masts**

Radio is basically quite safe, but no activity is completely without risk. As a General class licensee, you'll be using more different types of equipment, larger antennas and towers, and more complex stations. With this broader set of privileges comes an increased responsibility to be aware of potential hazards. Doing so helps you to take the necessary steps to protect yourself and others.

8.1 Electrical Safety

With the exception of mobile and portable operating, radio equipment gets its power from the ac power grid. Since that ac line voltage from the wall doesn't care whether a powerful radio or an indicator light is connected, the same safety practices apply for both low-power and high-power stations.

BASIC SAFETY

It's important to have a master OFF/ON switch for your station and workbench, just as in a shop full of power tools and machinery. If you are shocked, your rescuers should have been trained to remove power first so they are not also exposed to shock. The switch should be clearly labeled and somewhat away from the equipment. Don't place the OFF/ON switch in an obscure, hard-to-find or reach location. Show your family how to turn off power at the master switch and from your home's circuit-breaker box.

Don't put yourself in a position to be shocked or hard to rescue. Don't work on "live" equipment unless absolutely necessary. Avoid working alone on energized equipment. Never assume equipment is off or de-energized — check with a meter or tester first. If you are working on feed lines or antennas, be sure that a

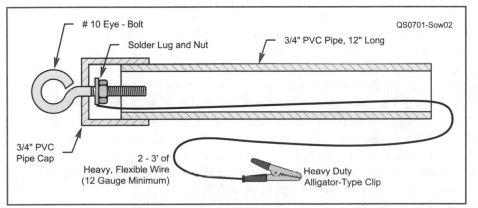

Figure 8-1 — A grounding or "chicken" stick is touched to all circuitry inside an enclosure to insure that no high voltage is present. The alligator clip is attached to an electrical ground and the eyebolt is put in contact with the circuitry.

10 Eye - Bolt

Solder Lug and Nut

3/4" PVC Pipe, 12" Long

QS0701-Sow02

3/4" PVC Pipe Cap

2 - 3' of Heavy, Flexible Wire (12 Gauge Minimum)

Heavy Duty Alligator-Type Clip

Soldering and Lead

Soldering is part of the electronic experience and has been for more than 100 years. Solder is primarily lead-based, with tin added to lower the melting point. Lead is a known toxin and so it is prudent to avoid unnecessary exposure. Solder in a well-ventilated area to avoid breathing the small amounts of lead vapor that result from melting the solder. The rosin flux smoke is also likely not good for you in high doses. After you are finished soldering, wash your hands to remove any solder or flux residue.

In 2006, a new set of environmental regulations called "Reduction of Hazardous Substances" or RoHS went into effect. The goal of those regulations is to reduce the amount of toxic materials that are used in electronics manufacturing, reducing them when the equipment is discarded or recycled, as well. Part of the regulations require that solder become lead-free.

Most amateurs will never be exposed by soldering to enough lead to pose a health hazard, but as industry changes, so will amateur practices. Lead-based solder will continue to be available for some time, but newer equipment will likely contain the new solders. Consult the owner's manual or manufacturer of your equipment to find out what type of solder was used. Mixing types of solder may lead to unreliable solder joints and erratic operation.

transmitter or amplifier can't be activated while you're working. Keep one hand in your pocket while probing or testing energized equipment, wear shoes with an insulated sole and remove unnecessary jewelry.

Before you go on, study test question G0B10. Review this section if you have difficulty.

When working inside equipment, remove, insulate or otherwise secure loose wires and cables. Remember that the residual charge on a capacitor can present hazardous voltages for a long time and use bleeder resistors to drain it off. A grounding stick (shown in **Figure 8-1**) should be used to positively remove charge from capacitors and be sure that all exposed conductors are at ground potential.

ELECTRICAL SHOCK

Shocks result from current flow through the body, and shocks that result from ac current are the most dangerous. Remember that it is not voltage that causes the shock, but current flow. Electrical currents of 100 mA or more may disrupt normal heart rhythm, although **Table 8-1** shows that shocks from lesser currents can be painful. Electrical current of more than a few mA can cause involuntary muscle spasms that in turn cause falls and sudden large movements. Burns can be caused by large ac or dc currents through the body or along the skin. The largest current that has been shown to have no adverse effects is 50 μA.

The most dangerous currents are those that travel through the heart, such as arm-to-arm or arm-to-foot. The current flow disrupts the heart's normal beating rhythm. Low-frequency ac current, such as 50 or 60 Hz household power, is the most dangerous because it penetrates the body easily and is of a frequency that can disrupt the heart.

After a shock, the heart may resynchronize to its usual rhythm, enter an uncoordinated state called *fibrillation*, or stop beating altogether. Depending on the body's resistance, voltages as low as 30 volts can cause enough current flow to be dangerous.

Both fibrillation and lack of beating cause immediate unconsciousness from which you'll need assistance to recover. It is a good idea for you and every other adult to get CPR training from your local fire or police department or from the American Red Cross

Table 8-1
Effects of Electric Current Through the Body of an Average Person

Current (1 sec contact)	Effect
50 µA	Maximum harmless current.
1 mA	Just perceptible.
10-20 mA	Lower limit for sustained muscular contractions.
30-50 mA	Pain.
50 mA	Pain, possible fainting. "Can't let go" current.
100-300 mA	Normal heart rhythm disrupted. Electrocution if sustained current.
6 A	Sustained heart contractions.

(**www.redcross.org**). It could come in handy not just for you, but as a lifesaver to anyone in need. A comprehensive discussion of electrical injury is available on the Web site **www.healthopedia.com/electrical-injury/**.

Before you go on, study test questions G0B04, G0B13 and G0B14. Review this section if you have difficulty.

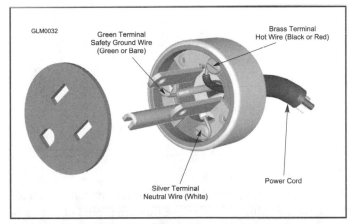

Figure 8-2 — Here's the correct wiring of a 120-V ac line cord to a new plug. Connect the black or red wire (hot) to the brass terminal, the white wire (neutral) to the silver terminal, and the green or bare wire (ground) to the green terminal.

WIRING AND SAFETY GROUNDING

When you are performing electrical maintenance in your home or in the shack, how can you tell what practices are safe? The National Electrical Code (NEC) contains detailed descriptions of how to handle ac wiring in your home and shack in a safe manner. (You can get a copy at many home improvement stores or at the library.) Local building codes should also be followed so that your home is properly wired to meet any special local conditions. This may be important for insurance purposes, as well. If you are in doubt about your ability to do the work properly, hire a professional electrician!

When wiring or repairing an ac power cord plug, be sure to follow the standard wire color conventions as shown in **Figure 8-2** and **Figure 8-3**:

● Hot is black or red insulation, connect to the brass terminal or screw

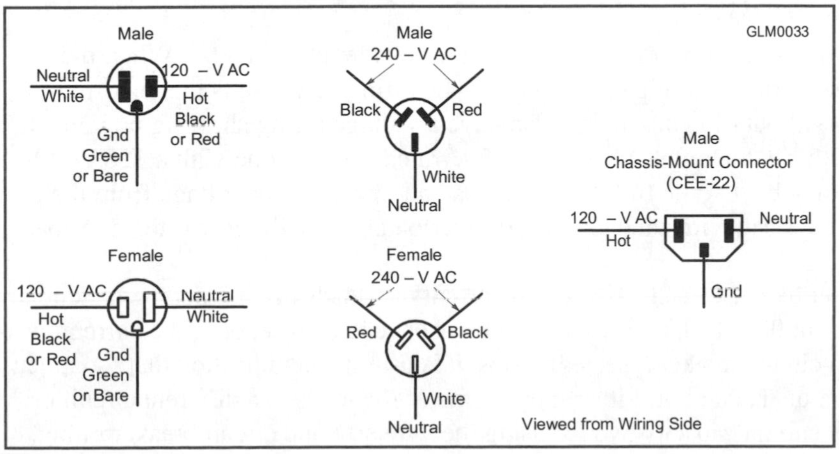

Figure 8-3 — Standard wiring conventions for 120 V and 240 V ac plugs and receptacles. It is critically important to follow the correct wiring techniques for ac power wiring. The white wire is neutral, the green wire is ground, and the black or red wire is the hot lead. Note that 240 V circuits have two hot wires and a neutral.

- Neutral is white insulation, connect to the silver terminal or screw
- Ground is green insulation or bare wire, connect to the green or bare copper terminal or screw

When connecting an ac power cord inside equipment, use the three-wire/three-prong cords. If the equipment has a metal chassis, always connect the ground wire or terminal to the chassis. This prevents hazardous voltages from appearing on the chassis. Do not use piping or structural metal as a safety ground unless you have verified that there is enough direct metal-to-ground contact to act as a ground rod. Many new homes and buildings use plastic piping in parts of the system.

Whether you are installing a new power circuit in your home or selecting a power cord, use cable and wire sufficiently rated for the expected current load as shown in **Table 8-2**. The rating of wire to carry current is called its *ampacity*. For house ac wiring, the two most common sizes are AWG number 12 wire for 20 A circuits and AWG number 14 for 15 A circuits. When you are finished with the wiring job, verify that you have the connections correct by using an ac circuit tester.

Table 8-2
Current Carrying Capacity of Some Common Wire Sizes

Copper Wire Size (AWG)	Allowable Ampacity (A)	Max Fuse or Circuit Breaker (A)
6	55	50
8	40	40
10	30	30
12	25 (20)[1]	20
14	20 (15)[1]	15

[1]The National Electrical Code limits the fuse or circuit breaker size (and as such, the maximum allowable circuit load) to 15 A for #14 AWG copper wire and to 20 A for #12 AWG copper wire conductors.

Before you go on, study test questions G4C10, G0B02, G0B03 and G0B06. Review this section if you have difficulty.

PROTECTIVE COMPONENTS

Protective components are used to prevent equipment damage or safety hazards such as fire or electrical shock caused by equipment malfunction. Those that are aimed at preventing shock hazards act when they detect current or voltage where it shouldn't be or indications that current is going where it's not supposed to go. Power control devices such as fuses and circuit breakers prevent equipment damage and fire by interrupting potentially large currents and disconnecting substantial voltages.

Fuses and Circuit Breakers

Fuses interrupt excessive current flow by melting a short length of metal. When the metal melts or "blows," the current path is broken. The rating of a fuse is the maximum current it can carry without blowing. Fuses also have a voltage rating showing how much voltage they will withstand. Do not substitute a 12 V rated fuse for one with a 120/240 V rating or the result may be that the fuse arcs over instead of removing voltage from the circuit. "Slow-blow" fuses can withstand temporary overloads, but will blow if the overload is sustained.

Circuit breakers act like fuses and "trip" when current overloads occur, opening the circuit and interrupting current flow. Unlike fuses, circuit breakers can be reset once the current overload is removed. If a circuit breaker repeatedly trips, it is usually an indication that too much power is being drawn on that circuit. Either move some of the loads to a different circuit or increase the circuit's current capacity by increasing the wire size and circuit breaker rating.

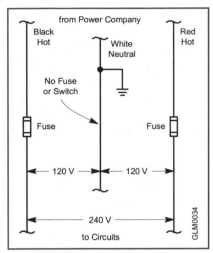

Figure 8-4 — Fuses and circuit breakers should be placed in the hot wire or wires of ac power wiring. Never install a fuse or circuit breaker in the neutral or ground wire of ac wiring. If a neutral or ground wire is disconnected, ac voltage is not removed from the equipment and may still present a shock or fire hazard.

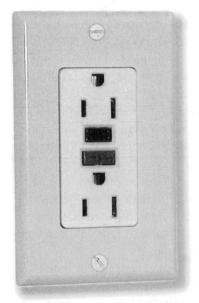

Figure 8-5 — *Ground fault circuit interrupter* (GFCI) circuit breakers are used in ac power circuits to prevent shock hazards. They are usually found in bathrooms, kitchens and other areas of the home with running water.

Use properly sized fuses and circuit breakers. Equipment manufacturers will specify the required fuse rating. Along with minimum wire size, building codes specify the size of the circuit breakers required at the power distribution panel. Never replace a fuse or circuit breaker with one of a larger current rating — fix the problem!

When installing fuses or circuit breakers in an ac power wiring circuit, be sure to place them in only the correct lines. Power is generally delivered to your home as a two-wire, 240 V circuit as shown in **Figure 8-4**. There is 120 V between each of the hot wires and the neutral wire. Most of your household circuits are connected between one of the hot wires and the neutral wire. Large household appliances and amplifiers should be connected between the two hot wires supplying 240 V because running from the higher voltage reduces the required amount of current for the same power consumption. For both types of wiring, only place a fuse or circuit breaker in the hot wire, never in the neutral wire. The reason is that opening the neutral does *not* remove voltage from the equipment and an electrical hazard may still be present.

Shock Prevention

A *safety interlock* is an example of a shock prevention device. Safety interlocks are switches that prevent dangerous voltages or intense RF from being present when a cabinet or enclosure is opened. One type of interlock physically disconnects high voltage (HV) or RF when activated. A second type shorts or grounds a HV circuit when activated, possibly blowing a circuit breaker or fuse in a power supply. Never bypass an interlock during testing unless specifically instructed to do so and then only in the way directed by the instructions. Be sure to enable the interlock before returning the equipment to service.

Ground fault circuit interrupter (GFCI) circuit breakers (**Figure 8-5**) are used in ac power circuits to prevent shock hazards. A GFCI circuit breaker will trip if an imbalance is sensed in the currents carried by the hot and neutral conductors. Current imbalances indicate the presence of an electrical shock hazard because the unbalanced current must be flowing through an unintended path, such as through a person from the hot wire to ground! GFCI breakers can be sensitive to just a few mA of imbalance between hot and neutral, well below the threshold for electrical injury.

> *Before you go on, study test questions G0B01, G0B05 and G0B12. Review this section if you have difficulty.*

GENERATOR SAFETY

Emergency and portable operation often makes use of an electrical generator driven by a gasoline or diesel engine. With generators easier and more convenient to use than ever, it's easy to overlook basic safety procedures.

Fueling and ventilation problems cause more injuries associated with generators than from any other cause. A generator should never be operated in an enclosed space or basement, or even a garage, where people are present or nearby. Install it outdoors, away from living areas, as shown in **Figure 8-6**. Carbon monoxide (CO) in the exhaust can quickly build up

Figure 8-6 — Install your generator in a well ventilated area, away from living areas.

to toxic levels. (For more information about CO safety, visit **www.epa.gov/iaq/pubs/coftsht.html.**) Even outside, exhaust fumes can be drawn into air intakes or windows or build up in poorly ventilated areas. If you plan on regularly using a generator, install CO detector alarms in living and working areas.

Flammable liquid fuels pose their own hazards. Generators should always be shut off when refueling to avoid igniting fumes or splashed liquid from the spark plug. Even if the generator engine is shut off, the engine block or exhaust may remain hot enough to pose an ignition hazard. Refueling should be done by a team of two, with one person equipped with a fire extinguisher. Store fuel well away from the generator, particularly from its hot exhaust, in approved containers. A fire extinguisher should be kept near the generator and separated from the fuel.

The metal frames of the generator housing and the engine act as an electrical ground, but they are not physically connected to the Earth. The best way to provide a generator safety ground is to use a ground rod near the generator and connected to the frame with heavy gauge wire. Most generators provide a special ground terminal just for this purpose.

If the generator is to be used at your home, connecting it to your household circuits requires special precautions. If you intend to connect the generator output directly to your home's wiring system, you must have the ability to disconnect your power service from the utility lines. This is usually accomplished by a pair of large circuit breakers labeled "Main." Opening these breakers completely disconnects your power distribution panel from the external electrical service. With these breakers open, you can then safely use a generator to power your home.

By not opening the main breakers, power supplied to your home's system is also connected back to the utility grid. The power system transformer that normally supplies your home works just as well in reverse — the voltage from your generator will be stepped up to lethal levels and placed on the utility lines. Known as *back-feeding*, this poses a serious hazard to electrical workers working on the system and to neighbors whose homes are likely still connected to the power system. If your generator is connected and running when power is restored, the resulting conflict between the utility and generator power is likely to cause damage to your generator.

The best way to connect a generator to your home is by using a *transfer switch* that transfers the power source for your distribution

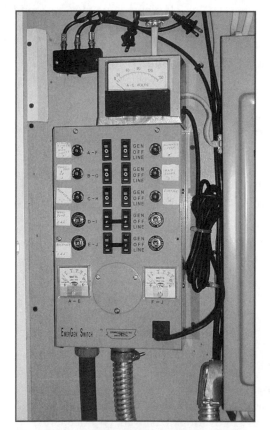

Figure 8-7 — A transfer switch connects your household circuits to the ac line *or* to a generator and isolates the generator from the line. This device eliminates the possibility of feeding generator power back into the ac line, or damaging the generator if ac power is restored.

panel from the utility lines to a special connector for your generator. Once the transfer switch is thrown, the power from your generator is connected only to your home's wiring and nothing else. The type of transfer switch in **Figure 8-7** switches selected household circuits between the ac line and the generator. A transfer switch should be installed by a professional electrician.

Before you go on, study test questions G4E06, G4E12 and G4E13. Review this section if you have difficulty.

LIGHTNING

The goal of lightning protection is to provide fire prevention for your home and to reduce or prevent electrical damage to your equipment. The best protection is to disconnect all cables outside the house and unplug equipment power cords inside the house before a storm. Don't forget that ac power lines, telephone and computer wiring can also conduct lightning.

When installing your station, a common metal entry panel where signal and control cables enter the house is a good place to provide a lightning ground (see **Figure 8-8**). The panel should be grounded to a nearby ground rod with a heavy, short metal strap. Lightning arrestors should be installed at the entry panel.

Figure 8-8 — A metal entrance panel serves as a common grounding point for all coaxial cable antenna feed lines entering your home. This helps to prevent damage to from nearby lightning strikes.

Grounding wires and straps should be as short and direct as possible. All towers, masts and antenna mounts should be grounded. Lightning grounds should be bonded to other safety grounds. Do not use solder to make the connections since it would likely vaporize if hit with a lightning-sized current pulse. Use mechanical clamps, brazing, or welding to be sure the ground connection is heavy enough.

Finally, you should also determine whether your renter's or homeowner's insurance covers you for lightning damage. Be sure to check for coverage of "external structures" and other types of property improvements that may be recognized by the insurance underwriters.

Before you go on, study test questions G0B09 and G0B11. Review this section if you have difficulty.

8.2 RF Exposure

Exposure to RF at low levels is not hazardous. At high power levels, for some frequencies, the amount of energy that the body absorbs can be a problem. There are a number of factors to consider along with the power level. These include frequency, average exposure and duty cycle of the transmission. The two primary factors that determine how much RF the body will absorb are power density and frequency. This section discusses how to take into account the various factors and arrive at a reasonable estimate of what RF exposure results from your transmissions and whether any safety precautions are required.

POWER DENSITY

Heating from exposure to RF signals is caused by the body tissue absorbing RF energy. The intensity of the RF energy is called *power density* and it is measured in mW/cm² (milliwatts per square centimeter), which is power per unit of area. For example, if the

Radiation

If there is a word guaranteed to cause apprehension, it is "radiation." Amateur Radio uses the word in a much broader sense — radiation pattern, feed line radiation, antennas radiate — and that can be confusing to the layman. It is true that radio frequency energy is a form of radiation, but it is far different from the radiation used for cancer treatment or emitted by radioactive materials.

Radiation from antennas is not the same as ionizing radiation from radioactivity. Radio frequencies are not nearly high enough for a photon of radio energy to cause an electron to leave the atom (ionize) as was discussed in the earlier section on ionospheric propagation. That is the difference between *ionizing* and *non-ionizing radiation* of which radio waves are the latter type.

Before radio waves can be considered ionizing, their frequency would have to be increased far beyond microwaves, through visible light and on to the upper reaches of the ultraviolet and x-ray spectrum. The radiation from radioactivity is carried by atomic particles such as the nucleus of a helium atom (alpha radiation), an electron (beta radiation), neutrons, or gamma-ray photons with frequencies even higher than X-rays. These are billions of times more energetic than the radio waves used by amateurs.

Biologic (athermal) effects such as genetic damage have never been observed at amateur frequencies and power levels. That requires the energy of ionizing radiation. The only demonstrated hazard from exposure to RF energy is heating (thermal effects) and that occurs only in very strong fields. RF "burns" are caused by touching conducting surfaces that have a high RF voltage present and are a very localized instance of heating that carries no more risk than thermal burns from hot objects.

power density in an RF field is 10 mW/cm² and your hand's surface area is 75 cm², then when exposed to that RF field, your hand is exposed to a total of 10 × 75 = 750 mW of RF power. RF field strengths can also be measured in V/m and A/m, but mW/cm² is the most useful for amateur requirements.

Power density is highest near antennas and in the directions in which antennas have the most gain. Increasing transmitter power increases power density around the antenna. Increasing distance from an antenna lowers power density.

ABSORPTION AND LIMITS

The rate at which energy is absorbed from the power to which the body is exposed is called the *specific absorption rate* (SAR). SAR is the best measure of RF exposure for amateur operators. The SAR varies with frequency, power density, average amount of exposure and the duty cycle of transmission. Injury is only caused when the combination of frequency and power cause too much energy to be absorbed in too short a time.

SAR depends on the frequency and the size of the body or body part affected and is highest where the body and body parts are naturally resonant. The limbs (arms and legs) and torso experience the highest SAR for RF fields in the VHF spectrum from 30 to 300 MHz. The head is most sensitive at UHF frequencies from 300 MHz to 3 GHz and the eyes are most affected by microwave signals above 1 GHz. The frequencies with highest SAR are between 30 and 1500 MHz.

Table 8-3
Maximum Permissible Exposure (MPE) Limits

Controlled Exposure (6-Minute Average)		Uncontrolled Exposure (30-Minute Average)	
Frequency Range (MHz)	Power Density (mW/cm²)	Frequency Range (MHz)	Magnetic Field Power Density (mW/cm²)
0.3-3.0	(100)*	0.3-1.34	(100)*
3.0-30	(900/f²)*	1.34-30	(180/f²)*
30-300	1.0	30-300	0.2
300-1500	f/300	300-1500	f/1500
1500-100,000	5	1500-100,000	1.0

f = frequency in MHz
* = Plane-wave equivalent power density

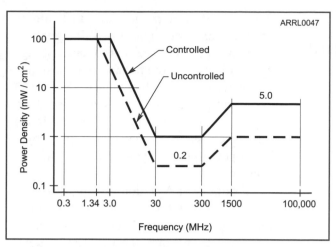

Figure 8-9 — Maximum Permissible Exposure (MPE) limits vary with frequency because the body responds differently to energy at different frequencies. The controlled and uncontrolled limits refer to the environment in which people are exposed to the RF energy.

At frequencies above and below the ranges of highest absorption, the body responds less and less to the RF energy, just like an antenna responds poorly to signals away from its natural resonant frequency.

Safe levels of SAR based on demonstrated hazards have been established for amateurs by the FCC in the form of *Maximum Permissible Exposure* (MPE) limits that vary with frequency as shown in **Figure 8-9** and **Table 8-3**. These take into account the variations in the body's sensitivity to RF energy at different frequencies.

Before you go on, study test questions G0A01, G0A02 and G0A03. Review this section if you have difficulty.

AVERAGING AND DUTY CYCLE

Exposure to RF energy is averaged over fixed time intervals because the response of the body to heating is different for short duration and long duration exposures. Time-averaging evaluates the total RF exposure over a fixed time interval. In addition, there are two types of environments with different averaging periods: controlled and uncontrolled.

Controlled and Uncontrolled Environments

People in *controlled environments* are considered to be aware of their exposure and are expected to take reasonable steps to minimize exposure. Examples of controlled environments are transmitting facilities (including Amateur Radio stations) and near antennas. In a controlled environment, access is restricted to authorized and informed individuals. The people expected to be in controlled environments would be station employees, licensed amateurs, and the families of licensed amateurs.

Uncontrolled environments are areas in which the general public has access, such as public roads and walkways, homes and schools, and even unfenced personal property. People in uncontrolled environments are not aware of their exposure, but are much less likely to receive continuous exposure. As a result, RF power density limits are higher for controlled environments and the averaging period is longer for uncontrolled environments. The averaging period is 6 minutes for *controlled environments* and 30 minutes for *uncontrolled environments*.

Duty Cycle

Duty cycle is the ratio of the time the transmitter is on to the total time during the exposure. Duty cycle has a maximum of 100%. (*Duty factor* is the same as duty cycle expressed as a fraction, instead of percent, such as 0.25 instead of 25%.) The lower the transmission duty cycle (the less the transmitter is on), the lower the average exposure. A lower transmission duty cycle permits greater short-term exposure levels for a given average exposure. This is the *operational duty cycle*. For most amateur operations, listening and transmitting time are about the same, so operational duty cycle is rarely higher than 50%.

Along with operational duty cycle, the different modes themselves have different

Table 8-4
Operating Duty Factor of Modes Commonly Used by Amateurs

Mode	Duty Cycle	Notes
Conversational SSB	20%	1
Conversational SSB	40%	2
SSB AFSK	100%	
SSB SSTV	100%	
Voice AM, 50% modulation	50%	3
Voice AM, 100% modulation	25%	
Voice AM, no modulation	100%	
Voice FM	100%	
Digital FM	100%	
ATV, video portion, image	60%	
ATV, video portion, black screen	80%	
Conversational CW	40%	
Carrier	100%	4

Notes
1) Includes voice characteristics and syllabic duty factor. No speech processing.
2) Includes voice characteristics and syllabic duty factor. Heavy speech processing.
3) Full-carrier, double-sideband modulation, referenced to PEP. Typical for voice speech. Can range from 25% to 100% depending on modulation.
4) A full carrier is commonly used for tune-up purposes.

emission duty cycles as shown in **Table 8-4**. For example, a normal SSB signal without speech processing to raise average power is considered to have an emission duty cycle of 20%. In contrast, FM is a constant-power mode so its emission duty cycle is 100%. Transmitter PEP multiplied by the emission duty cycle multiplied by the operating duty cycle gives the average power output.

Example 1: A station is using SSB without speech processing, transmitting and listening for equal amounts of time and with a PEP of 150 watts. The average power output = 150 × 20% × 50% = 15 watts.

Example 2: A station is sending a series of messages using SSB AFSK to transmit a digital signal at 100 watts PEP, listening only ¼ of the time. The average power output = 100 × 75% × 100% = 75 watts.

Antenna System

You must also take into account the amount of gain provided by your antenna and any significant losses from the feed line. High gain antennas increase a signal's average power considerably. For example, let's modify the two examples above by using an antenna with 6 dB of gain. In Example 1, the transmitter PEP is increased to 600 W by the antenna, increasing average power to 60 W. In Example 2, the same antenna would increase the average power to 300 W, larger than the transmitter PEP output.

> *Before you go on, study test questions G0A04 and G0A07. Review this section if you have difficulty.*

ESTIMATING EXPOSURE AND STATION EVALUATION

All fixed amateur stations must evaluate their capability to cause RF exposure, no matter whether they use high or low power. (Mobile and handheld transceivers are exempt from having to calculate exposure because they do not stay in one location.) A routine evaluation must then be performed if the transmitter PEP and frequency are within the FCC rule limits. The limits vary with frequency and PEP as shown in **Table 8-5**. You are required to perform the RF exposure evaluation only if your transmitter output power exceeds the levels shown for any band. For example, if your HF transmitter cannot output more than 25 watts, you are exempt from having to evaluate exposure caused by it.

You can perform the evaluation by actually measuring the RF field strength with calibrated field strength meters and calibrated antennas. You can also use computer modeling to determine the exposure levels. However, it's easiest for most hams to use the tables provided by the ARRL (**www.arrl.org/news/rfsafety/eval**) or an on-line calculator, such the one listed on the ARRL Web site.

Table 8-5
Power Thresholds for RF Exposure Evaluation

Band	Power (W)
160 meters	500
80	500
40	500
30	425
20	225
17	125
15	100
12	75
10	50
6	50
2	50
1.25	50
70 cm	70
33	150
23	200
13	250
SHF (all bands)	250
EHF (all bands)	250

Multitransmitter Environments

In a multitransmitter environment, such as at a commercial repeater site, each transmitter operator may be jointly responsible (with all other site operators) for ensuring that the total RF exposure from the site does not exceed the MPE limits. Any transmitter (including the antenna) that produces more than 5% of the total permissible exposure limit for transmissions at that frequency must be included in the site evaluation. (This is 5% of the permitted power density or 5% of the square of the E or H-field MPE limit. It is *not* 5% of the total exposure, which sometimes can be unknown.) The situation described by this question is common for amateur repeater installations, which often share a transmitting site.

If you choose to use the ARRL tables or calculators, you will need to know:

- Power at the antenna, including adjustments for duty cycle and feed line loss
- Antenna type (or gain) and height above ground
- Operating frequency

The ARRL tables are organized by frequency, antenna type and antenna height, and they show the distance required from the antenna to comply with MPE limits for certain levels of transmitter output power.

Exposure can be evaluated in one of two ways. The first way is to determine the power density at a known distance to see if exposure at that distance meets the MPE limit. The second way is to determine the minimum distance from your antenna at which the MPE limit is satisfied. Either way, the goal is to determine if your station meets MPE limits for all controlled and uncontrolled environments present at your station.

If you make changes to your station, such as changing to a higher power transmitter, increasing antenna gain or changing antenna height, you must re-evaluate the RF exposure from your station. If you reduce output power without making any other changes to a station already in compliance, you need not re-evaluate RF exposure.

Before you go on, study test questions G0A06, G0A08, G0A09, G0A10 and G0A15. Review this section if you have difficulty.

EXPOSURE SAFETY MEASURES

The measures you can take if your evaluation results exceed MPE limits are summarized in **Figure 8-10**. These are all "good practice" suggestions and can save time and expense if they are followed before doing your evaluation.

- Locate or move antennas away from where people can be exposed to excessive RF fields. Raise the antenna or place it away from where people will be. Keep the ends (high voltage) and center (high current) of antennas away from where people could come in contact with them. Locate the antenna away from property lines and place a fence around the base of ground-mounted antennas.
- Don't point gain antennas where people are likely to be. Use beam antennas to direct

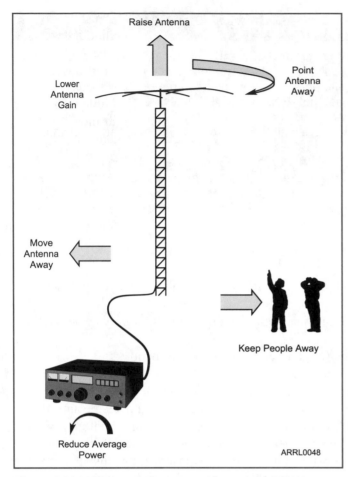

Raise Antenna

Lower Antenna Gain

Point Antenna Away

Move Antenna Away

Keep People Away

Reduce Average Power

ARRL0048

Figure 8-10 — There are many ways to reduce RF exposure to nearby people. Whatever lowers the power density in areas where people are present will work. Raising the antenna will even benefit your signal strength to other stations as it lowers power density on the ground!

the RF energy away from people. Remember that high-gain antennas have a narrower beam, but exposure in the beam will be more intense. Take special care with high-gain VHF/UHF/microwave antennas (such as long Yagis and dish antennas) and transmitters — don't transmit when you or other people are close to the antenna or when the antenna is pointed close to the horizon.

● If you have to use stealth or attic or other indoor antennas, carefully evaluate whether MPE limits are exceeded in your home's living quarters.

● On VHF and UHF, place mobile antennas on the roof or trunk of the car to maximize shielding of the passengers. Use a remote microphone to hold a handheld transceiver away from your head while transmitting.

● From the transmitter's perspective, use a dummy load or dummy antenna when testing a transmitter. You can also reduce the power and duty cycle of your transmissions. This is often quite effective and has a minimal effect on your signal.

> *Before you go on, study test questions G0A05, G0A11, G0A13 and G0A14. Review this section if you have difficulty.*

8.3 Outdoor Safety

Focusing on electrical safety associated with wiring and equipment is certainly justified, but there are many components of an Amateur Radio station outside the shack, as well. Outdoor safety involves mostly mechanical concerns that can be just as important as electrical safety indoors.

INSTALLING ANTENNAS

The most important rule for installing antennas is violated every year, usually with tragic results: *Place all antennas and feed lines well clear of power lines!* Poles and transmission lines like those in **Figure 8-11** are a common sight and must be given wide clearance. A good rule of thumb is to separate all parts of the antenna and support from the power lines by at least 150% of total height of tower or mast plus antenna. For example, if the combination of antenna and support mast is 40 feet tall, they should be 60 feet from the power lines. This effectively prevents an antenna from toppling over or blowing into power lines. Similarly, should a power line come down, it will have plenty of clearance from your antenna.

Speaking of power lines, don't run feed lines over power lines or service drops from a

Figure 8-11 — Utility poles and power lines must be given wide clearance from your antenna system.

transformer to the house. Even though they are "just" 240 V ac lines, they pack plenty of punch! If you are shooting lines through or over trees to support a wire antenna, be sure the projected flight path is completely safe and clear of people and power lines. Power lines can be hidden in or just beyond trees!

Once the antenna is up, people should not be able to come in contact with it. Place a fence around a ground-mounted antenna if there is a chance that people could come in contact with the antenna while you are transmitting. This also helps reduce RF exposure and reduces the chance of your antenna being knocked over.

Perhaps the most ignored safety advice is to follow the manufacturer's directions! Read the directions thoroughly before starting the job. The manufacturer wants you to have good results from their product and for you to be able to install it safely. Make sure you understand every step and that every part is on hand. When the mast is halfway up or the antenna is pulled up to the top of the tower is no time to discover that you didn't really understand the instructions or that a crucial part is missing!

TOWERS, MASTS AND HARDWARE

To increase range and reduce interference, a tower or mast is used to raise antennas above buildings and other obstructions. A fixed-length pipe mast of up to 20 feet is the simplest method of raising small antennas, such as ground planes or small directional antennas. Telescoping push-up masts for TV antennas can hold small amateur antennas. They are available up to 40 feet in height and require guy lines.

Fixed towers come in sections, often 10 feet each, and are used by amateurs at heights up to 200 feet. Most towers must be guyed or supported by a building, although some are specifically designed to be self-supporting. Fixed towers are required for large antennas due to the weight and torque. Because the towers are usually constructed with pipe legs and cross braces of rod welded to the legs, they are often referred to as *lattice towers*. Crank-up and tilt-over towers can support large antennas at heights up to 70 feet. Crank-up and tilt-over towers are generally self-supporting, but they require substantial concrete bases.

If the mast or tower requires guying, keep all lines and guys above head height wherever possible. If the guy anchor is low to the ground, flag or fence guy lines where they are lower than head height.

Building permits are generally required for lattice, crank-up and tilt-over towers. When erecting a tower near an airport, be sure to comply with FCC and FAA rules about maximum structure height near an airport. Make sure you follow grounding rules for external metal structures. Check with your local building codes. Towers should be grounded with separate 8-foot ground rods for each tower leg, with the ground rods bonded to the tower and each other.

Hardware used outdoors should be stainless steel or galvanized. The regular plated hardware used for indoor projects will rust quickly and become a real problem to deal with. If stainless steel screws and nuts are used, apply small amounts of anti-seize compound to prevent the surfaces from galling and seizing.

Plastic and ropes should be UV-resistant to avoid cracking or flaking after exposure to the sun. This is particularly important at the lower latitudes. This concern extends to the jacket of cables used outside. If you decide to bury the cables, use plastic conduit or cable rated for direct burial.

PERFORMING ANTENNA AND TOWER MAINTENANCE

Once you have the antenna and mast or tower up, regular maintenance is not something to scrimp on. You'll probably be experimenting with new antennas, as well. Whether you're climbing a tree, your roof or a tower, following basic safety rules will get the job done properly and without risking life and limb. Ignore that little voice saying, "Oh, I can just run up there in five minutes and do the job — why go to all the bother?"

First, both the climbers and ground crew should wear appropriate protective gear at all times. The climber must have a proper safety belt, or better yet a harness like the one shown in **Figure 8-12**. Other needed gear includes a hard hat, gloves, sun block and even goggles. Wear boots or work shoes to protect your feet and prevent sore arches from standing on tower rungs for extended periods. Plan for extra time on the job to handle the unexpected chores.

The ground crew is an important part of the team. Round up enough crew to do the job safely. If you don't have enough people, postpone the work. With everybody present and paying attention, review the job in detail and agree on who gives instructions. Make sure you can communicate clearly. Handheld FRS radios or ham radios are a lot easier to use than yelling and pointing. If you're going to use hand signals, make sure everybody understands them and uses the same ones!

Figure 8-12 — A harness specifically designed for tower climbing makes working on the tower more comfortable as well as providing essential safety features.

Before climbing or starting work, run through a safety checklist every time:
- Inspect all tower guying and support hardware.
- Crank-up towers must be fully nested and blocked.
- Double-check all belts and lanyards.
- Inspect all ropes and load-bearing hardware such as pulleys.
- Secure all electrical and RF equipment. Transmitters should be off and disconnected from the feed line to avoid shock or excessive RF exposure. Turn off and unplug all ac equipment, locking the circuits out and tagging them if possible (**Figure 8-13**).
- Check the weather report and don't be caught on the tower in a storm!

As you are climbing up or down, remember to take your time — it's not a race! Be sure your climbing gear is fully secure:
- Carabineers should be completely closed
- Latching hooks should close away from the tower
- Always use a safety lanyard or redundant lanyards

And remember that often forgotten rule to follow the manufacturer's directions!

Figure 8-13 — Before working on a tower or antenna, disconnect and if possible lock out the ac power circuits for your radio equipment.

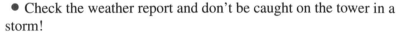
Before you go on, study test questions G0A12, G0B07 and G0B08. Review this section if you have difficulty.

Chapter 9

The Ham's International Language

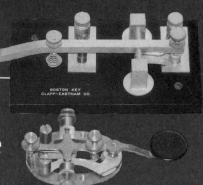

In this chapter, you'll learn about:
- Why hams enjoy using Morse code to communicate
- How to learn the Morse code alphabet
- Building your receiving speed
- How to send Morse code with a straight key
- Building a code practice oscillator

Although you no longer need to know Morse code to obtain any class of ham license, it is still a skill worth learning.

This book won't teach you the Morse code. In fact, you won't even find a copy of the Morse code printed in this book. That's because Morse code is best learned by sound, not by sight. Printed dots and dashes will only slow you down later. You'll need a method that teaches you the Morse code characters by producing the sounds for you.

ARRL's *Your Introduction to Morse Code* is available as a set of two audio CDs. The audio CDs are available directly from ARRL Headquarters or from the many dealers who sell ARRL publications. Write to ARRL, 225 Main Street, Newington, CT 06111 or call toll free at 888-277-5289 to order. You can even order directly over the Internet via **www.arrl.org**. In addition, there are several good computer programs that will teach you the code and give you unlimited practice without repeating the same text. Use your favorite Internet search engine to find programs that are currently available or check **www.arrl.org/FandES/ead/learncw**.

9.1 Code is Fun

Using the code is an exciting way to communicate. You become fluent in another complete language when you know the code. You can chat with hams from all around the world using this common language. With the practice gained from on-the-air contacts, your speed will increase quickly. There is great satisfaction in being able to communicate using Morse code. This is similar to the satisfaction you might feel from using any acquired skill.

How can one ham who speaks only English have a QSO with another ham who speaks no English? Using Morse code, of course! This chapter gives you some helpful hints and study suggestions for learning the skill of communicating by Morse code.

Morse code goes back to the very beginning of radio, and is still one of the most effective radio-communication methods. We send Morse code by interrupting the continuous-wave signal generated by a transmitter, and so we call it CW for short.

It takes far less power to establish reliable communications with CW than it does with voice (phone). On phone, we sometimes need high power and elaborate antennas to communicate with distant stations, or *DX* in the ham's lingo. On CW, less power and more modest stations will provide the same contacts.

CONSERVE TIME AND SPECTRUM SPACE

Another advantage of CW over phone is its very narrow bandwidth. Morse code makes efficient use of spectrum space. The ham bands are narrow portions of the whole spectrum. Many stations use the bands, and because they are crowded, interference is sometimes a problem. A CW signal occupies only about one-tenth the bandwidth of a phone signal. This means as many as 10 CW signals can fit into the space taken up by one phone signal.

Over the years, radio operators developed a vocabulary of three-letter *Q-signals*, that other radio-telegraphers throughout the world understand. For example, the Q-signal *QRM* means "you are being interfered with." Just imagine how hard it would be to communicate that thought to someone who didn't understand English. Another advantage to using Q-signals is speed. It's much faster to send three letters than to spell out each word. That's why you'll use Q-signals even when you're chatting by code with another English-speaking ham. Speed of transmission is also the reason radiotelegraphers use a code "shorthand." For example, to acknowledge that you heard what was transmitted to you, send the letter R. This means "I have received your transmission okay."

Many hams prefer to use CW in traffic nets, regular on-the-air meetings of hams to exchange and relay messages, called *traffic*. Using these nets, hams send messages across the country for just about anyone. When they send messages using CW, there is no confusion about the spelling of names such as Lee, Lea or Leigh.

CW: SOMETIMES THE ONLY CHOICE

When WA6INJ's jeep went over a cliff in a February snowstorm, he was able to call for help using his mobile rig. This worked well at first, but as the search for him continued, he became unable to speak. The nearly frozen man managed to tap out Morse code signals with his microphone push-to-talk button. That was all his rescuers had to work with to locate him. Morse code saved this ham's life.

Figure 9-1—Operation from just about anywhere is possible with a simple QRP transceiver, a piece of wire for an antenna and batteries or solar cells for power. CW is especially popular for backpacking and portable operation because it's more effective than voice modes with low power and simple antennas.

Some hams like to bounce VHF and UHF signals off the surface of the Moon to another ham station on the Earth. Because of its efficiency, hams often use CW to make *moon-bounce* QSOs.

Amateurs who enjoy making contacts using *QRP* (low power) enthusiastically embrace CW because of its ability to squeeze every mile out of a contact. **Figure 9-1** shows an example of a ham using portable equipment and antennas. Low-power CW transceivers can be packed to a mountaintop or packed in your baggage for some serious operating enjoyment.

On some frequencies, amateurs communicate by bouncing their signals off an auroral curtain in the northern sky. (Stations in the Southern Hemisphere would use an auroral curtain in the southern sky.) Phone signals become so distorted in the process of reflecting off an auroral curtain that they are difficult or impossible to understand. CW is the most effective way to communicate using signals bounced off an aurora.

You will feel a special thrill and a warm

satisfaction when you use the Morse code to communicate with someone. This feeling comes partly from sending messages to another part of the world. Sending and receiving Morse code is a skill that makes amateurs stand out. It provides a common bond between amateurs worldwide.

9.2 Getting Acquainted With the Code

The basic element of a Morse code character is a dot. The length of the dot determines how long a dash should be — three times as long as a dot. The dot length also determines the length of the spaces between elements, characters and words. **Figure 9-2** shows the proper timing of each piece. The time between dots and dashes in a character is equal to the length of a dot. The time between letters in a word is equal to three dot lengths and the space between words is seven dot lengths. Actual code heard on the air varies from these exact spacings, but those are the guidelines.

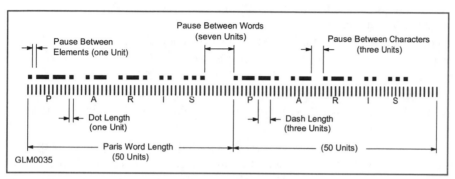

Figure 9-2—Whether you are a beginner or an expert, good sending depends on maintaining proper time ratios or "weight" between the dots, dashes and spaces, as shown.

The lengths of Morse code characters are not all the same, of course. Samuel Finley Breese Morse (1791-1872) developed the system of dots and dashes in 1838. He assigned the shortest combinations to the most-used letters in plain language text. The letter E has the shortest sound, because it is the most-used letter. T and I are the next most-used characters, and they are also short. Character lengths get longer for letters used less often.

An analysis of English plain-language text shows that the average word (including the space after the word) is 50 units long. By a unit we mean the time of a single dot or space between the parts of a character. The word PARIS is 50 units long, so we use it as a standard word to check code speed accurately. For example, to transmit at 5 words per minute (WPM), adjust your code-speed timing to send PARIS five times in one minute. To transmit at 10 WPM, accelerate your timing to send PARIS 10 times in one minute.

As you can see, the correct dot length (and the length of dashes and spaces) changes with code speed. As a result, the characters sound different when the speed changes. This leads to problems for a person learning the code. At slower speeds, the characters seem long and drawn out. The slow pace encourages students to learn the code by counting dots and dashes.

Counting dots and dashes introduces an extra translation step in the thought process of turning code into letters. (Learning the code by memorizing Morse-code-character dot/dash patterns from a printed copy introduces a similar extra translation.) That extra step may seem okay at first. As you try to increase your speed, however, you will soon find out what a problem it is. You won't be able to count the dots and dashes and translate them to a character fast enough! Having to re-learn the code copying process just as you're getting up to speed can be avoided by learning the characters as sound patterns from the start.

LEARNING MORSE CODE

Morse code is a communication method that depends on sounds. To understand the communication you must hear the sounds and interpret their meaning. This is why most code-teaching methods repeat the sounds for you to listen to and associate the characters with the sounds. It is also why you will not find a copy of the Morse code dots and dashes printed in this book. Audio CDs, cassette tapes, computer programs and even classroom or individual practice with a code-practice oscillator and a *code key* all rely on sounds to teach you the Morse code characters. (A code key is sometimes called a hand key, straight key or a telegraph key.)

Several other techniques have also been successful for teaching Morse code. Some of these methods involve memorizing a printed copy of the code. There are even a few commercial packages that picture the dots and dashes of the code characters in various "creative" patterns to help you remember them. You can learn Morse code by following any of these methods. Most people will learn faster, and will be able to increase their code speed easier, however, by using a "listening" method.

For those who find themselves unable to learn the Morse code using the audio CDs in *Your Introduction to Morse Code* or a computer program, one of these visual methods may prove helpful. Save that as a last resort, however. Practice faithfully with *Your Introduction to Morse Code* or a computer program every day for at least three to four weeks. Then, if you have not learned many of the characters, you may want to try one of the visual methods.

Many studies have been done, and various techniques tried, to teach Morse code as a listening process. The method that has met with the most success is called the *Farnsworth method*. That is the method used in the ARRL package, *Your Introduction to Morse Code*. With this technique, each character is sent at a faster speed (the ARRL uses a 15 WPM character speed) with lots of space between characters to reduce the overall number of words per minute. At speeds in this range, the characters — and even some short words — begin to take on a distinctive rhythmic pattern.

The 26 letters of the alphabet and the numbers 0 through 9 each have a different pattern. There are also different patterns for the period, comma, question mark, double dash (—), fraction bar (/) and some procedural signals that hams use, called *prosigns*. These two-letter combinations are written with a line over the letters to indicate that two letters are sent as one character to form a symbol. The + sign, which hams call $\overline{AR}$ (the overbar means that the letters are sent together without a space between them), means "end of message." $\overline{SK}$ means "end of work," or "end of contact." Hams sometimes refer to the double dash as $\overline{BT}$ and the fraction bar as $\overline{DN}$. That's a total of 43 character sounds. You'll learn the sounds of all these characters as you practice with your code CDs or computer program.

Your Introduction to Morse Code starts with code sent at an overall speed of 5 WPM. (You can still measure this timing by using the word PARIS, as described earlier.) Once you learn the character sounds and can copy at 5 WPM, it will be easy to increase your speed. Just decrease the spaces between letters and words, and your code speed increases without changing the rhythmic pattern of the characters at all. If you use a computer program to learn the code, or another method, we recommend this same technique, with the code characters sent at 15 WPM or faster.

Learn to recognize that rhythmic pattern and you'll associate it directly with the character without a translation step. You'll learn the code in the shortest possible time, and it will be much easier to increase your code speed. Decreasing the space between characters and words provides a natural progression to increase your code speed without changing the way you learn.

Sounding the Code

Some people find it helpful to say the sounds of Morse code characters, especially when they are first learning the code. Instead of saying the names of the Morse code elements, dot and dash, we use the sounds "dit" and "dah." If the dot is at the beginning or in the middle of the character, we sound it out as "di" instead of "dit," such as "didah" for the letter A.

Listen to the difference between the sounds you make saying the word "dit" and saying "dah." If you can tell the difference between those sounds, you have all the ability you need to learn the code. Being able to receive Morse code is really nothing more than being able to recognize a sound. Try it yourself. Say "didah." Now say "didahdit." Can you hear the difference? Congratulations! You now know the sounds for the letters A and R, and are on your way to learning the Morse code.

Using this method, you hear the sound "didah" and associate that sound with the letter A. With practice, you'll learn all the sounds and associate them with the correct letters, numbers and punctuation.

Learning to Write as You Copy Code

As you copy code sent at faster speeds, you may find that your ability to write the letters limits your speed. Practice writing the characters as quickly as possible. If you normally print, look for ways to avoid retracing lines. Don't allow yourself to be sloppy, though, because you may not be able to read your writing later.

Once you've begun to recognize the distinct patterns, the next step is to train your hand to write a certain letter, number or punctuation mark whenever you hear a specific pattern. You are forming a habit through practice. After all, forming a habit is nothing more than doing something the same way time after time. Eventually, whenever you want to do that thing, you automatically do it the same way without having to think about it.

You will need lots of practice writing the specific characters each time you hear a sound. Eventually you'll respond automatically to the sound by writing the corresponding character. This is important because it frees your thoughts for listening to the sound of the code.

Many people find that script, or cursive writing is faster than printing. Experiment with different writing methods, and find one that works for you. Then practice writing with that method so you don't have to think about forming the characters when you hear the sounds.

It is also perfectly okay to copy the code by typing it on a typewriter or computer keyboard. This method works especially well for people who can touch type already. The only problem is that you might not always have a keyboard available!

SOME STUDY SUGGESTIONS

The secret to easy and painless mastery of the Morse code is regular practice. Set aside two 15 to 30-minute periods every day to practice the code. If you try longer sessions, you may become over tired, and you will not learn as quickly. Likewise, if you only practice every other day or even less often, you will tend to forget more between practice sessions. It's a good idea to work your practice sessions into your daily routine. For instance, practice first thing in the morning and before dinner. Daily practice gives quick results.

One trick that some people use while learning the code is to whistle or hum the code while walking or driving. You can also say the sounds di, dit and dah to sound out the characters. Send the words on street signs, billboards and store windows. This extra practice may be just the help you need to master the code!

Start by learning the sound of each letter. Learn to associate the sound of each character with its unique pattern. Don't try to remember how many dots and dashes make up each character. Practice until you automatically recognize each Morse code character.

Feel free to review. You're learning a new way of communicating, by using the Morse code. If you are having trouble with a particular character, spend some extra time with it. If you are using ARRL's *Your Introduction to Morse Code*, replay the difficult CD track again. If you are using one of the computer programs, spend some extra time drilling on the problem character. After you've listened to the practice on one character two or three times, however, go on to the next one. You will get more practice with the problem character later, because you will be constantly copying all of the characters learned so far. You can even come back to study the problem character again in a later practice session. Be sure to listen to the practice tracks for at least three different characters during each practice session, however.

If you hear a Morse code character you don't immediately know, just draw a short line on your copy paper and go on to the next letter. This keeps you flowing with the sending rhythm. If you ignore your mistakes while copying code, you'll make fewer of them. If you sit there worrying about the letter you missed, you'll miss more before you get back in the groove! You shouldn't expect to copy perfectly while you are learning the code. You will get better with more practice.

When you think you've recognized a word after copying a few letters, concentrate all the more on the actual code sent. If you try to anticipate what comes next, your guess may turn out to be wrong. When that happens, you'll probably get confused and miss the next few letters as well. Write each letter just after it is sent. With more practice, you'll learn to "copy behind," hearing and writing whole words at one time. For now, when you are just learning the code, concentrate on writing each character as it is sent. This helps reinforce the association of a sound and a character in your mind.

Learning Morse code is like learning a language. Eventually you'll begin to recognize common syllables and words. With practice you will know many complete words, and won't even listen to the individual letters. When you become this familiar with the code, it really starts to be fun!

Don't be discouraged if you don't seem to be breaking any speed records. Some people have an ear for code and can learn the entire code in a week or less. Others require a month or more to learn it. Be patient, continue to practice and you will reach your goal.

9.3 Comfortable Sending

There's more to the code than just learning to receive it; you'll also have to learn to send it. To accomplish this, you'll need a telegraph key and a code-practice oscillator. You can get these items at most electronics-parts stores, or you can build your own simple oscillator. The "Assembling a Code-Practice Oscillator" sidebar at the end of this chapter

(A)

(B)

Figure 9-3 — Electronic keyers like those shown here can store messages in memory to be sent at the touch of a button. Thanks to the use of a sophisticated microprocessor, the Logikey unit at A is fully programmable and gives you complete control over the way your CW sounds. The MFJ keyer at B offers various training features to help you learn Morse code and increase your speed. It sends 5-character groups and random 1 to 8 character groups that can be composed of letters, numbers, punctuation and prosigns.

gives you step-by-step instructions for building one such oscillator that even includes a key for you to practice with. The code key with this project is not a true telegraph key, but it will allow you to do some practice sending. You should consider adding a real telegraph key to the project — the circuit board has two holes to connect wires to a straight key.

Many experienced amateurs prefer to use an electronic keyer to send Morse code. An electronic keyer produces properly timed dots and dashes because it uses one circuit to produce dots and another circuit to produce dashes. In general, it is probably better to learn to send Morse code with a hand key at first. Some students may have good success with a keyer.

Commercial keyers range from simple, basic units to full-featured Morse code machines. While they are comparatively expensive, some of the full-featured machines offer features that are quite helpful to a beginner. One of the keyers shown in **Figure 9-3** can send random-character code practice at any speed you desire. There are numerous electronic keyers and kits available as new or used equipment.

Figure 9-4 shows two different standard straight key models (one in the foreground and one to the left). There is a semiautomatic "bug" in the background and a popular Bencher paddle used with modern electronic keyers on the right. You'll want to obtain some type of code key for your on-the-air operating! Most hams new to CW start with an inexpensive straight key.

Just as with receiving, it is important that you be comfortable when sending. It helps to rest your arm on the table, letting your wrist and hand do all the work. Grasp the key lightly with your fingertips. Don't tap the key with a fingertip. Don't grip it tightly, either. If you do, you'll soon discover a few muscles you didn't know you had, and each one will ache. With a light grasp, you'll be able to send for long periods without fatigue. See **Figure 9-5** for a good example of how to hold the key to send. Experiment with position and grip until you are comfortable.

Another important part of sending code is the proper adjustment of your telegraph key. There are only two adjustments that you will normally have to make on a straight key, but you'll find they are very important. **Figure 9-6** illustrates these adjustments.

The first adjustment is the spacing between the contacts, which determines the distance the key knob must move to send a letter. Adjust the contacts so the knob moves about the thickness of a dime (1/16 inch). Try it. If you're not satisfied with this setting, try a wider or narrower spacing. Eventually, you'll find a spacing that works best for you. Don't be surprised if your feelings change from time to time, however, especially when your sending speed increases.

The second adjustment you must make is the spring tension that keeps the contacts apart. Just as there is no "correct" contact spacing, there is no correct tension adjustment for everyone. You will find, however, that adjusting the spacing

Figure 9-4 — Older than radio itself, code is still an efficient and effective communications mode; some hams use it almost exclusively. A modern straight key, the device most beginners use, is in the foreground.

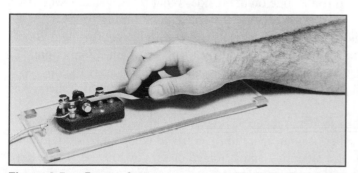

Figure 9-5 — Proper forearm support, with the wrist off the table, a gentle grip and a smooth up-and-down motion make for clean, effortless sending.

may also require a tension adjustment. Adjust the both the tension and spacing to provide what you think is the best "feel" when sending.

You will probably find that as your skill improves, your spacing and tension preferences change. Every operator is different, so don't hesitate to experiment with different settings. Eventually, you will settle on adjustments that allow you to operate comfortably for long periods.

Some straight keys have ball bearing pivot points on either side of the crossarms. These normally need no adjustment, but you should be sure the crossarms move freely in these pivots. If the bearings are too tight the key will bind or stick. If they are too loose there will be excessive play in the bearings that allows the key to twist. The side screws also adjust the crossarms from side to side so the contact points line up.

All of these adjustment screws have lock nuts, so be sure you loosen them before you make any adjustments. Tighten the lock nuts securely after making the adjustment.

Some better-quality keys have a shorting bar like the one shown in **Figure 9-6**. This shorting bar can be used to close the key contacts for transmitter tuning or adjustments. (The shorting bar was originally used to allow telegraph signals to pass through the key when the operator wasn't present.)

You'll probably want to fasten the key to a piece of wood or other heavy weight to prevent it from sliding around as you send. You might even want to fasten the key directly to the table. It's best to experiment with different positions before permanently attaching the key to any surface, however.

Some operators use a board that extends under their forearm and allows their arm to hold the key in position. This way the key can be moved aside for storage, or to clean off the table for other activities. A piece of ¼-inch plywood or Plexiglas about 12 inches long works well for this type of key base. This technique also allows you to reposition the key to find the most comfortable sending position.

Learning to send good code, like learning to receive, requires practice. A good way to start is to send along with your code practice. Try to duplicate the sounds as much as possible.

Always remember that you're trying to send a complete sound, not a series of dots and dashes. With that in mind, take a moment to think about the sound you're trying to send. It consists of dits, dahs and pauses (or spaces). The key to good sending, then, is timing. Try to keep the length of your dots and dashes and spaces consistent. It's especially important not to run letters and words together with too little space.

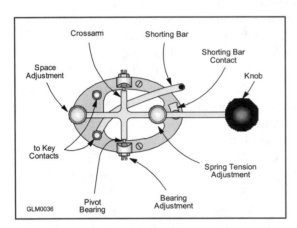

Figure 9-6 — A few simple adjustments to suit your style allow you to send for hours without fatigue. The contact spacing and spring tension should be set to provide the most comfortable feel.

If you're not convinced, listen to some code on the bands. What transmissions would you prefer to receive? Why? That's right — because they have good timing.

Some people send code that is very easy and enjoyable to copy. Others are not so good, and require a lot of concentration to understand. Since your *fist* is your on-the-air signature, try to make it as easy to read as possible. Learn to send code that is easy to copy. Then you'll have a fist you can be proud of. It can make a big difference in your success as a CW operator.

One of the best ways to learn to send and receive code is to work with another person. That person may be another member of your own family, a friend who is also studying the code or a licensed ham. If you're attending an organized class, you may be able to get together with another student several times a week.

If you must work alone, make good use of tape or computer-based recording by recording your sending. After waiting a day or two, try receiving what you sent. The wait between sending and receiving will help prevent you from writing down the message from memory. Not only will this procedure provide practice in receiving, but it will also let you hear exactly how your sending sounds. If your timing is off, you'll hear it. If you're having trouble with a specific letter or number or punctuation mark, you'll soon know about it. If you can't understand your own sending, neither will anyone else!

Regardless of whether you're sending or receiving, the key to your success with Morse code is regular practice. After you've learned all the characters, you will want to continue regular practice to gain confidence and increase your speed.

If you can, listen to actual contacts between hams. Make use of the code-practice material transmitted by W1AW, the ARRL station heard nationwide from Newington, Connecticut. There is a W1AW schedule on-line at **www.arrl.org/w1aw.html**.

It isn't difficult to construct a code-practice oscillator. A complete oscillator that mounts on a small piece of wood is shown in **Figure A**. **Figure B** shows all the parts for this project laid out ready for assembly. The circuit board for this project can be ordered from FAR Circuits, 18 N. 640 Field Court, Dundee, IL 60118-9269. Contact FAR Circuits for the latest pricing or visit their web site at **www. farcircuits.net**.

Figure C shows the schematic diagram and a complete parts list follows. Please read all instructions carefully before mounting any parts. Check the parts-placement diagram for the location of each part.

Figure A

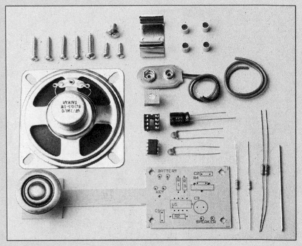

Figure B

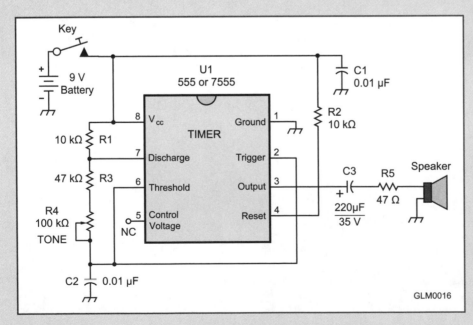

Figure C — Schematic diagram of a code-practice oscillator.

❑ **Check each box as that part is installed and soldered.**

Quantity	Description	RadioShack Part Number	Component Number	Used in Step Number
Capacitors				
❑ 1	0.01-µF	272-131	C1	3
❑ 1	0.01-µF	272-131	C2	6
❑ 1	220-µF, 35-V electrolytic	272-1029	C3	5
Resistors				
❑ 1	10-kilohm, ¼ W (brown-black-orange stripes)	271-1335	R2	4
❑ 1	47-kilohm, ¼ W (yellow-violet-orange stripes)	271-1342	R3	8
❑ 1	10-kilohm, ¼ W (brown-black-orange stripes)	271-1335	R1	9
❑ 1	47-ohm, ¼ W (yellow-violet-black stripes)		R5	11
Miscellaneous				
❑ 1	100-kilohm potentiometer	271-284	R4	7
❑ 1	8-pin IC socket	276-1995		2
❑ 1	7555 CMOS Timer IC (or 555 Timer IC)	276-1718	U1	13
❑ 1	Loudspeaker — 2-inch, 8-ohm		LS1	11
❑ 1	Six to 10 inches of insulated wire, about 18 or 22 gauge			11
❑ 1	9-V battery connector	270-325		10
❑ 1	9-V battery		BT1	10
❑ 1	U-shaped battery holder	270-326		12
❑ 1	Brass rod, 2 inches long, approximately 18 gauge (about the diameter of a coat hanger). Available at hobby shops.			
❑ 4	¼-inch spacers			12
❑ 1	2 × 4 × ½-inch piece of wood for base			12
❑ 5	No. 6 wood screws, ¾-inch long			12
❑ 2	No. 6 wood screws, ⅜-inch long			12
❑ 1	Five-lug tie point, used to mount speaker (optional)	274-688		11

❑ **Check each box as that step is completed.**

❑ **Step 1: Attach the brass rod. Check the parts-placement diagram (Figure E) for location.**

Clean the brass rod with sandpaper or steel wool. Bend one end of the rod slightly less than 90 degrees. Lay the circuit board on the table with foil side up. Place the hooked end of the brass rod over the large hole near the handle (see **Figure D**). Make sure the rod extends out over the handle area. Solder the rod to the board on the foil side. The end of the brass rod should not extend past the marked oval on the handle. This is your contact point. If it does extend beyond this point, cut the rod off just before the end of the oval.

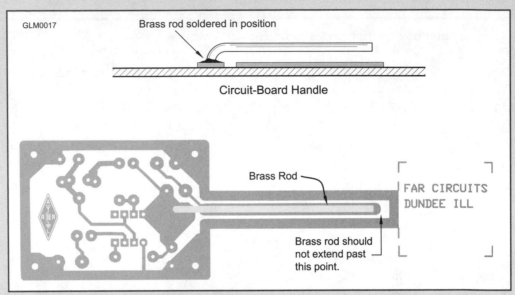

Figure D — Solder the brass rod in position on the foil side of the PC board. You can also use this figure as a circuit-board etching pattern if you want to make your own circuit board, since the pattern is printed full size.

❑ **Step 2: Solder the IC socket to the board.**

The socket for the IC is placed on the component (non-foil) side of the board first. Do not plug the IC into the socket now. After all the other parts are soldered to the board you will be instructed to plug the IC into the socket (Step 13). Identify the notched end of the socket. Insert the socket into the circuit board. Turn the board over and gently spread the pins on the socket so they make contact with the foil side of the board. Solder the socket in place.

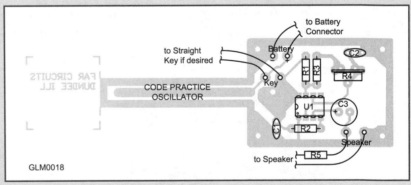

Figure E — Parts-placement diagram.

❑ **Step 3: Place C1 (0.01-µF capacitor) on the component side of the board.**

Thread the wire leads on C1 through the holes on the board. (See **Figure F**.) Solder the wires onto the foil side of the board. Cut the extra wire off above the solder joint.

❑ **Step 4: Place R2 (10-kilohm resistor) on the component side of the board.**

Prepare resistors for mounting by bending each lead (wire) of the resistor to approximately a 90° angle. (See **Figure G**.) Insert the leads into the board holes and bend them over to hold the resistor in place. Solder the leads to the foil and trim them close to the foil.

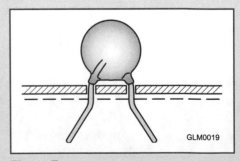

Figure F

❑ **Step 5: Place C3 (220-µF, 35-volt electrolytic capacitor) on the component side of the board.**

This capacitor has a plus (+) side and a negative (–) side. The (–) side is placed on the board facing away from the handle. (Notice the + sign printed on the circuit board at this location.) Insert the capacitor leads into the circuit board holes, solder them in place and trim off the extra wire.

❏ Step 6: Place C2 (0.01-µF capacitor) on the component side of the board.

Thread the wire leads from C2 through the holes on the circuit board. (See Step 3 and Figure F.) Solder the wires onto the board. Cut the extra wire off above the solder joint.

❏ Step 7: Place R4 (100-kilohm potentiometer) on the component side of the circuit board.

This component has three pins. All three pins must be plugged into the holes on the board. (It fits only one way.) Solder them in place and cut off any excess lead length.

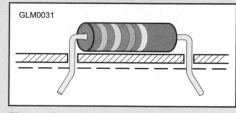

Figure G

❏ Step 8: Place R3 (47-kilohm resistor) on the component side of the circuit board.

Bend the wires on the resistor to plug it into the board. (See Step 4 and Figure G.) Plug the resistor into the board, spread the wires and solder it in place. Trim off the extra wire lengths.

❏ Step 9: Place R1 (10-kilohm resistor) on the component side of the board.

Bend the wires on the resistor to plug it into the board. (See Step 4 and Figure G.) Plug the resistor into the board, spread the wires and solder it in place. Trim the excess wire lengths.

❏ Step 10: Hook up the battery connector leads.

The battery connector consists of two wires, one red and one black, attached to a snap-on cap. Remove ¼ inch of plastic insulation from the end of both wires. The black wire is negative and the red wire is positive. The positive and negative battery connections are marked on the component side of the board. Be sure the red wire goes in the hole marked "+" and the black wire goes in the hole marked "–". Solder the wires in place and trim any excess length close to the solder joint.

❏ Step 11: Hook up the speaker.

If you are using the tie lug to hold the speaker in place, solder the speaker lugs to tie-point lugs on each side of the center post. (If you are not using the tie lug then you will solder the wires directly to the speaker lugs.) Cut the speaker wire into two equal lengths. Remove ¼ inch of plastic insulation from each end of both wires. Solder one end of each wire to one of the tie-point solder lugs below the speaker terminals. Solder one end of R5 (47-ohm resistor) to the circuit board as shown in Figure E. Solder one wire to the other end of this resistor and the second speaker wire to the circuit board.

❏ Step 12: Attach the circuit board to the wood base.

Place the completed circuit board on the wood. Trace through the four corner holes with a pencil. Take the circuit board off the wood and lay it aside. Place the spacers on the wood, standing upright. Carefully put the circuit board on top of the spacers. Put the ¾-inch screws through the holes in the circuit board and through the spacers and screw them into the board until snug. Be sure not to overtighten the screws, or you may crack the circuit board. Attach the speaker to the end of the board opposite the handle with a ⅜-inch screw through the tie-point mounting hole, or mount the speaker to the board using two screws and holes in the outside edge of the speaker's metal frame. Attach the U-shaped metal battery holder to the wooden base with a ⅜-inch screw.

❏ Step 13: Plug the integrated circuit (IC) into the socket, being careful to position it so the notch or dot on one end of the IC is toward the handle.

CAUTION — The static electricity from your body could destroy the IC. Before touching the IC, be sure you have discharged any static that may be built up on your body. While sitting at your table or workbench, touch a metal pipe or other large metal object for a few seconds. Carefully remove the IC from its foam padding. Hold it by the black body and avoid touching the wires. Plug it into the socket, being sure that the notched end of the IC is facing toward the handle. The notch on the IC should line up with the notch on the socket.

Attach the battery to the snap-on battery connector and place it in the U-shaped battery holder. This unit uses electricity only when the telegraph key handle is pushed down. No ON/OFF switch is necessary, and you may leave the battery connected at all times.

You're done! The oscillator should produce a tone when you press the key. If your oscillator does not work, check all your connections carefully. Make sure the IC is positioned correctly in the socket, and that you have a fresh battery. If it still doesn't work check all your solder connections.

Once you have the oscillator working, you're ready to use it to practice Morse code. If you are studying with a friend, you can use the oscillator to send code to each other. If you are studying alone, tape record your sending and play it back later. Can you copy what you sent? How would it sound on the air? Good luck!

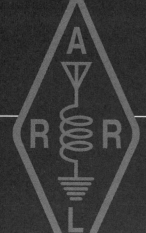

Chapter 10

Glossary

Absorption — The dissipation of the energy of a radio wave as it travels through a medium such as the ionosphere.

AC hum — Unwanted 60- or 120-Hz modulation of a RF signal due to inadequate filtering in a power supply.

Active — A device that requires a source of power to function.

Adapters — Special connectors that convert one style of connector to another.

Air link — That part of a digital communications system implemented using radio transmission and reception.

Alternating current (ac) — Electrical current that flows first in one direction and then in the other. The applied voltage is also changing polarity. This direction reversal continues at a rate that depends on the frequency of the ac.

Amateur Satellite Corporation (AMSAT) — The organization that manages many of the amateur satellite programs.

Amateur operator — A person holding a written authorization to be the control operator of an amateur station.

Amateur Radio Emergency Service (ARES)—Sponsored by the ARRL and provides emergency communications by working with groups such as the American Red Cross and local Emergency Operations Centers.

Amateur service — A radio communication service for the purpose of self-training, intercommunication and technical investigations carried out by amateurs, that is, duly authorized persons interested in radio technique solely with a personal aim and without **pecuniary** interest.

Amateur station — A station licensed in the amateur service, including necessary equipment, used for amateur communication.

Amateur television (ATV) — A wideband TV system that uses commercial transmission standards. ATV is only permitted on the 70-cm band (420 to 450 MHz) and higher frequencies.

American Radio Relay League (ARRL) — The national association for Amateur Radio.

Ammeter — A test instrument that measures current.

Ampacity — A wire's current rating.

Ampere (A) — The basic unit of electrical current, also abbreviated **amp**. Current is a measure of the electron flow through a circuit. 1 Ampere is the flow of 1 **Coulomb** per second.

Amplifier — A device or piece of equipment used to increase the strength of a signal.

Amplitude modulated phone — **AM** transmission in which voice (phone) signals are used to modulate the carrier. Most AM transmission is *double-sideband* in which the signal is composed of two sidebands and a carrier. Shortwave broadcast stations use this type of AM, as do stations in the Standard Broadcast Band (535-1710 kHz). Few amateurs use double-sideband voice AM, but a variation, known as **single sideband (SSB)**, is very popular.

Amplitude modulation (AM) — The process of adding information to a signal or *carrier* by varying its amplitude characteristics.

Analog (linear) — Circuits or devices that operate over a continuous range of voltage and current.

Analog signals — A signal (usually electrical) that can have any amplitude (voltage or current) value, and whose amplitude can vary smoothly over time. Also see **digital signals**.

Anode — In semiconductor diodes and vacuum tubes (the **plate**), the electrode to which electrons flow during conduction.

Antenna — A device that radiates or receives radio frequency energy.

Antenna switch — A switch used to connect one transmitter, receiver or transceiver to several different antennas.

Antenna tuner — A device that matches the antenna system input impedance to the transmitter, receiver or transceiver output impedance. Also called an *antenna-matching network, impedance matcher* or *Transmatch*.

Antipode — Locations directly opposite each other on a globe.

Apogee — That point in a satellite's orbit when it is farthest from the Earth.

Array — An antenna that uses more than one element to direct radiated energy in a specific direction.

Automatic Position Reporting System (APRS) — A system by which amateurs can report their position automatically by radio to central servers from which their locations can be observed. (APRS is a registered trademark of Bob Bruninga, WB4APR.)

Amateur Radio Direction Finding (ARDF) — Competitions in which amateurs combine orienteering with direction finding.

Atmosphere — The mass of air surrounding the Earth. Radio signals travel through the atmosphere and different conditions in the atmosphere affect how those signal travel or propagate.

Attenuate — To reduce the strength of a signal.

Audio frequency (AF) signal — An ac electrical signal in the range of 20 hertz to 20 kilohertz (20,000 hertz). This is called an audio signal because your ears respond to sound waves in the same frequency range.

Automatic gain control (AGC) — Receiver circuitry used to maintain a constant audio output level.

Automatic level control (ALC) — Transmitter circuitry that prevents excessive modulation of an AM or SSB signal.

Automatic control — A station operating under the control of devices or procedures that insure compliance with FCC rules.

Autopatch — A device that allows repeater users to make telephone calls through a repeater.

Back feeding — Supplying electrical power to the utility grid through a home power distribution panel when using a generator.

Balun — Contraction of "balanced to unbalanced". A device to couple a balanced load to an unbalanced feed line or device, or vice versa.

Band-pass filter (BPF) — A circuit that allows signals to pass through it only if they are within a certain range of frequencies. It attenuates signals above and below this range.

Band plan — Organization of communications activity on a frequency band by general consensus.

Bandwidth — (1) Bandwidth describes the range of frequencies that a radio signal occupies. (2) FCC Part 97 defines bandwidth for regulatory purposes as "The width of a frequency band outside of which the mean power is attenuated at least 26 dB below the mean power of the transmitted signal within the band." [§97.3 (8)]

Battery — A device that converts chemical energy into electrical energy.

Battery chemistry — The type of chemicals used to store energy in a battery.

Battery pack — A package of several individual batteries connected together (usually in series to provide higher voltages) and treated as a single battery.

Baud (also **bauds**) — The rate at which individual data symbols are transmitted (see also **symbol rate**).

Beacon station — An amateur station transmitting communications for the purposes of observation of propagation and reception or other related experimental activities.

Beam antenna — A directional antenna. A beam antenna must be rotated to provide coverage in different directions.

Beamwidth — The angle between the points in the main lobe at which gain is 3 dB less than the maximum value.

Binary data (number) — Information represented by 1s and 0s. A binary number consists entirely of 1s and 0s representing powers of 2.

Bipolar transistor — A transistor made from P- and N-type material whose functions are controlled by current.

Bit rate — The rate at which digital bits are carried by a transmitted signal.

Bleeder resistor — A high-value resistor that discharges a filter capacitor when power is removed.

Block diagram — A drawing using boxes to represent sections of a complicated device or process. The block diagram shows the connections between sections. A block diagram shows the internal functions of a complex piece of equipment without the unnecessary detail of a schematic diagram.

BNC connector — A type of connector for RF signals.

Break-in — Switching rapidly between transmit and receive so that signals can be heard between keying elements (full break-in) or words (semi break-in).

Broadcasting — Transmissions intended to be received by the general public, either direct or relayed.

Buffer — An amplifier intended to isolate a circuit from loads connected to its output.

Bug — A mechanical Morse key that uses a spring to send dots automatically.

Call district — The ten administrative areas established by the FCC.

Call sign — The letters and numbers that identify a specific amateur and the country in which his or her license was granted.

Calling frequency — A frequency on which amateurs establish contact before moving to a different frequency. Usually used by hams with a common interest or activity.

Capacitance — A measure of the ability of a capacitor to store energy in an **electric field**.

Capacitor — An electrical component usually formed by separating two conductive plates with an insulating material. A capacitor stores energy in an **electric field**.

Cathode — In semiconductor diodes and vacuum tubes, the electrode from which electrons flow during conduction.

Cathode ray tube (CRT) — A vacuum tube used to create visual displays on its phosphor-coated face.

CB — Citizen's Band. An unlicensed radio service operating near 27 MHz intended for use by individuals and businesses over ranges of a few miles. Also known as "11-meters" for the wavelength of its signals.

Center tapped — A transformer winding that is split into two equal halves with a connection (tap) at the center point

Centi (or lower case **c**) — The metric prefix for 10^{-2}, or divide by 100.

Certificate of Successful Completion of Examination (CSCE) — A document that verifies that an individual has passes one or more exam elements. A CSCE is good for 365 days and may be used as evidence of having passed an element at any other amateur license exam session.

Channel amplifiers (vertical and horizontal) — Circuits that apply external signals to the deflection plates of a cathode ray tube.

Characteristic impedance — The ratio of RF voltage and current for power flowing in a feed line.

Chassis ground — The common connection for all parts of a circuit that connect to the metal enclosure of the circuit. Chassis ground is usually connected to the negative side of the power supply.

Checksum — The output of an algorithm that allows the receiving system to detect errors in transmitted data.

Choke filter — A filter that uses an inductor to reduce ac ripple from a power supply output voltage.

Circuit breaker — A protective component that opens a circuit or *trips* when an excessive amount of current flow occurs.

Class A — Amplifier operation in which the amplifying device is active during the entire cycle of the signal.

Class AB — Amplifier operation in which the amplifying device is active for between one-half and the entire signal cycle.

Class B — Amplifier operation in which the amplifying device is active for one-half of the signal's cycle.

Class C — Amplifier operation in which the amplifying device is only active during a fraction of the signal.

Closed repeater — A repeater that restricts access to members of a certain group of amateurs.

Closed circuit — An electrical circuit with an uninterrupted path for the current to follow. Turning a switch on, for example, closes or completes the circuit, allowing current to flow. Also called a **complete circuit**.

Coaxial cable — Coax (pronounced kó-aks). A type of feed line with one conductor inside the other and both sharing a concentric central axis.

Color code — A system in which numerical values are assigned to various colors. For example, colored stripes representing the different values are painted on the body of resistors and sometimes other components to show their value.

Compiler — A program that translates a text program into machine language.

Common mode — Currents that flow equally on all conductors of a multiconductor cable, such as speaker wires or telephone cables.

Communications emergency — A situation in which communications is required for immediate safety of human life or protection of property.

Complete circuit — (see **closed circuit**).

Compression — Increasing gain during periods of low signal level while holding gain steady for high signal levels to increase the average power of the signal.

Conductor — A material whose electrons move freely in response to voltage, so an electrical current can pass through it.

Continuous wave (CW) — Radio communications transmitted by on/off keying of a continuous radio-frequency signal. Another name for international Morse code.

Control operator — An amateur operator designated by the licensee of a station to be responsible for the transmissions of an amateur station.

Control point — The locations at which a station's control operator function is performed.

Controlled environment — Any area in which an RF signal may cause radiation exposure to people who are aware of the radiated electric and magnetic fields and who can exercise some control over their exposure to these fields. The FCC generally considers amateur operators and their families to be in a controlled RF exposure environment to determine the maximum permissible exposure levels.

Conversion efficiency — The percentage of solar energy that is converted to electricity by a solar cell.

Coordinated repeater — A repeater system whose input and output frequencies are approved by the regional frequency coordination organization.

Coulomb (C) — The basic unit of charge. 1 Coulomb is the quantity of 6.25×10^{18} electrons. 1 Ampere equals the flow of 1 Coulomb of electrons per second.

Counter — A circuit that accumulates a total number of events or a device that displays the frequency of an input signal.

Coupling — The sharing of energy between two components or circuits.

Courtesy tone — A tone or beep transmitted by a repeater to indicate that the transmitting station is finished and the next station may begin transmitting. The courtesy tone is designed to allow a pause between transmissions on a repeater, so other stations can call. It also indicates that the **time-out timer** has been reset.

CQ — "Calling any station": the general call when requesting a conversation with anyone.

Critical angle — The largest angle at which a radio wave of a specified frequency can be returned to a specific point on Earth by the ionosphere.

Crossband — Able to receive and transmit on different amateur frequency bands. For example, a repeater might retransmit at 2 meters a signal received on 70 cm.

Crowbar — A circuit that places a short-circuit across a power supply output when excessive voltage is detected.

CTCSS — Continuous Tone Coded Squelch System. A low frequency tone system used on most repeaters. When added to a carrier, a CTCSS tone allows a receiver to output the received information. Also called **PL** or **sub-audible tone**.

Current — A flow of electrons in an electrical circuit.

Current gain (beta) — The control of a large collector-emitter current by a small base-emitter current, numerically equal to the ratio of collector-emitter current to base-emitter current. Beta (β) is the symbol for dc current gain. h_{fe} is the symbol for ac current gain.

Cutoff — The point at which current flow in a transistor or vacuum tube is reduced to zero.

CW (Morse code) — Radio communications transmitted by on/off keying of a continuous radio-frequency signal. Another name for international Morse code.

D region — The lowest region of the ionosphere. The D region (or layer) contributes very little to short-wave radio propagation. It acts mainly to absorb energy from radio waves as they pass through it. This absorption has a significant effect on signals below about 7.5 MHz during daylight.

Data modes — Computer-to-computer communication, such as by **packet radio** or **radioteletype (RTTY)**, which can be used to transmit and receive computer characters, or digital information.

DE — The Morse code abbreviation for "from" or "this is."

Deceptive signals — Transmissions that are intended to mislead or confuse those who may receive the transmissions. For example, distress calls transmitted when there is no actual emergency are false or deceptive signals.

Decibel (dB) — In electronics decibels are used to express ratios of power, voltage, or current. One dB = 10 log (power ratio) or 20 log (voltage or current ratio). The smallest change in sound level that can be detected by the human ear is 1 dB.

Deci (or lower case **d**) — The metric prefix for 10^{-1}, or divide by 10.

Deflection plates — The electrodes that control the position of an electron beam in a cathode ray tube.

Delta loop antenna — A variation of the quad antenna with triangular elements.

Detector — The stage in a receiver in which the modulation (voice or other information) is recovered from the RF signal.

Deviation — The change in frequency of an FM carrier due to a modulating signal.

Dielectric — The insulating material that separates the two conducting surfaces of a capacitor and stores electrical energy.

Diffract — To alter the direction of a radio wave as it passes by the edges of obstructions such as buildings or hills.

Digipeater — A digital station that stores and forwards digital packets from one station to another.

Digital (logic) — Circuits or devices that operate with discrete values of voltage and current.

Digital communications (see **data modes**)

Digital signal — (1) A signal (usually electrical) that can only have certain specific amplitude values, or steps—usually two; 0 and 1 or ON and OFF. (2) On the air, a digital signal is the same as a **data signal**.

Digital Signal Processing (DSP) — The process of converting an **analog signal** to **digital** form and using a microprocessor to process the signal in some way such as filtering or reducing noise.

Diode — An electronic component that allows electric current to flow in only one direction.

Dip meter — A tunable oscillator with an output voltage meter that is tuned until the meter shows a sharp dip at the frequency where the circuit under test is resonant.

Dipole antenna — An antenna consisting of two symmetrical linear halves. Also see **half-wave dipole**. A dipole need not be ½ wavelength long, nor is it required to have a feed point in the middle.

Direct current (dc) — Electrical current that flows in one direction only.

Direct detection — A type of **RF interference** caused by a device being disrupted by the presence of an RF signal it is not intended to receive.

Directional wattmeter — An RF power meter that can measure both forward and reflected power in a transmission line (also see **wattmeter**).

Director — A parasitic element in front of the driven element in a directional antennas.

Display (visual) — A device that is capable of presenting text or graphics information in visual form.

Distress call — A transmission made in order to attract attention in an emergency. (See also **MAYDAY** and **SOS**)

Doping — Adding impurities (*dopants*) to a semiconductor material to control its electrical properties.

Doppler shift or effect — A change in observed frequency of a signal caused by relative motion between the transmitter and receiver. Your ears hear Doppler shift when a car or train drives past you and you hear the pitch of the engine noise change. You will have to adjust your receive frequency to hear a satellite as it passes overhead because of Doppler shift.

Doubling — The undesirable act of two or more operators transmitting at the same time on the same frequency. Both operators are usually unaware of the other's presence, sometimes during the entire transmission!

Downlink — The frequency or frequency range on which a satellite transmits to the ground.

Driven (array) — An array antenna in which all of the elements are connected to the antenna feed line.

Driven element — The part of an antenna that connects directly to the feed line.

Driver — An amplifier that brings low-power signals to a level suitable to drive a power amplifier to full power output.

Dual-band antenna — An antenna designed for use on two different amateur bands.

Dummy antenna or **dummy load** — A station accessory that allows you to test or adjust transmitting equipment without sending a signal out over the air. Also called **dummy load**.

Duplex — (1) Transmitting on one frequency and receiving on another, such as for repeater operation. (2) A mode of communications (also known as *full duplex*) in which a user transmits on one frequency and receives on another frequency simultaneously. This is in contrast to half duplex, where the user transmits at one time and receives at another time.

Duplexer — A device that allows radios on two different bands to share a single antenna. Duplexers are often used to allow a dual-band radio to use a single dual-band antenna.

Duty cycle — A measure of the amount of time a transmitter is operating at full output power during a single transmission. A lower duty cycle reduces **RF radiation** exposure for the same PEP output.

DX — Distance, distant stations, foreign countries.

E region — The second lowest ionospheric region, the E region (or layer) exists only during the day. Under certain conditions, it may refract radio waves enough to return them to Earth.

Earth ground — A circuit connection to a ground rod driven into the Earth or to a metallic cold-water pipe that goes into the ground.

Earth station — An amateur station located on, or within 50 km of, the Earth's surface intended for communications with space stations or with other Earth stations by means of one or more other objects in space.

Earth-Moon-Earth (EME) or **Moonbounce** — A method of communicating with other stations by reflecting radio signals off the Moon's surface.

EchoLink — A system of linking repeaters and computer-based users by using the Voice-Over-Internet Protocol.

Effective radiated power (ERP) — The power level that would be required to be applied to a dipole to achieve the same signal strength in the direction of maximum radiation.

Electric field — An electric field exists in a region of space if an electrically charged object placed in the region is subjected to an electrical force.

Electromagnetic wave — A wave of energy composed of electric and magnetic fields.

Electromotive force (EMF) — The force or pressure that pushes a current through a circuit.

Electron — A tiny, negatively charged particle, normally found in the volume surrounding the nucleus of an atom. Moving electrons make up an electrical current.

Electronic keyer — A device that makes it easier to send well-timed Morse code. It sends a continuous string of either dots or dashes, depending on which lever of the *paddle* is pressed.

Element — (1) The conducting part or parts of an antenna designed to radiate or receive radio waves. (2) An electrode in a vacuum tube used to control the tube's operation.

Elmer — A ham radio mentor or teacher.

Emergency — A situation where there is a danger to human life or property.

Emergency communications — Communications conducted under adverse conditions where normal channels of communications are not available.

Emergency traffic — Messages with life and death urgency or requests for medical help and supplies that leave an area shortly after an emergency.

Emission — The transmitted signal from an amateur station.

Emission mode designator — A combination of letters and numbers used by the FCC to identify a particular transmission mode.

Emission privilege — Permission to use a particular emission type (such as Morse code or voice).

Emission types — Term for the different modes authorized for use on the Amateur Radio bands. Examples are CW, SSB, RTTY and FM.

Encapsulation — The process of packaging information from one protocol inside another.

Encoding — Changing the form of a signal into one suitable for storage or transmission. *Decoding* is the process of returning the signal to its original form.

Encryption — Changing the form of a signal into a privately-known format intended to obscure the meaning of the signal. *Decryption* is the process of reversing the encoding.

Energy — The ability to do work; the ability to exert a force to move some object.

Equivalent — An electrically identical circuit or component.

Equivalent series resistance — A single parasitic resistance that accounts for all of a capacitor's losses.

Equivalent series inductance — A single parasitic inductance that accounts for all of the inductance exhibited by a capacitor.

Extended-coverage receiver — A receiver that tunes frequencies from around 30 MHz to several hundred MHz or into the GHz frequencies. Also known as a **wide-range receiver**.

F region — A combination of the two highest ionospheric regions (or layers), the F1 and F2 regions. The F region refracts radio waves and returns them to Earth. Its height varies greatly depending on the time of day, season of the year and amount of sunspot activity.

False or deceptive signals — Transmissions that are intended to mislead or confuse those who may receive the transmissions. For example, distress calls transmitted when there is no actual emergency are false or deceptive signals.

Family (logic) — Digital gates and circuits that are all designed with the same type of electronic circuit technology.

Farad (F) — The basic unit of capacitance.

Federal Communications Commission (FCC) — Federal agency in the United States that regulates use and allocation of the frequency spectrum among many different services, including Amateur Radio.

Federal Registration Number (FRN) — An identification number assigned to an individual by the FCC to use when performing license modification or renewal.

Feed line — The wires or cable used to connect a transmitter, receiver or transceiver to an antenna. The feed line connects to an antenna at its **feed point**. Also see **transmission line**.

Feed point — The point at which a feed line is electrically connected to an antenna.

Feed point impedance — The ratio of RF voltage to current at the feed point of an antenna.

Feedback (circuit) — The process of applying some fraction of a circuit's output to its input.

Ferrite — A ceramic material that can store or dissipate magnetic energy. A ferrite core can be used to increase inductance and ferrite beads can be used to block RF current flow.

Field effect transistor — A transistor whose functions are controlled by voltages.

Field strength meter — A calibrated meter that measures the electric field strength of a transmitted signal.

Filter — A circuit that will allow some signals to pass through it but will greatly reduce the strength of others.

Filter capacitor — A capacitor used to reduce **ripple** in a power supply.

Fixed resistor — An electronic component specifically designed to oppose or control current through a circuit. The **resistance** value of a fixed resistor cannot be changed or adjusted.

Form 605 — An FCC form that serves as the application for your Amateur Radio license, or for modifications to an existing license.

Forward bias — Voltage applied so that current flows across a semiconductor PN junction. Voltage applied in the opposite direction is called **reverse bias**.

Forward power — The power traveling from the transmitter to the antenna along a transmission line.

Forward voltage — The voltage required to force electrons across a semiconductor PN junction.

Fox hunting — Exercises in which a hidden transmitter (the fox) is located in order to test direction-finding skills. Also called a *bunny hunt*.

Frequency — The number of complete cycles of an alternating current that occur per second.

Frequency band — A continuous range of frequencies. An **amateur band** is a frequency band in which amateur communications take place.

Frequency coordination — Allocating repeater input and output frequencies to minimize interference between repeaters and to other users of the band.

Frequency coordinator — An individual or group that recommends repeater frequencies to reduce or eliminate interference between repeaters operating on or near the same frequency in the same geographical area.

Frequency discriminator — A type of detector used in some FM receivers.

Frequency modulated phone — The type of signals used to communicate by voice (phone) over most repeaters. FM broadcast stations and most professional communications (police, fire, taxi) use FM. VHF/UHF FM phone is the most popular amateur mode.

Frequency modulation (FM) — The process of adding information to an RF signal or *carrier* by varying its frequency characteristics.

Frequency privilege — Permission to use a particular group of frequencies.

Front-end overload — Interference to a receiver caused by a strong signal that causes the receiver's sensitive input circuitry ("front end") to be overloaded or saturated. Front-end overload results in distortion of the desired signal and the generation of unwanted spurious signals within the receiver. See also **receiver overload**.

FRS — Family Radio Service. An unlicensed radio service that uses low-power radios operating near 460 MHz and intended for short-range communications by family members.

FSK — Frequency shift keying.

Full wave rectifier — A rectifier circuit that converts every half-cycle (360 degrees) of the input waveform to dc.

Function generator — Test equipment that can generate sine, square, and other waveforms in the audio and lower RF range.

Fuse — A thin metal strip mounted in a holder. When too much current passes through the fuse, the metal strip melts and opens the circuit.

Gain — (1) Focusing of an antenna's radiated energy in one direction. Gain in one direction means that gain in other directions is diminished. (2) The amount of amplification of a signal in a piece of equipment, such as AF Gain (volume) or RF Gain (sensitivity).

Gain (amplifier) — The amount by which a circuit increases signal amplitude.

Gain compression (blocking) — A reduction in gain due to the presence of strong signals.

Gate (logic) — A circuit that performs a specific logic function such as inversion, NOR, NAND, XOR, and so on.

General-coverage receiver — A receiver used to listen to a wide range of frequencies, not just specific bands. Most general-coverage receivers tune from frequencies below the AM broadcast band (550 - 1700 kHz) to around 30 MHz. (See also **extended-coverage receiver**.)

GFCI (or **GFI**) — Ground-fault interrupting circuit breaker that opens a circuit when an imbalance of current flow is detected between the hot and neutral wires of an ac power circuit.

Giga (or lower case **G**) — The metric prefix for 10^9, or multiply by 1,000,000,000.

GMRS — General Mobile Radio Service. A licensed radio service operating at 460 MHz intended for family businesses and members to communicate within a city or region.

Go kit — A pre-packaged collection of equipment or supplies kept at hand to allow an operator to quickly report where needed in time of need.

Grace period — The time the FCC allows following the expiration of an amateur license to renew that license without having to retake an examination. Those who hold an expired license may not operate an amateur station until the license is reinstated.

Great circle — The direct path across the Earth between two points.

Grid square — A locator in the Maidenhead Locator System.

Ground connection — A connection made to the earth for electrical safety. This connection can be made inside (to a metal cold-water pipe) or outside (to a **ground rod**).

Ground loop — A current path that connects two or more pieces of equipment in a loop in which voltage can be induced by RF or magnetic fields.

Ground rod — A copper or copper-clad steel rod that is driven into the earth. A heavy copper wire or strap connects all station equipment to the ground rod.

Ground-plane — A conducting surface of continuous metal or discrete wires that acts to create an electrical image of an antenna. **Ground-plane antennas** require a ground-plane in order to operate properly.

Ground-wave propagation — The method by which radio waves travel along the Earth's surface.

Ham-band receiver — A receiver designed to receive only frequencies in the amateur bands.

Half-wave dipole — A basic antenna used by radio amateurs. It consists of a length of wire or tubing with a feed point frequently at the center. The entire antenna is ½ wavelength long at the desired operating frequency.

Half wave rectifier — A rectifier circuit that converts every other half-cycle (180 degrees) of the input waveform to dc.

Hand-held radio — A VHF or UHF transceiver that can be carried in the hand or pocket.

Harmful interference — Interference that seriously degrades, obstructs or repeatedly interrupts a radio communication service operating in accordance with the Radio Regulations. [§97.3 (a) (22)]

Harmonics — Signals from a transmitter or oscillator occurring on whole-number multiples (2×, 3×, 4×, etc) of the original or *fundamental* frequency.

Harmonically related — Frequencies that are integer multiples of some fundamental frequency, such as 3.5, 7, 14, 21 and 28 MHz.

Header — The portion of a packet that contains information about the packet for routing or other control functions.

Health and Welfare traffic – Messages about the well-being of individuals in a disaster area. Such messages must wait for **Emergency** and **Priority traffic** to clear, and results in advisories to those outside the disaster area awaiting news from family and friends.

Henry (H) — The basic unit of inductance.

Hertz (Hz) — The basic unit of frequency. One Hertz is the same as one cycle per second.

Heterodyne — Mixing two signals together in order to obtain signals at the sum and difference of the frequencies of the original signals.

High frequency (HF) — The term used for the frequency range between 3 MHz and 30 MHz. The amateur HF bands are where you are most likely to make long-distance (worldwide) contacts.

High-pass filter (HPF) — A filter designed to pass signals above a specified *cutoff* frequency, while attenuating lower-frequency signals.

Impedance — The opposition to electric current in a circuit. Impedance includes both reactance and resistance, and applies to both alternating and direct currents.

Impedance match — To adjust impedances to be equal or the case in which two impedances are equal. Usually refers to the point at which a feed line is connected to an antenna or to transmitting equipment. If the impedances are different, that is a *mismatch*.

Impedance matcher — A device that matches one impedance level to another. For example, it may match the impedance of an antenna system to the impedance of a transmitter or receiver. Amateurs also call such devices a *Transmatch*, *antenna-matcher* or *antenna tuner*.

Impedance matching (circuit) — A circuit that transforms impedance from one value to another. Adjustable impedance matching circuits are used at the output of transmitters and amplifiers to allow maximum power output over a wide range of load impedances.

Impedance transformer — A transformer designed specifically for transforming impedances in RF equipment.

Indicator — Characters added after a slash or other separating phrase at the end of a call sign to modify the license class or location implied by the call sign. For example, "temporary AG" added after a call sign indicates that the operator has obtained General class privileges.

Indicator (visual) — A device that presents on/off information visually by the presence, absence, or color of light.

Inductance — A measure of the ability of a coil to store energy in a *magnetic field*.

Inductor — An electrical component usually composed of a coil of wire wound on a central core. An inductor stores energy in a *magnetic field*.

Input frequency — A repeater's receiving frequency. To use a repeater, transmit on the input frequency and receive on the **output frequency**.

Insulator — A material whose electrons do not move easily, so that an electric current cannot pass through it (within voltage limits).

Integrated circuit (IC) — Multiple semiconductor devices in a circuit created on a single substrate.

Intermediate frequency (IF) — The stages in a receiver that follow the input amplifier and mixer circuits. Most of the receiver's gain and selectivity are achieved at the IF stages.

Intermodulation — Two signals mixing together in a receiver circuit or non-linear contact in a strong RF field to produce mixing products that are received along with actual signals.

International Telecommunication Union (ITU) — The organization of the United Nations responsible for coordinating international telecommunications agreements.

Internet Repeater Linking Project (IRLP) — A system of linking repeaters by using the Voice-Over-Internet Protocol.

Ion — An atom that is missing one or more electrons.

Ionizing radiation — Electromagnetic radiation that has sufficient energy to knock electrons free from their atoms, producing positive and negative ions. X-rays, gamma rays and ultraviolet radiation are examples of ionizing radiation.

Ionosphere — A region of electrically charged (ionized) gases high in the atmosphere. The ionosphere bends radio waves as they travel through it, returning them to Earth. Also see **sky-wave propagation**.

Isotropic antenna — An antenna that radiates and receives equally in all possible directions.

Junction capacitance (C_J) — The capacitance formed by a junction diode's P- and N-type material.

K — The Morse code abbreviation for "end of transmission" or "go ahead." Any station may respond.

K factor — A measure of a dielectric material's ability to store electrical energy.

Keplerian elements — Mathematical values for a satellite's orbit that can be used to compute the position of a satellite at any point in time, for any position on Earth.

Key — A manually operated switch that turns a transmitter on and off to send Morse code.

Keyer or **electronic keyer** — A piece of equipment that generates Morse code automatically.

Kilo (or lower case **k**) — The metric prefix for 10^3, or multiply by 1000.

LCD — Liquid crystal display.

LC circuit — A circuit made entirely from inductors (L) and capacitors (C).

LED — Light-emitting diode.

Lightning protection — Methods to prevent lightning damage to your equipment (and your house), such as unplugging equipment, disconnecting antenna feed lines and using a lightning arrestor.

Line-of-sight propagation — The term used to describe VHF and UHF propagation in a straight line directly from one station to another.

Linear amplifier — Also known as a **linear**, a piece of equipment that amplifies the output of a transmitter, often to the full legal amateur power limit of 1500 W PEP.

Linear supply — A power supply that uses capacitor- or inductor-filter output circuits.

Loading — the technique of increasing an antenna's electrical size by adding inductive (coils) or capacitive (capacity hats) reactance to the antenna.

Local control — Operation of a station with a control operator physically present at the transmitter.

Log — The documents or log of a station that detail operation of the station. They can be used as supporting evidence, and for troubleshooting interference-related problems or complaints.

Long path — The longest of the two great circle paths between two stations.

Loop antenna — An antenna with element(s) constructed as continuous lengths of wire or tubing.

Loss — A reduction in power, voltage, or current due to dissipation of energy. (see also **attenuation**).

Lower sideband (LSB) — (1) In an AM signal, the sideband located below the carrier frequency. (2) The common single-sideband operating mode on the 40, 80 and 160-meter amateur bands.

Low-pass filter (LPF) — A filter designed to pass signals below a specified *cutoff* frequency, while attenuating higher-frequency signals.

Machine language — Binary data directly useable as instructions by digital logic circuits.

Malicious (willful) interference — Intentional, deliberate obstruction of radio transmissions.

Maximum useable frequency (MUF) — The highest-frequency radio signal that will reach a particular destination using **sky-wave propagation**, or *skip*. The MUF may vary for radio signals sent to different destinations.

MAYDAY — From the French *m'aidez* (help me), MAYDAY is used when calling for emergency assistance in voice modes.

Maximum permissible exposure (MPE) — The maximum intensity of RF radiation to which a human being may be exposed. FCC rules establish maximum permissible exposure values for humans to RF radiation. [§1.1310 and §97.13 (c)]

Mean — The average value.

Mega (or capital **M**) — The metric prefix for 10^6, or times 1,000,000.

Memory bus — The interface between a microprocessor and memory devices that supports high-speed data transfer.

Memory channel — Frequency and mode information stored by a radio and referenced by an alphanumeric designator.

Meteor scatter — Communicating by reflecting signals off of the ionized trails left by meteors in the upper atmosphere.

Metric prefixes — A series of terms used in the metric system of measurement. We use metric prefixes to describe a quantity as compared to a basic unit. The metric prefixes indicate multiples of 10.

Metric system — A system of measurement developed by scientists and used in most countries of the world. This system uses a set of prefixes that are multiples of 10 to indicate quantities larger or smaller than the basic unit.

Micro (or **μ**) — The metric prefix for 10^{-6}, or divide by 1,000,000.

Microphone — A device that converts sound waves into electrical energy. (abbreviated mic or mike)

Microprocessor — An integrated circuit that contains all of the digital circuitry necessary to read and execute a program.

Microwave — Radio waves or signals with frequencies greater than 1000 MHz (1 GHz). This is not a strict definition, just a conventional way of referring to those frequencies.

Milli (or lower case **m**) — The metric prefix for 10^{-3}, or divide by 1000.

Mismatch — A difference between the impedance of a load from the equipment or feed line to which it is connected.

Mixer — Circuitry that combines two signals and generates signals at both their sum and difference frequencies. Mixers are used in receivers and transmitters to convert signals from one frequency to another.

Mobile station — A radio transmitter designed to be mounted in a vehicle. A push-to-talk (PTT) switch generally activates the transmitter. Any station that can be operated on the move, typically in a car, but also on a boat, a motorcycle, truck or RV.

Mode — The combination of a type of information and a method of transmission. For example, FM radiotelephony or *FM phone* consists of using FM modulation to carry voice information.

Modem — Short for *mo*dulator/*dem*odulator. A modem changes data into audio signals that can be transmitted by radio and demodulates a received signal to recover transmitted data.

Modulate or **modulation** — The process of adding information to an RF signal or *carrier* by varying its amplitude, frequency, or phase.

Monitor — Observe by listening or watching.

Morse code (see **CW**)

Multiband antenna — An antenna capable of operating on more than one amateur frequency band, usually using a single feed line.

Multihop propagation — Long-distance radio propagation using several skips or hops between the Earth and the ionosphere.

Multimeter — An electronic test instrument used to measure current, voltage and resistance in a circuit. Describes all meters capable of making these measurements, such as the volt-ohm-milliammeter (VOM), vacuum-tube voltmeter (VTVM) and field-effect transistor VOM (FET VOM).

Multimode radio — Transceiver capable of SSB, CW and FM operation.

Multiple protocol controller (MPC) — A piece of equipment that can act as a **TNC** for several **protocols**.

Mutual inductance — The ability of inductors to share or transfer magnetic energy through a common magnetic field

N or **type N connector** — A type of RF connector.

National Electrical Code — A set of guidelines governing electrical safety, including antennas.

National Incident Management System (NIMS) — The method by which emergency situations are managed by US public safety agencies.

Net — An formal system of operation in order to exchange or manage information

Net control station (NCS) — The station in charge of a net.

Network — (1) A term used to describe several digital stations linked together to relay data over long distances. (2) A general term for any circuit or set of electrical connections.

Neutralization — The technique of preventing self-oscillation in an amplifier.

Noise blanker — A circuit that mutes the receiver during noise pulses.

Noise reduction — Removing random noise from a receiver's audio output.

Nominal value — The rated amount of ohms, farads, henrys and so forth that a component is supposed to present to a circuit.

Nonionizing radiation — Electromagnetic radiation that does not have sufficient energy to knock electrons free from their atoms. Radio frequency (RF) radiation is nonionizing.

Notch filter — A filter that removes a very narrow range of frequencies, usually from a receiver's audio output to remove interfering tones.

Offset frequency — The difference between a repeater's transmitter and receiver frequencies. Also known as the *repeater split*.

Ohm — The basic unit of electrical resistance.

Ohm's Law — A basic law of electronics. Ohm's Law states the relationship between voltage (E), current (I) and resistance (R). The voltage applied to a circuit is equal to the current through the circuit times the resistance of the circuit (E = IR).

Ohmmeter — A device used to measure resistance.

Omnidirectional — An antenna that radiates and receives equally in all horizontal directions.

One-way communications — Radio signals not directed to a specific Amateur Radio station, or for which no reply is expected. The FCC Rules provide for limited types of one-way communications on the amateur bands. [§97.111 (b)]

Open circuit — An electrical circuit that does not have a complete path, so current can't flow through the circuit.

Open circuit voltage — The voltage at the output of a circuit with no load connected.

Open repeater — A repeater that can be used by all hams who have a license that authorizes operation on the repeater frequencies.

Operator/primary station license — An amateur license actually includes two licenses in one. The operator license is that portion of an Amateur Radio license that gives permission to operate an amateur station. The **primary station license** is that portion of an Amateur Radio license that authorizes an amateur station at a specific location. The station license also lists the call sign of that station.

Oscillate — To vibrate continuously at a single frequency. An **oscillator** is a device or circuit that generates a signal at a single frequency.

Oscillator — A circuit that produces a single frequency output signal.

Oscilloscope — Test instrument that visually displays voltage versus time.

Output frequency — A repeater's transmitting frequency. To use a repeater, transmit on the **input frequency** and receive on the output frequency.

Packet radio — A digital mode in which packets are constructed and exchanged according to the rules of standard AX.25. On HF, packets are exchanged as FSK modulation by SSB equipment, while on VHF and UHF, FM is used.

Paddle — Similar to a **key** or **bug**, a paddle has a pair of contacts operated by one or two levers that is used to control an electronic **keyer** that generates Morse code automatically.

Parallel circuit — An electrical circuit in which the electrons may follow more than one path in traveling between the negative supply terminal and positive terminal.

Parallel-conductor line — A type of transmission line that uses two parallel wires spaced apart from each other by insulating material. Also known as *open-wire, ladder, or window line*.

Parallel interface — A data interface through which multiple bits of data are transferred at one time. A byte-wide interface transfers 8 data bits in each operation.

Parasitic (array) — An array antenna in which one or more of the elements is not directly connected to the antenna feed line.

Parasitic element — Part of a directional antenna that derives energy from mutual coupling with the driven element. Parasitic elements are not connected directly to the feed line.

Parity bit — A bit that indicates whether there is an odd or even number of 1 bits in an encoded character.

Part 15 — The section of the FCC's rules that deal with unlicensed devices likely to transmit or receive RF signals.

Part 97 — The section of the FCC's rules that regulate Amateur Radio.

Passive — A device that functions without requiring a source of power.

Peak envelope power (PEP) — The average power of an RF signal at its largest amplitude peak.

Pecuniary — Payment of any type, whether money or other goods. Amateurs may not operate their stations in return for any type of payment.

Perigee — That point in the orbit of a satellite when it is closest to the Earth.

Permeability — The ability of a material to contain magnetic energy.

Phase — A measure of position in time within a repeating waveform, such as a sine wave. Phase is measured in degrees or radians. There are 360 degrees or 2π radians in one complete cycle.

Phase angle — The phase angle of a signal is a measure of the relative difference in phase between the signal and a reference signal or some point in time.

Phase modulation (PM) — The process of adding information to a signal by varying its phase characteristics. Phase modulation is very similar to **FM** and PM signals can be received by FM receivers.

Phone — Another name for voice communications. An abbreviation for *radiotelephone*.

Phone emission — The FCC name for voice or other sound transmissions.

Phone patch — Using radio to transmit and receive audio from the public telephone system.

Phonetic alphabet — Standard words used on voice modes to make it easier to understand letters of the alphabet, such as those in call signs. The call sign KA6LMN stated phonetically is *Kilo Alfa Six Lima Mike November*.

Photovoltaic conversion — The direct conversion of sunlight to electricity.

Pi (π) — A mathematical constant approximately equal to 3.14159.

Pico (or lower case p) — The metric prefix for 10^{-12}, or divide by 1,000,000,000,000.

PL (see **CTCSS**) — Private Line. PL is a Motorola trademark.

PN junction — The interface where P-type and N-type semiconductor materials are in contact. A diode made from a PN junction is called a **junction diode.**

Polarization — The orientation of the electrical-field of a radio wave. An antenna that is parallel to the surface of the Earth, such as a dipole, produces horizontally polarized waves. One that is perpendicular to the Earth's surface, such as a quarter-wave vertical, produces vertically polarized waves. An antenna that has both horizontal and vertical polarization is said to be circularly polarized.

Polarized capacitor — A capacitor to which dc voltage may only be applied with one polarity without damage (non-polarized capacitors are insensitive to the polarity of the applied voltage).

Portable device — Generally considered to be a radio transmitting device designed to be transported easily and set up for operation independently of normal infrastructure. For purposes of RF exposure regulations, a portable device is one designed to have a transmitting antenna that is generally within 20 centimeters of a human body.

Potentiometer — Another name for a **variable resistor**. The resistance value of a potentiometer can be changed over a range of values without removing it from a circuit.

Power — The rate of energy consumption or expenditure. We calculate power in an electrical circuit by multiplying the voltage applied to the circuit times the current through the circuit ($P = IE$).

Power amplifier (see **linear amplifier**)

Power (or voltage or current) rating — The rated ability of the component to withstand electrical stress.

Power resistor — A resistor designed to dissipate several watts of power or more.

Power supply — A circuit that provides a direct-current output at some desired voltage from an ac input voltage.

Preamplifier — An amplifier placed ahead of a receiver's input circuitry to increase the strength of a received signal. Preamplifier circuits are often included in a receiver and may be turned on or off. Preamplifiers for VHF, UHF, and microwave frequencies are sometimes located at the antenna to amplify signals before loss in the feed line reduces their strength.

Prefix — The leading letters and numbers of a call sign that indicate the country in which the call sign was assigned.

Primary battery — A battery that is discarded after it is discharged.

Primary service — When a frequency band is shared among two or more different radio services, the primary service is preferred. Stations in the **secondary service** must not cause harmful interference to, and must accept interference from stations in the primary service. [§97.303]

Primary station license — An amateur license actually includes two licenses in one. The **operator license** is that portion of an Amateur Radio license that gives permission to operate an amateur station. The primary station license is that portion of an Amateur Radio license that authorizes an amateur station at a specific location. The station license also lists the call sign of that station.

Primary winding — The winding on a transformer to which power is applied.

Priority traffic — Emergency-related messages, but not as important as **Emergency traffic**.

Procedural signals (prosigns) — For Morse code communications, one or two letters sent as a single character. Amateurs use prosigns in CW contacts as a short way to indicate the operator's intention. Some examples are к for "Go Ahead or $\overline{AR}$ for "End of Message." (A bar over the letters is used to indicate that the prosign is sent as one character.) For phone communications, words such as "Break" or "Over" that control the flow of the communications.

Product detector — A type of mixer circuit that allows a receiver to demodulate CW and SSB signals.

Propagation — The process through which radio waves travel.

Protocol — A method of encoding, packaging, exchanging, and decoding digital data.

PSK — Phase shift keying.

Push-pull (see **Class B**)

Push to talk (PTT) — Turning a transmitter on and off manually with a switch, usually thumb- or foot-activated.

Q signals — Three-letter symbols beginning with Q used on CW to save time and to improve communication. Some examples are QRS (send slower), QTH (location), QSO (ham conversation) and QSL (acknowledgment of receipt).

Q system — A method of providing signal quality reports on a scale of 1 ("Q1") to 5 ("Q5").

QSL card — A postcard that serves as a confirmation of communication between two hams. QSL is a Q-signal meaning "received and understood."

QSO — A conversation between two radio amateurs. QSO is a Q-signal meaning "I am in contact."

Quad antenna — An antenna built with its elements in the shape of four-sided loops.

Quarter-wavelength vertical antenna — An antenna constructed of a quarter-wavelength long radiating element placed perpendicular to the Earth.

Radiation pattern — A graph showing how an antenna radiates and receives in different directions. An *azimuthal pattern* shows radiation in horizontal directions. An *elevation pattern* shows how an antenna radiates and receives at different vertical angles.

Radio Amateur Civil Emergency Service (RACES) — A part of the Amateur Service that provides radio communications for civil defense organizations during local, regional or national civil emergencies.

Radio frequency (RF) exposure — FCC Rules establish maximum permissible exposure (MPE) values for humans to RF radiation. [§1.1310 and §97.13 (c)]

Radio frequency (RF) radiation or **waves** — Electromagnetic energy that travels through space without wires.

Radio frequency (RF) signals — RF signals are generally considered to be any electrical signals with a frequency higher than 20,000 Hz, up to 300 GHz.

Radio-frequency interference (RFI) — Disturbance to electronic equipment caused by radio-frequency signals.

Radiogram — The standard format for messages relayed by Amateur Radio.

Radio horizon — The most distant point to which radio signals can be sent directly without reflections.

Radioteletype (RTTY) — Radio signals sent from one teleprinter machine to another machine. Anything that one operator types on his teleprinter will be printed on the other machine. Also known as narrow-band direct-printing telegraphy.

Ragchew — An informal conversation.

Random access memory (RAM) — Memory that can be read from or written to in any order.

Range — The longest distance over which radio signals can be exchanged.

Read-only memory (ROM) — Stores data permanently and cannot be changed.

Receiver — A device that converts radio waves into signals we can hear or see (abbreviated RCVR).

Receiver overload — Interference to a receiver caused by a RF signal too strong for the receiver input circuits. A signal that overloads the receiver RF amplifier (front end) causes **front-end overload**. Receiver overload is sometimes called *RF overload*.

Reciprocal operating authority — Permission for Amateur Radio operators from another country to operate in the US using their home license. This permission is based on various treaties between the US government and the governments of other countries.

Rectifier — A diode intended for use with high current or voltage in power supplies.

Rectifier string — Rectifier diodes connected in series to rectify a higher voltage than any single diode could withstand.

Reflected power — The power that returns to the transmitter from the antenna along a transmission line.

Reflection — Signals that travel by **line-of-sight propagation** are reflected by large objects like buildings.

Reflector — A parasitic element behind the driven element in a directional antennas.

Refract — Bending of an electromagnetic wave as it travels through materials with different properties. Light refracts as it travels from air into water. Radio waves refract as they travel through the ionosphere. If the radio waves refract enough they will return to Earth. This is the basis for long-distance communication on the **HF bands**.

Region — One of the three administrative areas defined by the **ITU**.

Register (shift) — A register is a digital circuit that accepts (loads) and stores digital data. A shift register accepts data as a sequence of 1s and 0s applied to its input.

Reliable transport — A protocol capable of delivering only data in which no transmission errors have occurred within the limits of its error correction and detection mechanisms.

Remote control — Operation of a station in which the control functions of the station are operated by a control operator over a control link.

Repeater station — A station that retransmits the signals of other stations to give them greater range.

Reradiation — Radiation from a parasitic antenna element resulting from energy received from a driven element.

Resistance — The ability to oppose an electric current.

Resistor — An electronic component specifically designed to oppose or control current through a circuit.

Resonance — (1) The frequency at which the maximum response of a circuit or antenna occurs. (2) The frequency at which a circuit's capacitive and inductive reactances are equal and cancel.

Resonant frequency — The desired operating frequency of a tuned circuit. In an antenna, the resonant frequency is one where the feed-point impedance is composed only of resistance.

RF burn — A burn produced by coming in contact with exposed RF voltages.

RF carrier — A steady radio frequency signal that is modulated to add an information signal to be transmitted. For example, a voice signal is added to the RF carrier to produce a **phone emission** signal.

RF feedback — Distortion caused by RF signals disturbing the function of an audio circuit.

RF overload — Another term for receiver overload.

RF safety — Preventing injury or illness to humans from the effects of radio-frequency energy.

Rig — The radio amateur's term for a transmitter, receiver or transceiver.

Ripple — Variations in power supply output voltage due to current pulses in a rectifier circuit.

Root Mean Square (RMS) — A measure of voltage of an ac signal that would deliver the same amount of power as a dc voltage of the same value. Root Mean Square refers to the method used to calculate the voltage.

RST — A system of numbers used for signal reports: R is readability, S is strength and T is tone. (On phone, only R and S reports are used.)

Rubber duck antenna — A flexible rubber-coated antenna that is inexpensive, small, lightweight and difficult to break. Rubber ducks are used mainly with hand-held VHF or UHF transceivers.

S meter — A meter that provides an indication of the relative strength of received signals.

Safety interlock — A switch that automatically turns off power to a piece of equipment when the enclosure is opened.

Saturation — The point at which an increase in input signal results in no change in the output signal.

Scattering — Radio wave propagation by means of multiple reflections in the layers of the atmosphere or from an obstruction.

Schematic diagram — A drawing that describes the electrical connections in a piece of electric or electronic equipment.

Schematic symbol — A standardized symbol used to represent an electrical or electronic circuit component on a schematic diagram.

Secondary battery — A battery that can be recharged and reused (also known as a **storage battery**).

Secondary service — When a frequency band is shared among two or more different radio services, the **primary service** is preferred. Stations in the secondary service must not cause harmful interference to, and must accept interference from stations in the primary service. [§97.303]

Secondary winding — The winding or windings on a transformer from which power is extracted.

Selectivity — The ability of a receiver to distinguish between signals. Selectivity is important when many signals are present and when it is desired to receive weak signals in the presence of strong signals.

Self policing — The practice of amateurs encouraging and assisting other amateurs to abide by FCC regulations.

Self-resonance — Resonance caused when the reactance from a component's parasitic reactance cancels the component's designed reactance.

Sensitivity — The ability of a receiver to detect weak signals.

Serial interface — A data interface through which data is transferred one bit at a time.

Series circuit — An electrical circuit in which all the electrons must flow through every part of the circuit because there is only one path for the electrons to follow.

Shack — The room where an Amateur Radio operator keeps his or her station equipment.

Shielding — Surrounding an electronic circuit to block RF signals from being radiated or received.

Short circuit — An electrical circuit in which the current does not take the desired path, but finds a shortcut instead. Often the current flows directly between the negative power-supply terminal and the positive one, bypassing the rest of the circuit.

Short path — The shortest of the two great circle paths between two stations.

Sidebands — The sum or difference frequencies generated when an RF carrier is mixed with an audio signal. Single-sideband phone (SSB) signals have an upper sideband (USB — that part of the signal above the carrier) and a lower sideband (LSB — the part of the signal below the carrier). SSB transceivers allow operation on either USB or LSB.

Signal diode (switching diode) — A diode designed for use with low power signals.

Signal generator — A device that produces low-level signals similar to those received over the air; used for testing receivers and other equipment.

Signal report — An evaluation of the transmitting station's signal and reception quality.

Signal tracer — A device used for receiver testing that can both generate and detect or demodulate signals.

Simplex operation — Receiving and transmitting on the same frequency.

Sine wave — A waveform whose amplitude is equal to the sine of frequency × time.

Single sideband (SSB) phone — SSB is a form of double-sideband amplitude modulation in which one sideband and the carrier are removed. SSB is a common mode of voice operation on the amateur bands.

Skip — Propagation by means of ionospheric reflection. Traversing the distance to the ionosphere and back to the ground is called a *hop*.

Skip zone — A ring-shaped area of poor radio communication, too distant for ground waves and too close for sky waves.

Sky-wave propagation — The method by which radio waves travel through the ionosphere and back to Earth. Sometimes called *skip*, sky-wave propagation has a far greater range than **line-of-sight** and **ground-wave propagation**.

Slow-scan television (SSTV) — A television system used by amateurs to transmit pictures within a signal bandwidth allowed on the HF or VHF/UHF bands by the FCC. It takes approximately 8 seconds to send a single black and white SSTV frame, and between 12 seconds and 4½ minutes for the various color systems currently in use on the HF bands.

SMA connector — A type of RF connector.

Solar cycle — The 10.7 year period of variation in solar activity.

Solenoidal winding — An inductor winding along a straight axis.

SOS — A Morse code call for emergency assistance.

Space station — An amateur station located more than 50 km above the Earth's surface.

Specific absorption rate (SAR) — A term that describes the rate at which RF energy is absorbed into the human body. Maximum permissible exposure (MPE) limits are based on whole-body SAR values.

Speech compression or **processing** — Increasing the average power and intelligibility of a voice signal by amplifying low-level components of the signal more than high-level components.

Splatter — A type of interference to stations on nearby frequencies. Splatter occurs when a transmitter is overmodulated.

Sporadic E — A form of enhanced radio-wave propagation that occurs when radio signals are reflected from small, dense ionization patches in the E region of the ionosphere. Sporadic E is observed on the 15, 10, 6 and 2-meter bands, and occasionally on the 1.25-meter band.

Spurious emissions — Signals from a transmitter on frequencies other than the operating frequency.

Spurs — Spurious signals not harmonically related to the desired signal.

Squelch — Circuitry that mutes an FM receiver when no signal is received.

SSB — Abbreviation for the **single sideband phone** mode of communication. This is the most widely used mode for phone operation on the HF bands.

Standard frequency offset — The standard transmitter/receiver frequency offset used by a repeater on a particular amateur band. For example, the standard offset on 2 meters is 600 kHz. Also see **offset frequency**.

Standing-wave ratio (SWR) — Sometimes called voltage standing-wave ratio (VSWR). A measure of the impedance match between the feed line's characteristic impedance and the load (usually an antenna). Also, with a Transmatch in use, a measure of the match between the feed line from the transmitter and the antenna system. The system includes the Transmatch and the line to the antenna. VSWR is the ratio of maximum voltage to minimum voltage along the feed line, also the ratio of antenna impedance to feed-line impedance.

Start bit — A bit preceding the data bits in a character in order to synchronize the receiving system.

Station grounding — The practice of connecting all station equipment to a good earth ground to improve both safety and station performance.

Station license — An amateur license actually includes two licenses in one. The **operator license** is that portion of an Amateur Radio license that gives permission to operate an amateur station. The primary station license is that portion of an Amateur Radio license that authorizes an amateur station at a specific location. The station license also lists the call sign of that station.

Station records/station log — The documents or log of a station that detail operation of the station. The log can be used as supporting evidence, and for troubleshooting interference-related problems or complaints.

Stop bit — A bit following the data bits in a character in order to synchronize the receiving system.

Storage battery (see **secondary battery**)

Stratosphere — The part of the Earth's atmosphere that extends from about 7 miles to 30 miles above the earth. Clouds rarely form in the stratosphere.

Sub-audible tone (see **CTCSS**)

Substrate — The base material from which transistors and ICs are made.

Suffix — The letters that follow a call sign prefix identifying a specific amateur.

Sunspot cycle — The number of **sunspots** increases and decreases in a predictable cycle that lasts about 11 years.

Sunspots — Dark spots on the surface of the Sun. When there are few sunspots, long-distance radio propagation is poor on the higher-frequency bands. When there are many sunspots, long-distance HF propagation improves.

Surface mount technology (SMT) — Printed-circuit board components that solder directly to connection pads without mounting holes.

Surge protector — A device that limits voltage by changing from an insulator to a conductor when excessive voltage occurs. Surge protectors are used to prevent temporary or *transient* excessive voltages from damaging sensitive electronic equipment.

Switch — A device used to connect or disconnect electrical contacts.

Switch mode supply (switching supply) — A power supply that uses high-frequency current pulses in an inductor to regulate output voltage.

SWR meter — A measuring instrument that senses forward and reflected power to display SWR.

Symbol rate (signaling rate) — The rate at which individual data symbols are transmitted (see also **baud**).

Tactical call signs — Names used to identify a location or function during local emergency communications.

Tactical communications — A first-response communications under emergency conditions that involves a few people in a small area.

Telecommand operation — A one-way radio transmission to start, change or end functions of a device at a distance.

Telegraph key — A telegraph key (also called a *straight key*) is the simplest type of Morse code sending device.

Teleprinter — A machine that can convert keystrokes (typing) into electrical impulses. The teleprinter can also convert the proper electrical impulses back into text. Computers have largely replaced teleprinters for amateur radioteletype work.

Television interference (TVI) — Interruption of television reception caused by another signal.

Temperature coefficient — The type of variation of a component's actual value with temperature.

Temperature inversion — A condition in the atmosphere in which a region of cool air is trapped beneath warmer air.

Terminal — An inexpensive piece of equipment that can be used in place of a computer in a packet radio station. A terminal can only send and display characters and does not execute programs or store information.

Third-party — An unlicensed person on whose behalf communications is passed by amateur radio.

Third-party communications — Messages passed from one amateur to another on behalf of a third person.

Third-party communications agreement — An official understanding between the United States and another country that allows amateurs in both countries to participate in third-party communications.

Third-party participation — An unlicensed person participating in amateur communications. A control operator must ensure compliance with FCC rules.

Through hole mount — Printed-circuit board components that have wire leads that are inserted into holes through connection pads and then soldered to the pads.

Ticket — A common name for an Amateur Radio license.

Time base — A circuit that generates a regular timing signal.

Time-out timer — A device that limits the amount of time any one person can talk continuously through a repeater.

Terminal Node Controller (TNC) — A device that acts as an interface between a computer and a radio. It includes a **modem** and implements the rules of a **protocol**.

Tolerance — The amount the actual value is allowed to vary from the nominal value, usually expressed in percent.

Toroidal winding — An inductor wound around a circular core with a center hole (a toroid).

T-R switch — Transmit-Receive switch. A circuit or device that switches an antenna between transmitter and receiver circuits or equipment.

Traffic — Formal messages exchanged via radio. *Traffic handling* is the process of exchanging traffic. A *traffic net* is a net specially created and managed to handle traffic. Can also refer, in the general sense, to activity on a band.

Transconductance — The ratio of output current to input voltage.

Transfer switch — A switch that connects a home power distribution panel to either a generator or the utility lines.

Transform (impedance) — To alter the ratio of voltage and current (impedance) from an undesired value to a desired value.

Transceiver (XCVR) — A radio transmitter and receiver combined in one unit.

Transistor — A solid-state device made of three layers of semiconductor material. A transistor can be used as a switch or amplifier.

Transmission line — The wires or cable used to connect a transmitter or receiver to an antenna. Also called **feed line**.

Transmitter (XMTR) — A device that produces radio-frequency signals.

Trip — Activate based on some physical action (current, signal level, voltage) exceeding a threshold. A circuit breaker trips, opening a circuit, when excessive current flow occurs, for example.

Troposphere — The region in Earth's atmosphere just above the Earth's surface and below the ionosphere.

Tropospheric bending — When radio waves are bent in the troposphere, they return to Earth farther away than the visible horizon.

Tropospheric ducting — A type of VHF propagation that can occur when warm air overruns cold air (a temperature inversion).

Turns ratio — The ratio of the number of turns in a transformer's primary winding to the number of turns in the secondary winding.

UHF connector — A type of RF connector.

Ultra high frequency (UHF) — The term used for the frequency range between 300 MHz and 3000 MHz (3 GHz). Technician licensees have full privileges on all amateur UHF bands.

Ultraviolet (UV) — Electromagnetic waves with frequencies higher than visible light. Literally, "above violet," which is the high-frequency end of the visible range.

Unbalanced line — Feed line with one conductor at ground potential, such as coaxial cable.

Uncontrolled environment — Any area in which an RF signal may cause radiation exposure to people who may not be aware of the radiated electric and magnetic fields. The FCC generally considers members of the general public and an amateur's neighbors to be in an uncontrolled **RF radiation** exposure environment to determine the maximum permissible exposure levels.

Uncoordinated repeater — A repeater system whose input and output frequencies are not approved by the regional frequency coordination organization.

Unidentified communications or signals — Signals or radio communications in which the transmitting station's call sign is not transmitted.

Unintentional interference — Interference created accidentally that is not intended to disrupt communications.

Universal Licensing System (ULS) — FCC database for all FCC radio services.

Uplink — The frequency or frequency range on which signals are transmitted from the ground to a satellite.

Upper sideband (USB) — (1) In an AM signal, the sideband located above the carrier frequency. (2) The common single-sideband operating mode on the 20, 17, 15, 12 and 10-meter HF amateur bands, and all the VHF and UHF bands.

Vanity call — A call sign selected by an amateur instead of sequentially assigned by the FCC.

Variable resistor — A resistor whose value can be adjusted over a certain range, without removing it from a circuit.

Variable-frequency oscillator (VFO) — An oscillator used in receivers and transmitters. The frequency is set by a tuned circuit using capacitors and inductors and can be changed by adjusting the components of the tuned circuit.

Vertical antenna — A common amateur antenna whose radiating element is vertical. There are usually four or more radial elements parallel to or on the ground.

Very high frequency (VHF) — The term used for the frequency range between 30 MHz and 300 MHz.

Visible horizon — The most distant point one can see by line of sight.

Voice communications — Any of the several methods used by amateurs to transmit speech. Hams can use several voice modes, including FM and SSB.

Volatile (memory) — Memory that loses its stored data when power is removed (**nonvolatile** memory retains the data when power is removed).

Volt (V) — The basic unit of electrical potential or EMF.

Voltage — The EMF or electrical potential difference that causes electrons to move through an electrical circuit.

Voltmeter — A test instrument used to measure voltage.

Volunteer Examiner (VE) — A licensed amateur who is accredited by a Volunteer Examiner Coordinator (VEC) to administer amateur license examinations.

Volunteer Examiner Coordinator (VEC) — An organization that has entered into an agreement with the FCC to coordinate amateur license examinations.

Voice-operated transmission (VOX) — Turning a transmitter on and off under control of the operator's voice.

Watt (W) — The unit of power in the metric system. The watt describes the rate at which a circuit uses electrical energy.

Wattmeter — Also called a *power meter*, a test instrument used to measure the power output (in watts) of a transmitter. A directional wattmeter measures both forward and reflected power in a feed line.

Wavelength — Often abbreviated λ. The distance a radio wave travels in one RF cycle. The wavelength relates to frequency. Higher frequencies have shorter wavelengths.

Wavemeter — A tunable LC circuit that when absorbs energy from an oscillator or amplifier at the LC circuit's resonant frequency. When the wavemeter is tuned to the operating frequency, it is visible as a change in operating parameters of the circuit under test.

Weak-signal modes — Usually SSB or CW modes, used in relation to operating on the VHF and UHF bands, where many amateurs only operate FM phone.

Whip antenna — An antenna with an element made of a single, flexible rod or tube.

Willful interference — Interference created deliberately so as to disrupt ongoing communications (also called **intentional interference**).

Windings — The inductors that share a common core in a transformer

Winlink — A system of email transmission and distribution using Amateur Radio for the connection between individual amateurs and mailbox stations known as *Participating Mailbox Operators (PMBO)*.

Wiring diagram — A pictorial or descriptive drawing that shows how the wiring of a piece of electric or electronic equipment is to be done.

WWV/WWVH — Radio stations run by the US NIST (National Institute of Standards and Technology) to provide accurate time and frequencies.

XCVR — Transceiver.

XMTR — Transmitter.

Yagi antenna — The most popular type of directional (beam) antenna. It has one driven element and one or more additional parasitic elements.

73 — Ham lingo for "best regards." Used on both phone and CW toward the end of a contact.

88 — Ham lingo for "love and kisses" (not meant literally) when concluding a contact with a female operator.

Chapter 11

Question Pool

There are significant differences between the order of topics in the Question Pool subelements and the arrangement of material in the text. An alternate arrangement of the questions that follows the text more closely is available at **www.arrl.org/gclm**. Follow the Study Guide link to download the material as a PDF file you can print or view.

General Class Question Pool ♦ Effective July 1, 2007

SUBELEMENT G1
Commission's Rules
5 exam questions — 5 groups

G1A — General class control operator frequency privileges; primary and secondary allocations

G1A01
On which of the following bands is a General Class license holder granted all amateur frequency privileges?
A. 20, 17, and 12 meters
B. 160, 80, 40, and 10 meters
C. 160, 30, 17, 12, and 10 meters
D. 160, 30, 17, 15, 12, and 10 meters

G1A01
(C)
[97.301(d)]
Page 3-9

G1A02
On which of the following bands is phone operation prohibited?
A. 160 meters
B. 30 meters
C. 17 meters
D. 12 meters

G1A02
(B)
[97.305]
Page 3-9

G1A03
On which of the following bands is image transmission prohibited?
A. 160 meters
B. 30 meters
C. 20 meters
D. 12 meters

G1A03
(B)
[97.305]
Page 3-9

G1A04
Which amateur band restricts communication to specific channels, using only USB voice, and prohibits all other modes, including CW and data?
A. 11 meters
B. 12 meters
C. 30 meters
D. 60 meters

G1A04
(D)
[97.303(s)]
Page 3-9

G1A05
(A)
[97.301(d)]
Page 3-5

G1A05
Which of the following frequencies is in the General Class portion of the 40 meter band?
A. 7.250 MHz
B. 7.500 MHz
C. 40.200 MHz
D. 40.500 MHz

G1A06
(D)
[97.301(d)]
Page 3-5

G1A06
Which of the following frequencies is in the 12 meter band?
A. 3.940 MHz
B. 12.940 MHz
C. 17.940 MHz
D. 24.940 MHz

G1A07
(C)
[97.301(d)]
Page 3-5

G1A07
Which of the following frequencies is within the General Class portion of the 75 meter phone band?
A. 1875 kHz
B. 3750 kHz
C. 3900 kHz
D. 4005 kHz

G1A08
(C)
[97.301(d)]
Page 3-5

G1A08
Which of the following frequencies is within the General Class portion of the 20 meter phone band?
A. 14005 kHz
B. 14105 kHz
C. 14305 kHz
D. 14405 kHz

G1A09
(C)
[97.301(d)]
Page 3-5

G1A09
Which of the following frequencies is within the General Class portion of the 80 meter band?
A. 1855 kHz
B. 2560 kHz
C. 3560 kHz
D. 3650 kHz

G1A10
(C)
[97.301(d)]
Page 3-5

G1A10
Which of the following frequencies is within the General Class portion of the 15 meter band?
A. 14250 kHz
B. 18155 kHz
C. 21300 kHz
D. 24900 kHz

G1A11
(D)
[97.301(d)]
Page 3-5

G1A11
Which of the following frequencies is available to a control operator holding a General Class license?
A. 28.020 MHz
B. 28.350 MHz
C. 28.550 MHz
D. All of these answers are correct

G1A12
When a General Class licensee is not permitted to use the entire voice portion of a particular band, which portion of the voice segment is generally available to them?
A. The lower end
B. The upper end
C. The lower end on frequencies below 7.3 MHz and the upper end on frequencies above 14.150 MHz
D. The upper end on frequencies below 7.3 MHz and the lower end on frequencies above 14.150 MHz

G1A13
Which amateur band is shared with the Citizens Radio Service?
A. 10 meters
B. 11 meters
C. 12 meters
D. None

G1A14
Which of the following applies when the FCC rules designate the amateur service as a secondary user and another service as a primary user on a band?
A. Amateur stations must obtain permission from a primary service station before operating on a frequency assigned to that station
B. Amateur stations are allowed to use the frequency band only during emergencies
C. Amateur stations are allowed to use the frequency band only if they do not cause harmful interference to primary users
D. Amateur stations may only operate during specific hours of the day, while primary users are permitted 24 hour use of the band

G1A15
What must you do if, when operating on either the 30 or 60 meter bands, a station in the primary service interferes with your contact?
A. Notify the FCC's regional Engineer in Charge of the interference
B. Increase your transmitter's power to overcome the interference
C. Attempt to contact the station and request that it stop the interference
D. Stop transmitting at once and/or move to a clear frequency

G1A16
Which of the following operating restrictions applies to amateur radio stations as a secondary service in the 60 meter band?
A. They must not cause harmful interference to stations operating in other radio services
B. They must transmit no more than 30 minutes during each hour to minimize harmful interference to other radio services
C. They must use lower sideband, suppressed-carrier, only
D. They must not exceed 2.0 kHz of bandwidth

G1A12
(B)
[97.301]
Page 3-9

G1A13
(D)
[97.303]
Page 3-9

G1A14
(C)
[97.303]
Page 3-13

G1A15
(D)
[97.303]
Page 3-13

G1A16
(A)
[97.303(s)]
Page 3-13

G1B — Antenna structure limitations; good engineering and good amateur practice; beacon operation; restricted operation; retransmitting radio signals

G1B01
(C)
[97.15(a)]
Page 3-2

G1B01
What is the maximum height above ground to which an antenna structure may be erected without requiring notification to the FAA and registration with the FCC, provided it is not at or near a public-use airport?
A. 50 feet
B. 100 feet
C. 200 feet
D. 300 feet

G1B02
(D)
[97.203(b)]
Page 3-10

G1B02
With which of the following conditions must beacon stations comply?
A. Identification must be in Morse Code
B. The frequency must be coordinated with the National Beacon Organization
C. The frequency must be posted on the Internet or published in a national periodical
D. There must be no more than one beacon signal in the same band from a single location

G1B03
(A)
[97.1(a)(9)]
Page 3-10

G1B03
Which of the following is a purpose of a beacon station as identified in the FCC Rules?
A. Observation of propagation and reception, or other related activities
B. Automatic Identification of Repeaters
C. Transmission of bulletins of General interest to amateur radio licensees
D. Identifying Net Frequencies

G1B04
(A)
[97.113(b)]
Page 2-21

G1B04
Which of the following must be true before an amateur station may provide news information to the media during a disaster?
A. The information must directly relate to the immediate safety of human life or protection of property and there is no other means of communication available
B. The exchange of such information must be approved by a local emergency preparedness official and transmitted on officially designated frequencies
C. The FCC must have declared a state of emergency
D. Both amateur stations must be RACES stations

G1B05
(D)
[97.113(a)(4),
97.113(e)]
Page 3-15

G1B05
When may music be transmitted by an amateur station?
A. At any time, as long as it produces no spurious emissions
B. When it is unintentionally transmitted from the background at the transmitter
C. When it is transmitted on frequencies above 1215 MHz
D. When it is an incidental part of a space shuttle or ISS retransmission

G1B06
(B)
[97.113(a)(4),
97.207(f)]
Page 3-15

G1B06
When is an amateur station permitted to transmit secret codes?
A. During a declared communications emergency
B. To control a space station
C. Only when the information is of a routine, personal nature
D. Only with Special Temporary Authorization from the FCC

G1B07
What are the restrictions on the use of abbreviations or procedural signals in the amateur service?
A. Only "Q" codes are permitted
B. They may be used if they do not obscure the meaning of a message
C. They are not permitted because they obscure the meaning of a message to FCC monitoring stations
D. Only "10-codes" are permitted

G1B07
(B)
[97.113(a)(4)]
Page 3-15

G1B08
Which of the following is prohibited by the FCC Rules for amateur radio stations?
A. Transmission of music as the primary program material during a contact
B. The use of obscene or indecent words
C. Transmission of false or deceptive messages or signals
D. All of these answers are correct

G1B08
(D)
[97.113(a)(4),
97.113(e)]
Page 3-15

G1B09
When may an amateur station transmit communications in which the licensee or control operator has a pecuniary (monetary) interest?
A. Only when other amateurs are being notified of the sale of apparatus normally used in an amateur station and such activity is not done on a regular basis
B. Only when there is no other means of communications readily available
C. At any time as long as the communication does not involve a third party
D. Never

G1B09
(A)
[97.113(a)(3)]
Page 3-15

G1B10
What is the power limit for beacon stations?
A. 10 watts PEP output
B. 20 watts PEP output
C. 100 watts PEP output
D. 200 watts PEP output

G1B10
(C)
[97.203(c)]
Page 3-10

G1B11
How does the FCC require an amateur station to be operated in all respects not covered by the Part 97 rules?
A. In conformance with the rules of the IARU
B. In conformance with amateur radio custom
C. In conformance with good engineering and good amateur practice
D. All of these answers are correct

G1B11
(C)
[97.101(a)]
Page 3-16

G1B12
Who or what determines "good engineering and good amateur practice" that apply to operation of an amateur station in all respects not covered by the Part 97 rules?
A. The FCC
B. The Control Operator
C. The IEEE
D. The ITU

G1B12
(A)
[97.101(a)]
Page 3-16

G1B13
What restrictions may the FCC place on an amateur station that is causing interference to a broadcast receiver of good engineering design?
A. Restrict the amateur station operation to times other than 8 pm to 10:30 pm local time every day, as well as on Sundays from 10:30 am to 1 pm local time
B. Restrict the amateur station from operating at times requested by the owner of the receiver
C. Restrict the amateur station to operation only during RACES drills
D. Restrict the amateur station from operating at any time

G1B13
(A)
[97.121(a)]
Page 3-12

G1C — Transmitter power regulations; HF data emission standards

G1C01
(A)
[97.313(c)(1)]
Page 3-17

G1C01
What is the maximum transmitting power an amateur station may use on 10.140 MHz?
A. 200 watts PEP output
B. 1000 watts PEP output
C. 1500 watts PEP output
D. 2000 watts PEP output

G1C02
(C)
[97.313(a),
97.313(b)]
Page 3-17

G1C02
What is the maximum transmitting power an amateur station may use on the 12 meter band?
A. 1500 PEP output, except for 200 watts PEP output in the novice portion
B. 200 watts PEP output
C. 1500 watts PEP output
D. Effective radiated power equivalent to 50 watts from a half wave dipole

G1C03
(B)
[97.313]
Page 3-17

G1C03
What is the maximum transmitting power a General class licensee may use when operating between 7025 and 7125 kHz?
A. 200 watts PEP output
B. 1500 watts PEP output
C. 1000 watts PEP output
D. 2000 watts PEP output

G1C04
(A)
[97.313]
Page 3-17

G1C04
What limitations, other than the 1500 watt PEP limit, are placed on transmitter power in the 14 MHz band?
A. Only the minimum power necessary to carry out the desired communications should be used
B. Power must be limited to 200 watts when transmitting between 14.100 MHz and 14.150 MHz
C. Power should be limited as necessary to avoid interference to another radio service on the frequency
D. Effective radiated power cannot exceed 3000 watts

G1C05
(C)
[97.313]
Page 3-17

G1C05
What is the maximum transmitting power a station with a General Class control operator may use on the 28 MHz band?
A. 100 watts PEP output
B. 1000 watts PEP output
C. 1500 watts PEP output
D. 2000 watts PEP output

G1C06
(D)
[97.313(b)]
Page 3-17

G1C06
What is the maximum transmitting power an amateur station may use on 1825 kHz?
A. 200 watts PEP output
B. 1000 watts PEP output
C. 1200 watts PEP output
D. 1500 watts PEP output

G1C07
(C)
[97.303(s)]
Page 3-17

G1C07
Which of the following is a requirement when a station is transmitting on the 60 meter band?
A. Transmissions may only use Lower Sideband (LSB)
B. Transmissions must use only CW or Data modes
C. Transmissions must not exceed an effective radiated power of 50 Watts PEP referred to a dipole antenna
D. Transmissions must not exceed an effective radiated power of 200 Watts PEP referred to a dipole antenna

G1C08
What is the maximum symbol rate permitted for RTTY emissions transmitted on frequency bands below 28 MHz?
A. 56 kilobaud
B. 19.6 kilobaud
C. 1200 baud
D. 300 baud

G1C09
What is the maximum symbol rate permitted for packet emission transmissions on the 2 meter band?
A. 300 baud
B. 1200 baud
C. 19.6 kilobaud
D. 56 kilobaud

G1C10
What is the maximum symbol rate permitted for RTTY or data emission transmissions on the 10 meter band?
A. 56 kilobaud
B. 19.6 kilobaud
C. 1200 baud
D. 300 baud

G1C11
What is the maximum symbol rate permitted for RTTY or data emission transmissions on the 6 and 2 meter bands?
A. 56 kilobaud
B. 19.6 kilobaud
C. 1200 baud
D. 300 baud

G1C12
What is the maximum authorized bandwidth for RTTY, data or multiplexed emissions using an unspecified digital code transmitted on the 6 and 2 meter bands?
A. 20 kHz
B. 50 kHz
C. The total bandwidth shall not exceed that of a single-sideband phone emission
D. The total bandwidth shall not exceed 10 times that of a CW emission

G1C13
What is the maximum bandwidth permitted by FCC rules for amateur radio stations when operating on USB frequencies in the 60-meter band?
A. 2.8 kHz
B. 5.6 kHz
C. ±2.8 kHz
D. 3 kHz

G1C08
(D)
[97.305(c),
97.307(f)(3)]
Page 3-18

G1C09
(C)
[97.305(c),
97.307(f)(5)]
Page 3-18

G1C10
(C)
[97.305(c),
97.307(f)(4)]
Page 3-18

G1C11
(B)
[97.305(c),
97.307(f)(5)]
Page 3-18

G1C12
(A)
[97.305(c),
97.307(f)(5)]
Page 3-18

G1C13
(A)
[97.303s]
Page 3-17

G1D — Volunteer Examiners and Volunteer Examiner Coordinators; temporary identification

G1D01
(C)
[97.119(f)(2)]
Page 3-5

G1D01
What is the proper way to identify when transmitting on General class frequencies if you have a CSCE for the required elements but your upgrade from Technician has not appeared in the ULS database?
A. Give your call sign followed by the words "General class"
B. No special identification is needed, since your license upgrade would already be shown in the FCC's database
C. Give your call sign followed by the words "temporary AG"
D. Give your call sign followed the abbreviation "CSCE"

G1D02
(C)
[97.509(b)(3)(i)]
Page 3-3

G1D02
What license examinations may you administer when you are an accredited VE holding a General Class operator license?
A. Novice
B. General
C. Technician
D. All elements

G1D03
(C)
[97.9(b)]
Page 3-5

G1D03
Which of the following band segments may you operate on if you are a Technician Class operator and have a CSCE for General Class privileges?
A. Only the Technician band segments until your upgrade is posted on the FCC database
B. Only on the Technician band segments until your license arrives in the mail
C. On any General Class band segment
D. On any General Class Band segment except 30 and 60 meters

G1D04
(A)
[97.509(a),
97.509(b)]
Page 3-4

G1D04
Which of the following are requirements for administering a Technician Class operator examination?
A. At Least three VEC-accredited General Class or higher VEs must be present
B. At least two VEC-accredited General Class or higher VEs must be present
C. At least two General Class or higher VEs must be present, but only one need be VEC accredited
D. At least three VEs of Technician Class or higher must be present

G1D05
(D)
[97.509(b)(3)(i)]
Page 3-3

G1D05
Which of the following is sufficient for you to be an administering VE for a Technician Class operator license examination?
A. Notification to the FCC that you want to give an examination
B. Receipt of a CSCE for General class
C. Possession of properly obtained telegraphy and written examinations
D. A FCC General class or higher license and VEC accreditation

G1D06
(A)
[97.119(f)(2)]
Page 3-5

G1D06
When must you add the special identifier "AG" after your call sign if you are a Technician Class licensee and have a CSCE for General Class operator privileges?
A. Whenever you operate using General class frequency privileges
B. Whenever you operate on any amateur frequency
C. Whenever you operate using Technician frequency privileges
D. A special identifier is not required as long as your General class license application has been filed with the FCC

G1D07
Who is responsible at a Volunteer Exam Session for determining the correctness of the answers on the exam?
A. The FCC
B. The administering VEs
C. The VEC
D. The local VE team liaison

G1D07
(B)
[97.509(h)]
Page 3-4

G1D08
What document must be issued to a person that passes an exam element?
A. FCC form 605
B. CSCE
C. CCSA
D. NCVEC form 605

G1D08
(B)
[97.509(i)]
Page 3-4

G1D09
How long is a Certificate of Successful Completion of Examination(CSCE)valid for exam element credit?
A. 30 days
B. 180 days
C. 365 days
D. For as long as your current license is valid

G1D09
(C)
[97.3(a)(15)]
Page 3-4

G1D10
What is the minimum age that one must be to qualify as an accredited Volunteer Examiner?
A. 12 years
B. 18 years
C. 21 years
D. There is no age limit

G1D10
(B)
[97.509(b)(2)]
Page 3-3

G1D11
What criteria must be met for a non U.S. citizen to be an accredited Volunteer Examiner?
A. The person must be a resident of the U.S. for a minimum of 5 years
B. The person must hold a U.S. amateur radio license of General class or above
C. The person's home citizenship must be in the ITU 2 region
D. None of these answers is correct; non U.S. citizens cannot be volunteer examiners

G1D11
(B)
[97.509(b)(3)]
Page 3-3

G1D12
Volunteer Examiners are accredited by what organization?
A. The Federal Communications Commission
B. The Universal Licensing System
C. A Volunteer Examiner Coordinator
D. The Wireless Telecommunications Bureau

G1D12
(C)
[97.509(b)(1)]
Page 3-3

G1D13
When may you participate as a VE in administering an amateur radio license examination?
A. Once you have notified the FCC that you want to give an examination
B. Once you have a Certificate of Successful Completion of Examination (CSCE) for General class
C. Once your General class license appears in the FCC's ULS database
D. Once you have been granted your General class license and received your VEC accreditation

G1D13
(D)
[97.509]
Page 3-3

G1E — Control categories; repeater regulations; harmful interference; third party rules; ITU regions

G1E01
(A)
[97.115(b)(2)]
Page 3-13

G1E01
Which of the following would disqualify a third party from participating in stating a message over an amateur station?
A. The third party is a person previously licensed in the amateur service whose license had been revoked
B. The third party is not a U.S. citizen
C. The third party is a licensed amateur
D. The third party is speaking in a language other than English, French, or Spanish

G1E02
(D)
[97.205(a)]
Page 3-15

G1E02
When may a 10 meter repeater retransmit the 2 meter signal from a station having a Technician Class control operator?
A. Under no circumstances
B. Only if the station on 10 meters is operating under a Special Temporary Authorization allowing such retransmission
C. Only during an FCC-declared General state of communications emergency
D. Only if the 10 meter control operator holds at least a General class license

G1E03
(A)
[97.3(a)(39)]
Page 3-15

G1E03
What kind of amateur station simultaneously retransmits the signals of other stations on another channel?
A. Repeater Station
B. Beacon Station
C. Telecommand Station
D. Relay Station

G1E04
(D)
[97.13(b),
97.311(b),
97.303]
Page 3-11

G1E04
Which of the following conditions require an amateur radio station to take specific steps to avoid harmful interference to other users or facilities?
A. When operating within one mile of an FCC Monitoring Station
B. When using a band where the amateur service is secondary
C. When a station is transmitting spread spectrum emissions
D. All of these answers are correct

G1E05
(C)
[97.115(a)(2),
97.117]
Page 3-13

G1E05
What types of messages for a third party in another country may be transmitted by an amateur station?
A. Any message, as long as the amateur operator is not paid
B. Only messages for other licensed amateurs
C. Only messages relating to amateur radio or remarks of a personal character, or messages relating to emergencies or disaster relief
D. No messages may be transmitted to foreign countries for third parties

G1E06
(A)
[97.205(c)]
Page 3-12

G1E06
Which of the following applies in the event of interference between a coordinated repeater and an uncoordinated repeater?
A. The licensee of the non-coordinated repeater has primary responsibility to resolve the interference
B. The licensee of the coordinated repeater has primary responsibility to resolve the interference
C. Both repeater licensees share equal responsibility to resolve the interference
D. The frequency coordinator bears primary responsibility to resolve the interference

G1E07

With which of the following is third-party traffic prohibited, except for messages directly involving emergencies or disaster relief communications?

A. Countries in ITU Region 2
B. Countries in ITU Region 1
C. Any country other than the United States, unless there is a third-party agreement in effect with that country
D. Any country which is not a member of the Internal Amateur Radio Union (IARU)

G1E07
(C)
[97.115(a)(2)]
Page 3-14

G1E08

Which of the following is a requirement for a non-licensed person to communicate with a foreign amateur radio station from a US amateur station at which a licensed control operator is present?

A. Information must be exchanged in English
B. The foreign amateur station must be in a country with which the United States has a third party agreement
C. The control operator must have at least a General class license
D. All of these answers are correct

G1E08
(B)
[97.115(a)(b)]
Page 3-14

G1E09

What language must you use when identifying your station if you are using a language other than English in making a contact?

A. The language being used for the contact
B. Any language if the US has a third party agreement with that country
C. English
D. Any language of a country that is a member of the ITU

G1E09
(C)
[97.119(b)(2)]
Page 3-5

G1E10

Which of the following is a permissible third party communication during routine amateur radio operations?

A. Permitting an unlicensed person to speak to a licensed amateur anywhere in the world
B. Sending a business message for another person, as long it is for a non-profit organization
C. Sending a business message for another person, as long as the control operator has no pecuniary interest in the message
D. Sending a message to a third party through a foreign station, as long as that person is a licensed amateur radio operator

G1E10
(D)
[97.115(a)(2)]
Page 3-13

SUBELEMENT G2
Operating Procedures
6 exam questions — 6 groups

G2A — Phone operating procedures; USB/LSB utilization conventions; procedural signals; breaking into a QSO in progress; VOX operation

G2A01
(A)
Page 2-8

G2A01
Which sideband is most commonly used for phone communications on the bands above 20 meters?
A. Upper Sideband
B. Lower Sideband
C. Vestigial Sideband
D. Double Sideband

G2A02
(B)
Page 2-8

G2A02
Which sideband is commonly used on the 160, 75, and 40 meter bands?
A. Upper Sideband
B. Lower Sideband
C. Vestigial Sideband
D. Double Sideband

G2A03
(A)
Page 2-8

G2A03
Which sideband is commonly used in the VHF and UHF bands?
A. Upper Sideband
B. Lower Sideband
C. Vestigial Sideband
D. Double Sideband

G2A04
(A)
Page 2-8

G2A04
Which mode is most commonly used for voice communications on the 17 and 12 meter bands?
A. Upper Sideband
B. Lower Sideband
C. Vestigial Sideband
D. Double Sideband

G2A05
(C)
Page 2-7

G2A05
Which mode of voice communication is most commonly used on the High Frequency Amateur bands?
A. FM
B. AM
C. SSB
D. PM

G2A06
(B)
Page 2-7

G2A06
Which of the following is an advantage when using single sideband as compared to other voice modes on the HF amateur bands?
A. Very high fidelity voice modulation
B. Less bandwidth used and high power efficiency
C. Ease of tuning on receive
D. Less subject to static crashes (atmospherics)

G2A07

Which of the following statements is true of the single sideband (SSB) voice mode?

A. Only one sideband and the carrier are transmitted; the other sideband is suppressed
B. Only one sideband is transmitted; the other sideband and carrier are suppressed
C. SSB voice transmissions have higher average power than any other mode
D. SSB is the only mode that is authorized on the 160, 75 and 40 meter amateur bands

G2A08

Which of the following statements is true of single sideband (SSB) voice mode?

A. It is a form of amplitude modulation in which one sideband and the carrier are suppressed
B. It is a form of frequency modulation in which higher frequencies are emphasized
C. It reproduces upper frequencies more efficiently than lower frequencies
D. It is the only voice mode authorized on the HF bands between 14 and 30 MHz

G2A09

Why do most amateur stations use lower sideband on the 160, 75 and 40 meter bands?

A. The lower sideband is more efficient at these frequency bands
B. The lower sideband is the only sideband legal on these frequency bands
C. Because it is fully compatible with an AM detector
D. Current amateur practice is to use lower sideband on these frequency bands

G2A10

Which of the following statements is true of VOX operation?

A. The received signal is more natural sounding
B. VOX allows "hands free" operation
C. Frequency spectrum is conserved
D. The duty cycle of the transmitter is reduced

G2A11

Which of the following user adjustable controls are usually associated with VOX circuitry?

A. Anti-VOX
B. VOX Delay
C. VOX Sensitivity
D. All of these choices are correct

G2A12

What is the recommended way to break into a conversation when using phone?

A. Say "QRZ" several times followed by your call sign
B. Say your call sign during a break between transmissions from the other stations
C. Say "Break" "Break" "Break" and wait for a response
D. Say "CQ" followed by the call sign of either station

G2A13

What does the expression "CQ DX" usually indicate?

A. A general call for any station
B. The caller is listening for a station in Germany
C. The caller is looking for any station outside their own country
D. This is a form of distress call

G2A07
(B)
Page 2-7

G2A08
(A)
Page 2-7

G2A09
(D)
Page 2-8

G2A10
(B)
Page 2-11

G2A11
(D)
Page 2-11

G2A12
(B)
Page 2-2

G2A13
(C)
Page 2-2

G2B — Operating courtesy; band plans

G2B01
(C)
Page 2-3

G2B01
What action should be taken if the frequency on which a net normally meets is in use just before the net begins?
A. Reduce your output power and start the net as usual
B. Increase your power output so that net participants will be able to hear you
C. Ask the stations if the net may use the frequency, or move the net to a nearby clear frequency if necessary
D. Cancel the net for that day

G2B02
(A)
Page 2-3

G2B02
What should be done if a net is about to begin on a frequency you and another station are using?
A. Move to a different frequency as a courtesy to the net
B. Tell the net that they must to move to another frequency
C. Reduce power to avoid interfering with the net
D. Pause between transmissions to give the net a chance to change frequency

G2B03
(C)
Page 2-6

G2B03
What should you do if you notice increasing interference from other activity on a frequency you are using?
A. Tell the interfering stations to change frequency since you were there first
B. Report the interference to your local Amateur Auxiliary Coordinator
C. Move your contact to another frequency
D. Turn on your amplifier

G2B04
(B)
Page 2-3

G2B04
What minimum frequency separation between CW signals should be allowed to minimize interference?
A. 5 to 50 Hz
B. 150 to 500 Hz
C. 1 to 3 kHz
D. 3 to 6 kHz

G2B05
(B)
Page 2-3

G2B05
What minimum frequency separation between SSB signals should be allowed to minimize interference?
A. Between 150 and 500 Hz
B. Approximately 3 kHz
C. Approximately 6 kHz
D. Approximately 10 kHz

G2B06
(B)
Page 2-3

G2B06
What minimum frequency separation between 170 Hz shift RTTY signals should be allowed to minimize interference?
A. 60 Hz
B. 250 to 500 Hz
C. Approximately 3 kHz
D. 170 Hz

G2B07
(A)
Page 2-4

G2B07
What is a band plan?
A. A voluntary guideline for band use beyond the divisions established by the FCC
B. A guideline from the FCC for making amateur frequency band allocations
C. A guideline from the ITU for making amateur frequency band allocations
D. A plan devised by a club to best use a frequency band during a contest

G2B08
What is the "DX window" in a voluntary band plan?
A. A portion of the band that should not be used for contacts between stations within the 48 contiguous United States
B. An FCC rule that prohibits contacts between stations within the United States and possessions on that band segment
C. An FCC rule that allows only digital contacts in that portion of the band
D. A portion of the band that has been set aside for digital contacts only

G2B08
(A)
Page 2-4

G2B09
What should you do to comply with good amateur practice when choosing a frequency for Slow-Scan TV (SSTV) operation?
A. Transmit only on lower sideband
B. Transmit your callsign as an SSTV image for 1 minute to ensure a clear frequency
C. Select a frequency in the portion of the band set aside for digital operation
D. Follow generally accepted band plans for SSTV operation

G2B09
(D)
Page 2-4

G2B10
What should you do to comply with good amateur practice when choosing a frequency for radio-teletype (RTTY) operation?
A. Call CQ in Morse code before attempting to establish a contact in RTTY
B. Select a frequency in the upper end of the phone band
C. Select a frequency in the lower end of the phone band
D. Follow generally accepted band plans for RTTY operation

G2B10
(D)
Page 2-4

G2B11
What should you do to comply with good amateur practice when choosing a frequency for HF PSK operation?
A. Call CQ in Morse code before attempting to establish a contact in PSK
B. Select a frequency in the upper end of the phone band
C. Select a frequency in the lower end of the phone band
D. Follow generally accepted band plans for PSK operation

G2B11
(D)
Page 2-4

G2B12
What is a practical way to avoid harmful interference when selecting a frequency to call CQ using phone?
A. Ask if the frequency is in use, say your callsign, and listen for a response
B. Keep your CQ to less than 2 minutes in length to avoid interference to contacts that may be in progress
C. Listen for 2 minutes before calling CQ to avoid interference to contacts that may be in progress
D. Call CQ at low power first and if there is no indication of interference, increase power as necessary

G2B12
(A)
Page 2-3

G2B13
What is a practical way to avoid harmful interference when calling CQ using Morse code or CW?
A. Send the letter "V" 12 times and then listen for a response
B. Keep your CQ to less than 2 minutes in length to avoid interference with contacts already in progress
C. Send "QRL? de" followed by your callsign and listen for a response
D. Call CQ at low power first; if there is no indication of interference then increase power as necessary

G2B13
(C)
Page 2-3

G2C — Emergencies, including drills and emergency communications

G2C01
(C)
[97.403]
Page 2-19

G2C01
When normal communications systems are not available, what means may an amateur station use to provide essential communications when there is an immediate threat to the safety of human life or the protection of property?
A. Only transmissions sent on internationally recognized emergency channels
B. Any means, but only to RACES recognized emergency stations
C. Any means of radiocommunication at its disposal
D. Only those means of radiocommunication for which the station is licensed

G2C02
(A)
[97.407(a)]
Page 2-22

G2C02
Who may be the control operator of an amateur station transmitting in RACES to assist relief operations during a disaster?
A. Only a person holding an FCC issued amateur operator license
B. Only a RACES net control operator
C. Only official emergency stations may transmit during a disaster
D. Any control operator when normal communication systems are operational

G2C03
(D)
[97.407(b)]
Page 2-22

G2C03
When may the FCC restrict normal frequency operations of amateur stations participating in RACES?
A. When they declare a temporary state of communication emergency
B. When they seize your equipment for use in disaster communications
C. Only when all amateur stations are instructed to stop transmitting
D. When the President's War Emergency Powers have been invoked

G2C04
(C)
[97.405(b)]
Page 2-21

G2C04
When is an amateur station prevented from using any means at its disposal to assist another station in distress?
A. Only when transmitting in RACES
B. Only when authorized by the FCC rule
C. Never
D. Only on authorized HF frequencies

G2C05
(B)
[97.403]
Page 2-22

G2C05
What type of transmission would a control operator be making when transmitting out of the amateur band without station identification during a life threatening emergency?
A. A prohibited transmission
B. An unidentified transmission
C. A third party communication
D. An auxiliary transmission

G2C06

G2C06 — This question has been withdrawn.

G2C07
(B)
Page 2-22

G2C07
What is the first thing you should do if you are communicating with another amateur station and hear a station in distress break in?
A. Continue your communication because you were on frequency first
B. Acknowledge the station in distress and determine what assistance may be needed
C. Change to a different frequency
D. Immediately cease all transmissions

G2C08
When are you prohibited from helping a station in distress?
A. When that station is not transmitting on amateur frequencies
B. When the station in distress offers no call sign
C. You are never prohibited from helping any station in distress
D. When the station is not another amateur station

G2C08
(C)
[97.405(b)]
Page 2-21

G2C09
What type of transmissions may an amateur station make during a disaster?
A. Only transmissions when RACES net is activated
B. Transmissions necessary to meet essential communications needs and to facilitate relief actions
C. Only transmissions from an official emergency station
D. Only one-way communications

G2C09
(B)
[97.111(a)(2)]
Page 2-19

G2C10
Which emission mode must be used to obtain assistance during a disaster?
A. Only SSB
B. Only SSB and CW
C. Any mode
D. Only CW

G2C10
(C)
Page 2-20

G2C11
What information should be given to a station answering a distress transmission?
A. The ITU region and grid square locator of the emergency
B. The location and nature of the emergency
C. The time that the emergency occurred and the local weather
D. The name of the local emergency coordinator

G2C11
(B)
Page 2-22

G2C12
What frequency should be used to send a distress call?
A. Whatever frequency has the best chance of communicating the distress message
B. 3873 kHz at night or 7285 kHz during the day
C. Only frequencies that are within your operating privileges
D. Only frequencies used by police, fire or emergency medical services

G2C12
(A)
Page 2-22

G2D — Amateur auxiliary; minimizing Interference; HF operations

G2D01
What is the Amateur Auxiliary to the FCC?
A. Amateur volunteers who are formally enlisted to monitor the airwaves for rules violations
B. Amateur volunteers who conduct amateur licensing examinations
C. Amateur volunteers who conduct frequency coordination for amateur VHF repeaters
D. Amateur volunteers who use their station equipment to help civil defense organizations in times of emergency

G2D01
(A)
Page 3-2

G2D02
What are the objectives of the Amateur Auxiliary?
A. To conduct efficient and orderly amateur licensing examinations
B. To encourage amateur self-regulation and compliance with the rules
C. To coordinate repeaters for efficient and orderly spectrum usage
D. To provide emergency and public safety communications

G2D02
(B)
Page 3-2

G2D03
(B)
Page 3-2

G2D03
What skills learned during "Fox Hunts" are of help to the Amateur Auxiliary?
A. Identification of out of band operation
B. Direction-finding skills used to locate stations violating FCC Rules
C. Identification of different call signs
D. Hunters have an opportunity to transmit on non-amateur frequencies

G2D04
(B)
Page 6-8

G2D04
What is an azimuthal projection map?
A. A world map projection centered on the North Pole
B. A world map projection centered on a particular location
C. A world map that shows the angle at which an amateur satellite crosses the equator
D. A world map that shows the number of degrees longitude that an amateur satellite appears to move westward at the equator with each orbit

G2D05
(A)
Page 6-8

G2D05
What is the most useful type of map to use when orienting a directional HF antenna toward a distant station?
A. Azimuthal projection
B. Mercator projection
C. Polar projection
D. Stereographic projection

G2D06
(C)
Page 7-5

G2D06
How is a directional antenna pointed when making a "long-path" contact with another station?
A. Toward the rising sun
B. Along the Gray Line
C. 180 degrees from its short-path heading
D. Toward the North

G2D07

Withdrawn Question

G2D08
(D)
Page 2-4, 3-16

G2D08
Why do many amateurs keep a log even though the FCC doesn't require it?
A. The ITU requires a log of all international contacts
B. The ITU requires a log of all international third party traffic
C. The log provides evidence of operation needed to renew a license without retest
D. To help with a reply if the FCC requests information on who was control operator of your station at a given date and time

G2D09
(D)
Page 2-4, 3-16

G2D09
What information is traditionally contained in a station log?
A. Date and time of contact
B. Band and/or frequency of the contact
C. Call sign of station contacted and the signal report given
D. All of these choices are correct

G2D10

What is QRP operation?

A. Remote Piloted Model control
B. Low power transmit operation, typically about 5 watts
C. Transmission using Quick Response Protocol
D. Traffic Relay Procedure net operation

G2D11

Which HF antenna would be the best to use for minimizing interference?

A. A bi-directional antenna
B. An isotropic antenna
C. A unidirectional antenna
D. An omnidirectional antenna

G2D12

Which of the following is required by the FCC rules when operating in the 60 meter band?

A. If you are using other than a dipole antenna, you must keep a record of the gain of your antenna
B. You must keep a log of the date, time, frequency, power level and stations worked
C. You must keep a log of all third party traffic
D. You must keep a log of the manufacturer of your equipment and the antenna used

G2E — Digital operating: procedures, procedural signals and common abbreviations

G2E01

Which mode should be selected when using a SSB transmitter with an Audio Frequency Shift Keying (AFSK) RTTY signal?

A. USB
B. DSB
C. CW
D. LSB

G2E02

How many data bits are sent in a single PSK31 character?

A. The number varies
B. 5
C. 7
D. 8

G2E03

What part of a data packet contains the routing and handling information?

A. Directory
B. Preamble
C. Header
D. Footer

G2E04

Which of the following 20 meter band segments is most often used for most data transmissions?

A. 14.000 - 14.050 MHz
B. 14.070 - 14.100 MHz
C. 14.150 - 14.225 MHz
D. 14.275 - 14.350 MHz

G2D10
(B)
Page 3-17

G2D11
(C)
Page 6-7

G2D12
(A)
[97.303(s)]
Page 3-15

G2E01
(D)
Page 5-5

G2E02
(A)
Page 2-16, 5-5

G2E03
(C)
Page 2-16, 5-6

G2E04
(B)
Page 2-14

G2E05
(C)
Page 2-15,
5-4

G2E05
Which of the following describes Baudot RTTY?
A. 7-bit code, with start, stop and parity bits
B. Utilizes error detection and correction
C. 5-bit code, with additional start and stop bits
D. Two major operating modes are SELCAL and LISTEN

G2E06
(B)
Page 2-15,
5-5

G2E06
What is the most common frequency shift for RTTY emissions in the amateur HF bands?
A. 85 Hz
B. 170 Hz
C. 425 Hz
D. 850 Hz

G2E07
(B)
Page 2-15

G2E07
What does the abbreviation "RTTY" stand for?
A. "Returning To You", meaning "your turn to transmit"
B. Radio-Teletype
C. A general call to all digital stations
D. Repeater Transmission Type

G2E08
(A)
Page 2-14

G2E08
What segment of the 80 meter band is most commonly used for data transmissions?
A. 3570 – 3600 kHz
B. 3500 – 3525 kHz
C. 3700 – 3750 kHz
D. 3775 – 3825 kHz

G2E09
(D)
Page 2-14

G2E09
Where are PSK signals generally found on the 20 meter band?
A. In the low end of the phone band
B. In the high end of the phone band
C. In the weak signal portion of the band
D. Around 14.070 MHz

G2E10
(D)
Page 2-16

G2E10
What is a major advantage of MFSK16 compared to other digital modes?
A. It is much higher speed than RTTY
B. It is much narrower bandwidth than most digital modes
C. It has built-in error correction
D. It offers good performance in weak signal environment without error correction

G2E11
(B)
Page 2-16

G2E11
What does the abbreviation "MFSK" stand for?
A. Manual Frequency Shift Keying
B. Multi (or Multiple) Frequency Shift Keying
C. Manual Frequency Sideband Keying
D. Multi (or Multiple) Frequency Sideband Keying

G2F — CW operating procedures and procedural signals, Q signals and common abbreviations; full break in

G2F01
Which of the following describes full break-in telegraphy (QSK)?
A. Breaking stations send the Morse code prosign BK
B. Automatic keyers are used to send Morse code instead of hand keys
C. An operator must activate a manual send/receive switch before and after every transmission
D. Incoming signals are received between transmitted code character elements

G2F01
(D)
Page 2-13

G2F02
What should you do if a CW station sends "QRS" when using Morse code?
A. Send slower
B. Change frequency
C. Increase your power
D. Repeat everything twice.

G2F02
(A)
Page 2-13

G2F03
What does it mean when a CW operator sends "KN" at the end of a transmission?
A. Listening for novice stations
B. Operating full break-in
C. Listening only for a specific station or stations
D. Closing station now

G2F03
(C)
Page 2-13

G2F04
What does it mean when a CW operator sends "CL" at the end of a transmission?
A. Keep frequency clear
B. Operating full break-in
C. Listening only for a specific station or stations
D. Closing station

G2F04
(D)
Page 2-13

G2F05
What is the best speed to use answering a CQ in Morse Code?
A. The speed at which you are most comfortable copying
B. The speed at which the CQ was sent
C. A slow speed until contact is established
D. 5 wpm, as all operators licensed to operate CW can copy this speed

G2F05
(B)
Page 2-13

G2F06
What does the term "zero beat" mean in CW operation?
A. Matching the speed of the transmitting station
B. Operating split to avoid interference on frequency
C. Sending without error
D. Matching the frequency of the transmitting station

G2F06
(D)
Page 2-13

G2F07
When sending CW, what does a "C" mean when added to the RST report?
A. Chirpy or unstable signal
B. Report was read from S meter reading rather than estimated
C. 100 percent copy
D. Key clicks

G2F07
(A)
Page 2-12

G2F08
(C)
Page 2-13

G2F08
What prosign is sent using CW to indicate the end of a formal message?
A. SK
B. BK
C. AR
D. KN

G2F09
(C)
Page 2-13

G2F09
What does the Q signal "QSL" mean when operating CW?
A. Send slower
B. We have already confirmed by card
C. I acknowledge receipt
D. We have worked before

G2F10
(B)
Page 2-13

G2F10
What does the Q signal "QRQ" mean when operating CW?
A. Slow down
B. Send faster
C. Zero beat my signal
D. Quitting operation

G2F11
(D)
Page 2-13

G2F11
What does the Q signal "QRV" mean when operating CW?
A. You are sending too fast
B. There is interference on the frequency
C. I am quitting for the day
D. I am ready to receive messages

SUBELEMENT G3
RADIO WAVE PROPAGATION
3 exam questions — 3 groups

G3A — Sunspots and solar radiation; ionospheric disturbances; propagation forecasting and indices

G3A01
What can be done at an amateur station to continue communications during a sudden ionospheric disturbance?
A. Try a higher frequency
B. Try the other sideband
C. Try a different antenna polarization
D. Try a different frequency shift

G3A01
(A)
Page 7-10

G3A02
What effect does a Sudden Ionospheric Disturbance (SID) have on the daytime ionospheric propagation of HF radio waves?
A. It disrupts higher-latitude paths more than lower-latitude paths
B. It disrupts signals on lower frequencies more than those on higher frequencies
C. It disrupts communications via satellite more than direct communications
D. None, because only areas on the night side of the Earth are affected

G3A02
(B)
Page 7-10

G3A03
How long does it take the increased ultraviolet and X-ray radiation from solar flares to affect radio-wave propagation on the Earth?
A. 28 days
B. Several hours depending on the position of the Earth in its orbit
C. Approximately 8 minutes
D. 20 to 40 hours after the radiation reaches the Earth

G3A03
(C)
Page 7-9

G3A04
What is measured by the solar flux index?
A. The density of the sun's magnetic field
B. The radio energy emitted by the sun
C. The number of sunspots on the side of the sun facing the Earth
D. A measure of the tilt of the Earth's ionosphere on the side toward the sun

G3A04
(B)
Page 7-7

G3A05
What is the solar-flux index?
A. A measure of the highest frequency that is useful for ionospheric propagation between two points on the Earth
B. A count of sunspots which is adjusted for solar emissions
C. Another name for the American sunspot number
D. A measure of solar activity at 10.7 cm

G3A05
(D)
Page 7-7

G3A06
What is a geomagnetic disturbance?
A. A sudden drop in the solar-flux index
B. A shifting of the Earth's magnetic pole
C. Ripples in the ionosphere
D. A significant change in the Earth's magnetic field over a short period of time

G3A06
(D)
Page 7-10

G3A07
(A)
Page 7-10

G3A07
Which latitudes have propagation paths that are more sensitive to geomagnetic disturbances?
A. Those greater than 45 degrees North or South latitude
B. Those between 5 and 45 degrees North or South latitude
C. Those at or very near to the equator
D. All paths are affected equally

G3A08
(B)
Page 7-10

G3A08
What can be an effect of a geomagnetic storm on radio-wave propagation?
A. Improved high-latitude HF propagation
B. Degraded high-latitude HF propagation
C. Improved ground-wave propagation
D. Improved chances of UHF ducting

G3A09
(C)
Page 7-6

G3A09
What is the effect on radio communications when sunspot numbers are high?
A. High-frequency radio signals become weak and distorted
B. Frequencies above 300 MHz become usable for long-distance communication
C. Long-distance communication in the upper HF and lower VHF range is enhanced
D. Long-distance communication in the upper HF and lower VHF range is diminished

G3A10
(A)
Page 7-6

G3A10
What is the sunspot number?
A. A measure of solar activity based on counting sunspots and sunspot groups
B. A 3 digit identifier which is used to track individual sunspots
C. A measure of the radio flux from the sun measured at 10.7 cm
D. A measure of the sunspot count based on radio flux measurements

G3A11
(D)
Page 7-6

G3A11
How long is the typical sunspot cycle?
A. Approximately 8 minutes
B. Between 20 and 40 hours
C. Approximately 28 days
D. Approximately 11 years

G3A12
(B)
Page 7-7

G3A12
What is the K-index?
A. An index of the relative position of sunspots on the surface of the sun
B. A measure of the short term stability of the Earth's magnetic field
C. A measure of the stability of the sun's magnetic field
D. An index of solar radio flux measured at Boulder, Colorado

G3A13
(C)
Page 7-8

G3A13
What is the A-index?
A. An index of the relative position of sunspots on the surface of the sun
B. The amount of polarization of the sun's electric field
C. An indicator of the long term stability of the Earth's geomagnetic field
D. An index of solar radio flux measured at Boulder, Colorado

G3A14
(B)
Page 7-10

G3A14
How are radio communications usually affected by the charged particles that reach the Earth from solar coronal holes?
A. HF communications are improved
B. HF communications are disturbed
C. VHF/UHF ducting is improved
D. VHF/UHF ducting is disturbed

G3A15

How long does it take charged particles from Coronal Mass Ejections to affect radio-wave propagation on the Earth?

A. 28 days
B. 14 days
C. The effect is instantaneous
D. 20 to 40 hours

G3A15
(D)
Page 7-10

G3A16

What is a possible benefit to radio communications resulting from periods of high geomagnetic activity?

A. Aurora that can reflect VHF signals
B. Higher signal strength for HF signals passing through the polar regions
C. Improved HF long path propagation
D. Reduced long delayed echoes

G3A16
(A)
Page 7-10

G3A17

At what point in the solar cycle does the 20 meter band usually support worldwide propagation during daylight hours?

A. At the summer solstice
B. Only at the maximum point of the solar cycle
C. Only at the minimum point of the solar cycle
D. At any point in the solar cycle

G3A17
(D)
Page 7-7

G3A18

If the HF radio-wave propagation (skip) is generally good on the 24-MHz and 28-MHz bands for several days, when might you expect a similar condition to occur?

A. 7 days later
B. 14 days later
C. 28 days later
D. 90 days later

G3A18
(C)
Page 7-7

G3A19

Which frequencies are least reliable for long distance communications during periods of low solar activity?

A. Frequencies below 3.5 MHz
B. Frequencies near 3.5 MHz
C. Frequencies at or above 10 MHz
D. Frequencies above 20 MHz

G3A19
(D)
Page 7-7

G3B — Maximum Usable Frequency; Lowest Usable Frequency; propagation "hops"

G3B01

Which band should offer the best chance for a successful contact if the maximum usable frequency (MUF) between the two stations is 22 MHz?

A. 10 meters
B. 15 meters
C. 20 meters
D. 40 meters

G3B01
(B)
Page 7-8

G3B02
(C)
Page 7-8

G3B02
Which band should offer the best chance for a successful contact if the maximum usable frequency (MUF) between the two stations is 16 MHz?
A. 80 meters
B. 40 meters
C. 20 meters
D. 2 meters

G3B03
(A)
Page 7-8

G3B03
Which of the following guidelines should be selected for lowest attenuation when transmitting on HF?
A. Select a frequency just below the MUF
B. Select a frequency just above the LUF
C. Select a frequency just below the critical frequency
D. Select a frequency just above the critical frequency

G3B04
(A)
Page 7-8

G3B04
What is a reliable way to determine if the maximum usable frequency (MUF) is high enough to support 28-MHz propagation between your station and Western Europe?
A. Listen for signals on a 28 MHz international beacon
B. Send a series of dots on the 28 MHz band and listen for echoes from your signal
C. Check the strength of TV signals from Western Europe
D. Listen to WWV propagation signals on the 28 MHz band

G3B05
(A)
Page 7-8

G3B05
What usually happens to radio waves with frequencies below the maximum usable frequency (MUF) when they are sent into the ionosphere?
A. They are bent back to the Earth
B. They pass through the ionosphere
C. They are completely absorbed by the ionosphere
D. They are bent and trapped in the ionosphere to circle the Earth

G3B06
(C)
Page 7-8

G3B06
What usually happens to radio waves with frequencies below the lowest usable frequency (LUF)?
A. They are bent back to the Earth
B. They pass through the ionosphere
C. They are completely absorbed by the ionosphere
D. They are bent and trapped in the ionosphere to circle the Earth

G3B07
(A)
Page 7-8

G3B07
What does LUF stand for?
A. The Lowest Usable Frequency for communications between two points
B. The Longest Universal Function for communications between two points
C. The Lowest Usable Frequency during a 24 hour period
D. The Longest Universal Function during a 24 hour period

G3B08
(B)
Page 7-8

G3B08
What does MUF stand for?
A. The Minimum Usable Frequency for communications between two points
B. The Maximum Usable Frequency for communications between two points
C. The Minimum Usable Frequency during a 24 hour period
D. The Maximum Usable Frequency during a 24 hour period

G3B09

What is the maximum distance along the Earth's surface that is normally covered in one hop using the F2 region?

A. 180 miles
B. 1,200 miles
C. 2,500 miles
D. 12,000 miles

G3B09
(C)
Page 7-4

G3B10

What is the maximum distance along the Earth's surface that is normally covered in one hop using the E region?

A. 180 miles
B. 1,200 miles
C. 2,500 miles
D. 12,000 miles

G3B10
(B)
Page 7-4

G3B11

What happens to HF propagation when the lowest usable frequency (LUF) exceeds the maximum usable frequency (MUF)?

A. No HF radio frequency will support communications over the path
B. HF communications over the path are enhanced at the frequency where the LUF and MUF are the same
C. Double hop propagation along the path is more common
D. Propagation over the path on all HF frequencies is enhanced

G3B11
(A)
Page 7-8

G3B12

What factors affect the maximum usable frequency (MUF)?

A. Path distance and location
B. Time of day and season
C. Solar radiation and ionospheric disturbance
D. All of these choices are correct

G3B12
(D)
Page 7-8

G3B13

How might a sky-wave signal sound if it arrives at your receiver by both short path and long path propagation?

A. Periodic fading approximately every 10 seconds
B. Signal strength increased by 3 dB
C. The signal will be cancelled causing severe attenuation
D. A well-defined echo can be heard

G3B13
(D)
Page 7-5

G3B14

Which of the following is a good indicator of the possibility of sky-wave propagation on the 6 meter band?

A. Short hop sky-wave propagation on the 10 meter band
B. Long hop sky-wave propagation on the 10 meter band
C. Severe attenuation of signals on the 10 meter band
D. Long delayed echoes on the 10 meter band

G3B14
(A)
Page 7-5

G3C — Ionospheric layers; critical angle and frequency; HF scatter; Near Vertical Incidence Sky waves

G3C01
(A)
Page 7-1

G3C01
Which of the following ionospheric layers is closest to the surface of the Earth?
A.   The D layer
B.   The E layer
C.   The F1 layer
D.   The F2 layer

G3C02
(A)
Page 7-3

G3C02
When can the F2 region be expected to reach its maximum height at your location?
A.   At noon during the summer
B.   At midnight during the summer
C.   At dusk in the spring and fall
D.   At noon during the winter

G3C03
(C)
Page 7-4

G3C03
Why is the F2 region mainly responsible for the longest distance radio wave propagation?
A.   Because it is the densest ionospheric layer
B.   Because it does not absorb radio waves as much as other ionospheric regions
C.   Because it is the highest ionospheric region
D.   All of these choices are correct

G3C04
(D)
Page 7-3

G3C04
What does the term "critical angle" mean as used in radio wave propagation?
A.   The long path azimuth of a distant station
B.   The short path azimuth of a distant station
C.   The lowest takeoff angle that will return a radio wave to the Earth under specific ionospheric conditions
D.   The highest takeoff angle that will return a radio wave to the Earth under specific ionospheric conditions

G3C05
(C)
Page 7-4

G3C05
Why is long distance communication on the 40, 60, 80 and 160 meter bands more difficult during the day?
A.   The F layer absorbs these frequencies during daylight hours
B.   The F layer is unstable during daylight hours
C.   The D layer absorbs these frequencies during daylight hours
D.   The E layer is unstable during daylight hours

G3C06
(B)
Page 7-10

G3C06
What is a characteristic of HF scatter signals?
A.   They have high intelligibility
B.   They have a wavering sound
C.   They have very large swings in signal strength
D.   All of these choices are correct

G3C07
(D)
Page 7-10

G3C07
What makes HF scatter signals often sound distorted?
A.   The ionospheric layer involved is unstable
B.   Ground waves are absorbing much of the signal
C.   The E-region is not present
D.   Energy is scattered into the skip zone through several radio wave paths

G3C08

Why are HF scatter signals in the skip zone usually weak?

A. Only a small part of the signal energy is scattered into the skip zone
B. Signals are scattered from the troposphere which is not a good reflector
C. Propagation is through ground waves which absorb most of the signal energy
D. Propagation is through ducts in F region which absorb most of the energy

G3C08
(A)
Page 7-10

G3C09

What type of radio wave propagation allows a signal to be detected at a distance too far for ground wave propagation but too near for normal sky wave propagation?

A. Ground wave
B. Scatter
C. Sporadic-E skip
D. Short-path skip

G3C09
(B)
Page 7-10

G3C10

Which of the following might be an indication that signals heard on the HF bands are being received via scatter propagation?

A. The communication is during a sunspot maximum
B. The communication is during a sudden ionospheric disturbance
C. The signal is heard on a frequency below the maximum usable frequency
D. The signal is heard on a frequency above the maximum usable frequency

G3C10
(D)
Page 7-10

G3C11

Which of the following is true about ionospheric absorption near the maximum usable frequency (MUF)?

A. Absorption will be minimum
B. Absorption is greater for vertically polarized waves
C. Absorption approaches maximum
D. Absorption is greater for horizontally polarized waves

G3C11
(A)
Page 7-8

G3C12

Which ionospheric layer is the most absorbent of long skip signals during daylight hours on frequencies below 10 MHz?

A. The F2 layer
B. The F1 layer
C. The E layer
D. The D layer

G3C12
(D)
Page 7-4

G3C13

What is Near Vertical Incidence Sky-wave (NVIS) propagation?
A. Propagation near the MUF
B. Short distance HF propagation using high elevation angles
C. Long path HF propagation at sunrise and sunset
D. Double hop propagation near the LUF

G3C13
(B)
Page 7-12

G3C14

Which of the following antennas will be most effective for skip communications on 40 meters during the day?
A. A vertical antenna
B. A horizontal dipole placed between ⅛ and ¼ wavelength above the ground
C. A left-hand circularly polarized antenna
D. A right-hand circularly polarized antenna

G3C14
(B)
Page 7-12

SUBELEMENT G4
Amateur Radio Practices
5 exam questions — 5 groups

G4A — Two-tone Test; amplifier tuning and neutralization; DSP

G4A01
(B)
Page 5-20

G4A01
Which of the following is one use for a DSP in an amateur station?
A. To provide adequate grounding
B. To remove noise from received signals
C. To increase antenna gain
D. To increase antenna bandwidth

G4A02
(B)
Page 5-14

G4A02
Which of the following instruments may be used to measure the output of a single-sideband transmitter when performing a two-tone test of amplitude linearity?
A. An audio distortion analyzer
B. An oscilloscope
C. A directional wattmeter
D. A high impedance audio voltmeter

G4A03
(D)
Page 5-20

G4A03
Which of the following is needed for a DSP IF filter?
A. An Analog to Digital Converter
B. Digital to Analog Converter
C. A Digital Processor Chip
D. All of the these answers are correct

G4A04
(A)
Page 5-20

G4A04
Which of the following is an advantage of a receiver IF filter created with a DSP as compared to an analog filter?
A. A wide range of filter bandwidths and shapes can be created
B. Fewer digital components are required
C. Mixing products are greatly reduced
D. The DSP filter is much more effective at VHF frequencies

G4A05
(B)
Page 5-20

G4A05
How is DSP filtering accomplished?
A. By using direct signal phasing
B. By converting the signal from analog to digital and using digital processing
C. By up-converting the signal to VHF
D. By converting the signal from digital to analog and taking the difference of mixing products

G4A06
(B)
Page 5-17

G4A06
What reading on the plate current meter of a vacuum tube RF power amplifier indicates correct adjustment of the plate tuning control?
A. A pronounced peak
B. A pronounced dip
C. No change will be observed
D. A slow, rhythmic oscillation

G4A07

What is the correct adjustment for the "Load" or "Coupling" control of a vacuum tube RF power amplifier?

A. Minimum SWR on the antenna
B. Minimum plate current without exceeding maximum allowable grid current
C. Highest plate voltage while minimizing grid current
D. Maximum power output without exceeding maximum allowable plate current

G4A07 (D) Page 5-17

G4A08

Which of the following techniques is used to neutralize an RF amplifier?

A. Feed-forward compensation
B. Feed-forward cancellation
C. Negative feedback
D. Positive feedback

G4A08 (C) Page 5-17

G4A09

What does a neutralizing circuit do in an RF amplifier?

A. It controls differential gain
B. It cancels the effects of positive feedback
C. It eliminates AC hum from the power supply
D. It reduces incidental grid modulation

G4A09 (B) Page 5-17

G4A10

What is the reason for neutralizing the final amplifier stage of a transmitter?

A. To limit the modulation index
B. To eliminate self oscillations
C. To cut off the final amplifier during standby periods
D. To keep the carrier on frequency

G4A10 (B) Page 5-17

G4A11

What type of transmitter performance does a two-tone test analyze?

A. Linearity
B. Carrier and undesired sideband suppression
C. Percentage of frequency modulation
D. Percentage of carrier phase shift

G4A11 (A) Page 5-14

G4A12

What type of signals are used to conduct a two-tone test?

A. Two audio signals of the same frequency shifted 90-degrees
B. Two non-harmonically related audio signals
C. Two swept frequency tones
D. Two audio frequency range square wave signals of equal amplitude

G4A12 (B) Page 5-14

G4A13

Which of the following performs automatic notching of interfering carriers?

A. Band pass tuning
B. A DSP filter
C. Balanced mixing
D. A noise limiter

G4A13 (B) Page 5-20

G4B — Test and monitoring equipment

G4B01
(D)
Page 4-41

G4B01
What item of test equipment contains horizontal and vertical channel amplifiers?
A. An ohmmeter
B. A signal generator
C. An ammeter
D. An oscilloscope

G4B02
(D)
Page 4-41

G4B02
Which of the following is an advantage of an oscilloscope versus a digital voltmeter?
A. An oscilloscope uses less power
B. Complex impedances can be easily measured
C. Input impedance is much lower
D. Complex waveforms can be measured

G4B03
(D)
Page 4-42

G4B03
How would a signal tracer normally be used?
A. To identify the source of radio transmissions
B. To make exact drawings of signal waveforms
C. To show standing wave patterns on open-wire feed-lines
D. To identify an inoperative stage in a receiver

G4B04
(C)
Page 4-43

G4B04
How is a noise bridge normally used?
A. It is connected at an antenna's feed point and reads the antenna's noise figure
B. It is connected between a transmitter and an antenna and tuned for minimum SWR
C. It is connected between a receiver and an antenna of unknown impedance and is adjusted for minimum noise
D. It is connected between an antenna and ground and tuned for minimum SWR

G4B05
(A)
Page 4-41

G4B05
Which of the following is the best instrument to use to check the keying waveform of a CW transmitter?
A. A monitoring oscilloscope
B. A field-strength meter
C. A sidetone monitor
D. A wavemeter

G4B06
(D)
Page 4-41

G4B06
What signal source is connected to the vertical input of a monitoring oscilloscope when checking the quality of a transmitted signal?
A. The local oscillator of the transmitter
B. The audio input of the transmitter
C. The transmitter balanced mixer output
D. The attenuated RF output of the transmitter

G4B07
(C)
Page 4-40

G4B07
What is an advantage of a digital voltmeter as compared to an analog voltmeter?
A. Better for measuring computer circuits
B. Better for RF measurements
C. Significantly better precision for most uses
D. Faster response

G4B08

What instrument may be used to monitor relative RF output when making antenna and transmitter adjustments?

A. A field-strength meter
B. An antenna noise bridge
C. A multimeter
D. A Q meter

G4B08
(A)
Page 4-44

G4B09

How much must the power output of a transmitter be raised to change the "S" meter reading on a distant receiver from S8 to S9?

A. Approximately 2 times
B. Approximately 3 times
C. Approximately 4 times
D. Approximately 5 times

G4B09
(C)
Page 5-21

G4B10

Which of the following can be determined with a field strength meter?

A. The radiation resistance of an antenna
B. The radiation pattern of an antenna
C. The presence and amount of phase distortion of a transmitter
D. The presence and amount of amplitude distortion of a transmitter

G4B10
(B)
Page 4-44

G4B11

Which of the following might be a use for a field strength meter?

A. Close-in radio direction-finding
B. A modulation monitor for a frequency or phase modulation transmitter
C. An overmodulation indicator for a SSB transmitter
D. A keying indicator for a RTTY or packet transmitter

G4B11
(A)
Page 4-44

G4B12

What is one way a noise bridge might be used?

A. Determining an antenna's gain in dBi
B. Pre-tuning an antenna tuner
C. Pre-tuning a linear amplifier
D. Determining the line loss of the antenna system

G4B12
(B)
Page 4-43

G4B13

What is one measurement that can be made with a dip meter?

A. The resonant frequency of a circuit
B. The tilt of the ionosphere
C. The gain of an antenna
D. The notch depth of a filter

G4B13
(A)
Page 4-43

G4B14

Which of the following must be connected to an antenna analyzer when it is being used for SWR measurements?

A. Receiver
B. Transmitter
C. Antenna and feedline
D. All of these answers are correct

G4B14
(C)
Page 4-43

G4B15
(A)
Page 4-44

G4B15
Which of the following can be measured with a directional wattmeter?
A. Standing Wave Ratio
B. Antenna front-to-back ratio
C. RF interference
D. Radio wave propagation

G4B16
(D)
Page 4-41

G4B16
Why is high input impedance desirable for a voltmeter?
A. It improves the frequency response
B. It decreases battery consumption in the meter
C. It improves the resolution of the readings
D. It decreases the loading on circuits being measured

G4C — Interference with consumer electronics; grounding

G4C01
(B)
Page 5-25

G4C01
Which of the following might be useful in reducing RF interference to audio-frequency devices?
A. Bypass inductor
B. Bypass capacitor
C. Forward-biased diode
D. Reverse-biased diode

G4C02
(B)
Page 5-24

G4C02
Which of the following should be installed if a properly operating amateur station is interfering with a nearby telephone?
A. An RFI filter on the transmitter
B. An RFI filter at the affected telephone
C. A high pass filter on the transmitter
D. A high pass filter at the affected telephone

G4C03
(C)
Page 5-24

G4C03
What sound is heard from a public-address system if there is interference from a nearby single-sideband phone transmitter?
A. A steady hum whenever the transmitter is on the air
B. On-and-off humming or clicking
C. Distorted speech
D. Clearly audible speech

G4C04
(A)
Page 5-24

G4C04
What is the effect on a public-address system if there is interference from nearby CW transmitter?
A. On-and-off humming or clicking
B. A CW signal at a nearly pure audio frequency
C. A chirpy CW signal
D. Severely distorted audio

G4C05
(D)
Page 5-23

G4C05
What might be the problem if you receive an RF burn when touching your equipment while transmitting on a HF band, assuming the equipment is connected to a ground rod?
A. Flat braid rather than round wire has been used for the ground wire
B. Insulated wire has been used for the ground wire
C. The ground rod is resonant
D. The ground wire is resonant

G4C06

Which of the following is an important reason to have a good station ground?

A. To reduce the likelihood of RF burns
B. To reduce the likelihood of electrical shock
C. To reduce interference
D. All of these answers are correct

G4C06
(D)
Page 5-23

G4C07

What is one good way to avoid stray RF energy in an amateur station?

A. Keep the station's ground wire as short as possible
B. Install an RF filter in series with the ground wire
C. Use a ground loop for best conductivity
D. Install a few ferrite beads on the ground wire where it connects to your station

G4C07
(A)
Page 5-23

G4C08

Which of the following is a reason to place ferrite beads around audio cables to reduce common mode RF interference?

A. They act as a series inductor
B. They act as a shunt capacitor
C. They lower the impedance of the cable
D. They increase the admittance of the cable

G4C08
(A)
Page 5-25

G4C09

Which of the following statements about station grounding is true?

A. The chassis of each piece of station equipment should be tied together with high-impedance conductors
B. If the chassis of all station equipment is connected with a good conductor, there is no need to tie them to an earth ground
C. RF hot spots can occur in a station located above the ground floor if the equipment is grounded by a long ground wire
D. A ground loop is an effective way to ground station equipment

G4C09
(C)
Page 5-23

G4C10

Which of the following is covered in the National Electrical Code?

A. Acceptable bandwidth limits
B. Acceptable modulation limits
C. Electrical safety inside the ham shack
D. RF exposure limits of the human body

G4C10
(C)
Page 8-3

G4C11

Which of the following can cause unintended rectification of RF signal energy and can result in interference to your station as well as nearby radio and TV receivers?

A. Induced currents in conductors that are in poor electrical contact
B. Induced voltages in conductors that are in good electrical contact
C. Capacitive coupling of the RF signal to ground
D. Excessive standing wave ratio (SWR) of the transmission line system

G4C11
(A)
Page 5-24

G4C12

What is one cause of broadband radio frequency interference at an amateur radio station?

A. Not using a balun or line isolator to feed balanced antennas
B. Lack of rectification of the transmitter's signal in power conductors
C. Arcing at a poor electrical connection
D. The use of horizontal, rather than vertical antennas

G4C12
(C)
Page 5-24

G4C13
(D)
Page 5-23

G4C13
How can a ground loop be avoided?
A. Series connect all ground conductors
B. Connect the AC neutral conductor to the ground wire
C. Avoid using lock washers and star washers in making ground connections
D. Connect all ground conductors to a single point

G4D — Speech processors; S meters; common connectors

G4D01
(D)
Page 5-15

G4D01
What is the reason for using a properly adjusted speech processor with a single sideband phone transmitter?
A. It reduces average transmitter power requirements
B. It reduces unwanted noise pickup from the microphone
C. It improves voice-frequency fidelity
D. It improves signal intelligibility at the receiver

G4D02
(B)
Page 5-15

G4D02
Which of the following describes how a speech processor affects a transmitted single sideband signal?
A. It increases the peak power
B. It increases the average power
C. It reduces harmonic distortion
D. It reduces intermodulation distortion

G4D03
(D)
Page 5-15

G4D03
Which of the following can be the result of an incorrectly adjusted speech processor?
A. Distorted speech
B. Splatter
C. Excessive background pickup
D. All of these answers are correct

G4D04
(C)
Page 5-21

G4D04
What does an S-meter measure?
A. Conductance
B. Impedance
C. Received signal strength
D. Transmitter power output

G4D05
(D)
Page 5-21

G4D05
How does an S-meter reading of 20 db over S-9 compare to an S-9 signal, assuming a properly calibrated S meter?
A. It is 10 times weaker
B. It is 20 times weaker
C. It is 20 times stronger
D. It is 100 times stronger

G4D06
(A)
Page 5-21

G4D06
Where is an S-meter generally found?
A. In a receiver
B. In a SWR bridge
C. In a transmitter
D. In a conductance bridge

G4D07
Which of the following describes a Type-N connector?
A. A moisture resistant RF connector useful to 10 GHz
B. A small bayonet connector used for data circuits
C. A threaded connector used for hydraulic systems
D. An audio connector used in surround sound installations

G4D08
Which of the following connectors would be a good choice for a serial data port?
A. PL-259
B. Type N
C. Type SMA
D. DB-9

G4D09
Which of these connector types is commonly used for RF service at frequencies up to 150 MHz?
A. Octal
B. RJ-11
C. UHF
D. DB-25

G4D10
Which of these connector types is commonly used for audio signals in amateur radio stations?
A. PL-259
B. BNC
C. RCA Phono
D. Type N

G4D11
What is the main reason to use keyed connectors over non-keyed types?
A. Prevention of use by unauthorized persons
B. Reduced chance of damage due to incorrect mating
C. Higher current carrying capacity
D. All of these choices are correct

G4E — HF mobile radio installations; emergency and battery powered operation

G4E01
Which of the following emission types are permissible while operating HF mobile?
A. CW
B. SSB
C. FM
D. All of these choices are correct

G4E02
What is alternator whine?
A. A DC emission from the alternator
B. A constant pitched tone or buzz in transmitted or received audio that occurs whenever the ignition key is in the on position
C. A tone or buzz in transmitted or received audio that varies with engine speed
D. A mechanical sound from the alternator indicating current overload

G4D07
(A)
Page 4-39

G4D08
(D)
Page 4-39

G4D09
(C)
Page 4-39

G4D10
(C)
Page 4-38

G4D11
(B)
Page 4-37

G4E01
(D)
Page 5-22

G4E02
(C)
Page 5-22

G4E03
(A)
Page 5-22

G4E03
Which of the following power connections would be the best for a 100-watt HF mobile installation?
A. A direct, fused connection to the battery using heavy gauge wire
B. A direct, fused connection to the alternator or generator using heavy gauge wire
C. A direct, fused connection to the battery using resistor wire
D. A direct, fused connection to the alternator or generator using resistor wire

G4E04
(B)
Page 5-22

G4E04
Why is it best NOT to draw the DC power for a 100-watt HF transceiver from an automobile's cigarette lighter socket?
A. The socket is not wired with an RF-shielded power cable
B. The socket's wiring may be inadequate for the current being drawn by the transceiver
C. The DC polarity of the socket is reversed from the polarity of modern HF transceivers
D. The power from the socket is never adequately filtered for HF transceiver operation

G4E05
(C)
Page 5-22

G4E05
Which of the following most limits the effectiveness of an HF mobile transceiver operating in the 75 meter band?
A. "Picket Fencing" signal variation
B. The wire gauge of the DC power line to the transceiver
C. The HF mobile antenna system
D. FCC rules limiting mobile output power on the 75 meter band

G4E06
(A)
Page 8-5

G4E06
Which of the following is true of an emergency generator installation?
A. The generator should be located in a well ventilated area
B. The generator should be insulated from ground
C. Fuel should be stored near the generator for rapid refueling in case of an emergency
D. All of these choices are correct

G4E07
(C)
Page 4-36

G4E07
When might a lead-acid storage battery give off explosive hydrogen gas?
A. When stored for long periods of time
B. When being discharged
C. When being charged
D. When not placed on a level surface

G4E08
(A)
Page 4-36

G4E08
What is the name of the process by which sunlight is changed directly into electricity?
A. Photovoltaic conversion
B. Photon emission
C. Photosynthesis
D. Photon decomposition

G4E09
(B)
Page 4-36

G4E09
What is the approximate open-circuit voltage from a modern, well illuminated photovoltaic cell?
A. 0.02 VDC
B. 0.5 VDC
C. 0.2 VDC
D. 1.38 VDC

G4E10
Which of these materials is used as the active element of a solar cell?
A. Doped Silicon
B. Nickel Hydride
C. Doped Platinum
D. Aluminum nitride

G4E10
(A)
Page 4-36

G4E11
Which of the following is a disadvantage to using wind power as the primary source of power for an emergency station?
A. The conversion efficiency from mechanical energy to electrical energy is less than 2 percent
B. The voltage and current ratings of such systems are not compatible with amateur equipment
C. A large energy storage system is needed to supply power when the wind is not blowing
D. All of these choices are correct

G4E11
(C)
Page 4-36

G4E12
Which of the following is a primary reason for not placing a gasoline-fueled generator inside an occupied area?
A. Danger of carbon monoxide poisoning
B. Danger of engine over torque
C. Lack of oxygen for adequate combustion
D. Lack of nitrogen for adequate combustion

G4E12
(A)
Page 8-6

G4E13
Why would it be unwise to power your station by back feeding the output of a gasoline generator into your house wiring by connecting the generator through an AC wall outlet?
A. It might present a hazard for electric company workers
B. It is prone to RF interference
C. It may disconnect your RF ground
D. None of the above; this is an excellent expedient

G4E13
(A)
Page 8-6

SUBELEMENT G5
ELECTRICAL PRINCIPLES
3 exam questions – 3 groups

G5A — Resistance; reactance; inductance; capacitance; impedance; impedance matching

G5A01
(C)
Page 4-20

G5A01
What is impedance?
A. The electric charge stored by a capacitor
B. The inverse of resistance
C. The opposition to the flow of current in an AC circuit
D. The force of repulsion between two similar electric fields

G5A02
(B)
Page 4-18

G5A02
What is reactance?
A. Opposition to the flow of direct current caused by resistance
B. Opposition to the flow of alternating current caused by capacitance or inductance
C. A property of ideal resistors in AC circuits
D. A large spark produced at switch contacts when an inductor is deenergized

G5A03
(D)
Page 4-20

G5A03
Which of the following causes opposition to the flow of alternating current in an inductor?
A. Conductance
B. Reluctance
C. Admittance
D. Reactance

G5A04
(C)
Page 4-19

G5A04
Which of the following causes opposition to the flow of alternating current in a capacitor?
A. Conductance
B. Reluctance
C. Reactance
D. Admittance

G5A05
(D)
Page 4-20

G5A05
How does a coil react to AC?
A. As the frequency of the applied AC increases, the reactance decreases
B. As the amplitude of the applied AC increases, the reactance increases
C. As the amplitude of the applied AC increases, the reactance decreases
D. As the frequency of the applied AC increases, the reactance increases

G5A06
(A)
Page 4-19

G5A06
How does a capacitor react to AC?
A. As the frequency of the applied AC increases, the reactance decreases
B. As the frequency of the applied AC increases, the reactance increases
C. As the amplitude of the applied AC increases, the reactance increases
D. As the amplitude of the applied AC increases, the reactance decreases

G5A07
What happens when the impedance of an electrical load is equal to the internal impedance of the power source?
A. The source delivers minimum power to the load
B. The electrical load is shorted
C. No current can flow through the circuit
D. The source can deliver maximum power to the load

G5A07
(D)
Page 4-21

G5A08
Why is impedance matching important?
A. So the source can deliver maximum power to the load
B. So the load will draw minimum power from the source
C. To ensure that there is less resistance than reactance in the circuit
D. To ensure that the resistance and reactance in the circuit are equal

G5A08
(A)
Page 4-21

G5A09
What unit is used to measure reactance?
A. Farad
B. Ohm
C. Ampere
D. Siemens

G5A09
(B)
Page 4-18

G5A10
What unit is used to measure impedance?
A. Volt
B. Ohm
C. Ampere
D. Watt

G5A10
(B)
Page 4-20

G5A11
Why should core saturation of a conventional impedance matching transformer be avoided?
A. Harmonics and distortion could result
B. Magnetic flux would increase with frequency
C. RF susceptance would increase
D. Temporary changes of the core permeability could result

G5A11
(A)
Page 4-22

G5A12
What is one reason to use an impedance matching transformer?
A. To reduce power dissipation in the transmitter
B. To maximize the transfer of power
C. To minimize SWR at the antenna
D. To minimize SWR in the transmission line

G5A12
(B)
Page 4-21

G5A13
Which of the following devices can be used for impedance matching at radio frequencies?
A. A transformer
B. A Pi-network
C. A length of transmission line
D. All of these choices are correct

G5A13
(D)
Page 4-21

G5A14
Which of the following describes one method of impedance matching between two AC circuits?
A. Insert an LC network between the two circuits
B. Reduce the power output of the first circuit
C. Increase the power output of the first circuit
D. Insert a circulator between the two circuits

G5A14
(A)
Page 4-21

G5B — The Decibel; current and voltage dividers; electrical power calculations; sine wave root-mean-square (RMS) values; PEP calculations

G5B01
(B)
Page 4-4

G5B01
A two-times increase or decrease in power results in a change of how many dB?
A. 2 dB
B. 3 dB
C. 6 dB
D. 12 dB

G5B02
(C)
Page 4-14

G5B02
How does the total current relate to the individual currents in each branch of a parallel circuit?
A. It equals the average of each branch current
B. It decreases as more parallel branches are added to the circuit
C. It equals the sum of the currents through each branch
D. It is the sum of the reciprocal of each individual voltage drop

G5B03
(B)
Page 4-2

G5B03
How many watts of electrical power are used if 400 VDC is supplied to an 800-ohm load?
A. 0.5 watts
B. 200 watts
C. 400 watts
D. 3200 watts

G5B04
(A)
Page 4-2

G5B04
How many watts of electrical power are used by a 12-VDC light bulb that draws 0.2 amperes?
A. 2.4 watts
B. 24 watts
C. 6 watts
D. 60 watts

G5B05
(A)
Page 4-2

G5B05
How many watts are being dissipated when a current of 7.0 milliamperes flows through 1.25 kilohms?
A. Approximately 61 milliwatts
B. Approximately 39 milliwatts
C. Approximately 11 milliwatts
D. Approximately 9 milliwatts

G5B06
(B)
Page 4-7

G5B06
What is the output PEP from a transmitter if an oscilloscope measures 200 volts peak-to-peak across a 50-ohm dummy load connected to the transmitter output?
A. 1.4 watts
B. 100 watts
C. 353.5 watts
D. 400 watts

G5B07
(C)
Page 4-5

G5B07
Which measurement of an AC signal is equivalent to a DC voltage of the same value?
A. The peak-to-peak value
B. The peak value
C. The RMS value
D. The reciprocal of the RMS value

G5B08
What is the peak-to-peak voltage of a sine wave that has an RMS voltage of 120 volts?
A. 84.8 volts
B. 169.7 volts
C. 240.0 volts
D. 339.4 volts

G5B09
What is the RMS voltage of sine wave with a value of 17 volts peak?
A. 8.5 volts
B. 12 volts
C. 24 volts
D. 34 volts

G5B10 — This question has been withdrawn.

G5B11
What is the ratio of peak envelope power to average power for an unmodulated carrier?
A. .707
B. 1.00
C. 1.414
D. 2.00

G5B12
What would be the voltage across a 50-ohm dummy load dissipating 1200 watts?
A. 173 volts
B. 245 volts
C. 346 volts
D. 692 volts

G5B13
What percentage of power loss would result from a transmission line loss of 1 dB?
A. 10.9 %
B. 12.2 %
C. 20.5 %
D. 25.9 %

G5B14
What is the output PEP from a transmitter if an oscilloscope measures 500 volts peak-to-peak across a 50-ohm resistor connected to the transmitter output?
A. 8.75 watts
B. 625 watts
C. 2500 watts
D. 5000 watts

G5B15
What is the output PEP of an unmodulated carrier if an average reading wattmeter connected to the transmitter output indicates 1060 watts?
A. 530 watts
B. 1060 watts
C. 1500 watts
D. 2120 watts

G5B08
(D)
Page 4-6

G5B09
(B)
Page 4-6

G5B10

G5B11
(B)
Page 4-7

G5B12
(B)
Page 4-7

G5B13
(C)
Page 4-5

G5B14
(B)
Page 4-7

G5B15
(B)
Page 4-7

G5C – Resistors, capacitors, and inductors in series and parallel; transformers

G5C01
(C)
Page 4-16

G5C01
What causes a voltage to appear across the secondary winding of a transformer when an AC voltage source is connected across its primary winding?
A. Capacitive coupling
B. Displacement current coupling
C. Mutual inductance
D. Mutual capacitance

G5C02
(B)
Page 4-16

G5C02
Where is the source of energy normally connected in a transformer?
A. To the secondary winding
B. To the primary winding
C. To the core
D. To the plates

G5C03
(A)
Page 4-17

G5C03
What is current in the primary winding of a transformer called if no load is attached to the secondary?
A. Magnetizing current
B. Direct current
C. Excitation current
D. Stabilizing current

G5C04
(C)
Page 4-15

G5C04
What is the total resistance of three 100-ohm resistors in parallel?
A. .30 ohms
B. .33 ohms
C. 33.3 ohms
D. 300 ohms

G5C05
(C)
Page 4-15

G5C05
What is the value of each resistor if three equal value resistors in parallel produce 50 ohms of resistance, and the same three resistors in series produce 450 ohms?
A. 1500 ohms
B. 90 ohms
C. 150 ohms
D. 175 ohms

G5C06
(C)
Page 4-16

G5C06
What is the voltage across a 500-turn secondary winding in a transformer if the 2250-turn primary is connected to 120 VAC?
A. 2370 volts
B. 540 volts
C. 26.7 volts
D. 5.9 volts

G5C07
(A)
Page 4-16

G5C07
What is the turns ratio of a transformer used to match an audio amplifier having a 600-ohm output impedance to a speaker having a 4-ohm impedance?
A. 12.2 to 1
B. 24.4 to 1
C. 150 to 1
D. 300 to 1

G5C08
What is the equivalent capacitance of two 5000 picofarad capacitors and one 750 picofarad capacitor connected in parallel?
A. 576.9 picofarads
B. 1733 picofarads
C. 3583 picofarads
D. 10750 picofarads

G5C09
What is the capacitance of three 100 microfarad capacitors connected in series?
A. .30 microfarads
B. .33 microfarads
C. 33.3 microfarads
D. 300 microfarads

G5C10
What is the inductance of three 10 millihenry inductors connected in parallel?
A. .30 Henrys
B. 3.3 Henrys
C. 3.3 millihenrys
D. 30 millihenrys

G5C11
What is the inductance of a 20 millihenry inductor in series with a 50 millihenry inductor?
A. .07 millihenrys
B. 14.3 millihenrys
C. 70 millihenrys
D. 1000 millihenrys

G5C12
What is the capacitance of a 20 microfarad capacitor in series with a 50 microfarad capacitor?
A. .07 microfarads
B. 14.3 microfarads
C. 70 microfarads
D. 1000 microfarads

G5C13
What component should be added to a capacitor in a circuit to increase the circuit capacitance?
A. An inductor in series
B. A resistor in series
C. A capacitor in parallel
D. A capacitor in series

G5C14
What component should be added to an inductor in a circuit to increase the circuit inductance?
A. A capacitor in series
B. A resistor in parallel
C. An inductor in parallel
D. An inductor in series

G5C15
What is the total resistance of a 10 ohm, a 20 ohm, and a 50 ohm resistor in parallel?
A. 5.9 ohms
B. 0.17 ohms
C. 10000 ohms
D. 80 ohms

G5C08
(D)
Page 4-15

G5C09
(C)
Page 4-15

G5C10
(C)
Page 4-15

G5C11
(C)
Page 4-15

G5C12
(B)
Page 4-15

G5C13
(C)
Page 4-14

G5C14
(D)
Page 4-14

G5C15
(A)
Page 4-15

G5C16 4
What component should be added to an existing resistor in a circuit to increase circuit resistance?
A. A resistor in parallel
B. A resistor in series
C. A capacitor in series
D. A capacitor in parallel

SUBELEMENT G6
Circuit Components
3 exam question – 3 groups

G6A — Resistors; capacitors; inductors

G6A01
What will happen to the resistance if the temperature of a carbon resistor is increased?
A. It will increase by 20% for every 10 degrees centigrade
B. It will stay the same
C. It will change depending on the resistor's temperature coefficient rating
D. It will become time dependent

G6A01
(C)
Page 4-9

G6A02
What type of capacitor is often used in power-supply circuits to filter the rectified AC?
A. Disc ceramic
B. Vacuum variable
C. Mica
D. Electrolytic

G6A02
(D)
Page 4-13

G6A03
Which of the following is the primary advantage of ceramic capacitors?
A. Tight tolerance
B. High stability
C. High capacitance for given volume
D. Comparatively low cost

G6A03
(D)
Page 4-13

G6A04
Which of the following is an advantage of an electrolytic capacitor?
A. Tight tolerance
B. Non-polarized
C. High capacitance for given volume
D. Inexpensive RF capacitor

G6A04
(C)
Page 4-13

G6A05
Which of the following is one effect of lead inductance in a capacitor used at VHF and above?
A. Effective capacitance may be reduced
B. Voltage rating may be reduced
C. ESR may be reduced
D. The polarity of the capacitor might become reversed

G6A05
(A)
Page 4-13

G6A06
What is the main disadvantage of using a conventional wire-wound resistor in a resonant circuit?
A. The resistor's tolerance value would not be adequate for such a circuit
B. The resistor's inductance could detune the circuit
C. The resistor could overheat
D. The resistor's internal capacitance would detune the circuit

G6A06
(B)
Page 4-9

G6A07
What is an advantage of using a ferrite core with a toroidal inductor?
A. Large values of inductance may be obtained
B. The magnetic properties of the core may be optimized for a specific range of frequencies
C. Most of the magnetic field is contained in the core
D. All of these choices are correct

G6A07
(D)
Page 4-12

G6A08
(C)
Page 4-11

G6A08
How should two solenoid inductors be placed so as to minimize their mutual inductance?
A. In line with their winding axis
B. With their winding axes parallel to each other
C. With their winding axes at right angles to each another
D. Within the same shielded enclosure

G6A09
(B)
Page 4-11

G6A09
Why might it be important to minimize the mutual inductance between two inductors?
A. To increase the energy transfer between both circuits
B. To reduce or eliminate unwanted coupling
C. To reduce conducted emissions
D. To increase the self-resonant frequency of both inductors

G6A10
(B)
Page 4-11

G6A10
What is an effect of inter-turn capacitance in an inductor?
A. The magnetic field may become inverted
B. The inductor may become self resonant at some frequencies
C. The permeability will increase
D. The voltage rating may be exceeded

G6A11
(D)
Page 4-13

G6A11
What is the common name for a capacitor connected across a transformer secondary that is used to absorb transient voltage spikes?
A. Clipper capacitor
B. Trimmer capacitor
C. Feedback capacitor
D. Suppressor capacitor

G6A12
(D)
Page 4-11

G6A12
What is the common name for an inductor used to help smooth the DC output from the rectifier in a conventional power supply?
A. Back EMF choke
B. Repulsion coil
C. Charging inductor
D. Filter choke

G6A13
(B)
Page 4-9

G6A13
What type of component is a thermistor?
A. A resistor that is resistant to changes in value with temperature variations
B. A device having a controlled change in resistance with temperature variations
C. A special type of transistor for use at very cold temperatures
D. A capacitor that changes value with temperature

G6B — Rectifiers; solid state diodes and transistors; solar cells; vacuum tubes; batteries

G6B01
(C)
Page 4-22

G6B01
What is the peak-inverse-voltage rating of a rectifier?
A. The maximum voltage the rectifier will handle in the conducting direction
B. 1.4 times the AC frequency
C. The maximum voltage the rectifier will handle in the non-conducting direction
D. 2.8 times the AC frequency

G6B02

What are the two major ratings that must not be exceeded for silicon-diode rectifiers?

A. Peak inverse voltage; average forward current
B. Average power; average voltage
C. Capacitive reactance; avalanche voltage
D. Peak load impedance; peak voltage

G6B03

What is the approximate junction threshold voltage of a germanium diode?

A. 0.1 volt
B. 0.3 volts
C. 0.7 volts
D. 1.0 volts

G6B04

When two or more diodes are connected in parallel to increase current handling capacity, what is the purpose of the resistor connected in series with each diode?

A. The resistors ensure the thermal stability of the power supply
B. The resistors regulate the power supply output voltage
C. The resistors ensure that one diode doesn't carry most of the current
D. The resistors act as swamping resistors in the circuit

G6B05

What is the approximate junction threshold voltage of a silicon diode?

A. 0.1 volt
B. 0.3 volts
C. 0.7 volts
D. 1.0 volts

G6B06

Which of the following is an advantage of using a Schottky diode in an RF switching circuit as compared to a standard silicon diode?

A. Lower capacitance
B. Lower inductance
C. Longer switching times
D. Higher breakdown voltage

G6B07

What are the stable operating points for a bipolar transistor that is used as a switch in a logic circuit?

A. Its saturation and cut-off regions
B. Its active region (between the cut-off and saturation regions)
C. Between its peak and valley current points
D. Between its enhancement and deletion modes

G6B08

Why is it often necessary to insulate the case of a large power transistor?

A. To increase the beta of the transistor
B. To improve the power dissipation capability
C. To reduce stray capacitance
D. To avoid shorting the collector or drain voltage to ground

G6B02
(A)
Page 4-22

G6B03
(B)
Page 4-22

G6B04
(C)
Page 4-32

G6B05
(C)
Page 4-22

G6B06
(A)
Page 4-23

G6B07
(A)
Page 4-24

G6B08
(D)
Page 4-25

G6B09
(B)
Page 4-24

G6B09
Which of the following describes the construction of a MOSFET?
A. The gate is formed by a back-biased junction
B. The gate is separated from the channel with a thin insulating layer
C. The source is separated from the drain by a thin insulating later
D. The source is formed by depositing metal on silicon

G6B10
(A)
Page 4-17

G6B10
Which element of a triode vacuum tube is used to regulate the flow of electrons between cathode and plate?
A. Control grid
B. Heater
C. Screen Grid
D. Suppressor grid

G6B11
(B)
Page 4-18

G6B11
Which of the following solid state devices is most like a vacuum tube in its general characteristics?
A. A bipolar transistor
B. An FET
C. A tunnel diode
D. A varistor

G6B12
(A)
Page 4-17

G6B12
What is the primary purpose of a screen grid in a vacuum tube?
A. To reduce grid-to-plate capacitance
B. To increase efficiency
C. To increase the high frequency response
D. To decrease plate resistance

G6B13
(B)
Page 4-35

G6B13
What is an advantage of the low internal resistance of Nickel Cadmium batteries?
A. Long life
B. High discharge current
C. High voltage
D. Rapid recharge

G6B14
(C)
Page 4-35

G6B14
What is the minimum allowable discharge voltage for maximum life of a standard 12 volt lead acid battery?
A. 6 volts
B. 8.5 volts
C. 10.5 volts
D. 12 volts

G6B15
(D)
Page 4-36

G6B15
When is it acceptable to recharge a carbon-zinc primary cell?
A. As long as the voltage has not been allowed to drop below 1.0 volt
B. When the cell is kept warm during the recharging period
C. When a constant current charger is used
D. Never

G6B16

Which of the following is a rechargeable battery?

A. Carbon-zinc
B. Silver oxide
C. Nickel Metal Hydride
D. Mercury

G6B16
(C)
Page 4-35

G6C — Analog and digital integrated circuits (IC's); microprocessors; memory; I/O devices; microwave IC's (MMIC's); display devices

G6C01

Which of the following is most often provided as an analog integrated circuit?

A. NAND Gate
B. Gallium Arsenide UHF Receiver "front end" Amplifier
C. Frequency Counter
D. Linear voltage regulator

G6C01
(D)
Page 4-25

G6C02

Which of the following is the most commonly used digital logic family of integrated circuits?

A. RTL
B. TTL
C. CMOS
D. PMOS

G6C02
(C)
Page 4-27

G6C03

Which of the following is an advantage of CMOS Logic integrated circuits compared to TTL logic circuits?

A. Low power consumption
B. High power handling capability
C. Better suited for RF amplification
D. Better suited for power supply regulation

G6C03
(A)
Page 4-27

G6C04

What is meant by the term ROM?

A. Resistor Operated Memory
B. Read Only Memory
C. Random Operational Memory
D. Resistant to Overload Memory

G6C04
(B)
Page 4-28

G6C05

What is meant when memory is characterized as "non-volatile"?

A. It is resistant to radiation damage
B. It is resistant to high temperatures
C. The stored information is maintained even if power is removed
D. The stored information cannot be changed once written

G6C05
(C)
Page 4-28

G6C06

Which type of integrated circuit is an operational amplifier?

A. Digital
B. MMIC
C. Programmable
D. Analog

G6C06
(D)
Page 4-25

G6C07
(D)
Page 4-29

G6C07
What is one disadvantage of an incandescent indicator compared to a LED?
A. Low power consumption
B. High speed
C. Long life
D. High power consumption

G6C08
(D)
Page 4-29

G6C08
How is an LED biased when emitting light?
A. Beyond cutoff
B. At the Zener voltage
C. Reverse Biased
D. Forward Biased

G6C09
(A)
Page 4-29

G6C09
Which of the following is a characteristic of a liquid crystal display?
A. It requires ambient or back lighting
B. It offers a wide dynamic range
C. It has a wide viewing angle
D. All of these choices are correct

G6C10
(B)
Page 4-27

G6C10
What is meant by the term MMIC?
A. Multi Megabyte Integrated Circuit
B. Monolithic Microwave Integrated Circuit
C. Military-specification Manufactured Integrated Circuit
D. Mode Modulated Integrated Circuit

G6C11
(B)
Page 4-28

G6C11
What is a microprocessor?
A. A low powered analog signal processor used as a microwave detector
B. A miniature computer on a single integrated circuit chip
C. A microwave detector, amplifier, and local oscillator on a chip
D. A low voltage amplifier used in a microwave transmitter modulator stage

G6C12
(A)
Page 4-29

G6C12
What two devices in an amateur radio station might be connected using a USB interface?
A. Computer and transceiver
B. Microphone and transceiver
C. Amplifier and antenna
D. Power supply and amplifier

SUBELEMENT G7
Practical Circuits
2 exam question – 2 groups

G7A — Power supplies; transmitters and receivers; filters, schematic drawing symbols

G7A01
What safety feature does a power-supply bleeder resistor provide?
A. It acts as a fuse for excess voltage
B. It discharges the filter capacitors
C. It removes shock hazards from the induction coils
D. It eliminates ground-loop current

G7A02
What components are used in a power-supply filter network?
A. Diodes
B. Transformers and transistors
C. Quartz crystals
D. Capacitors and inductors

G7A03
What should be the minimum peak-inverse-voltage rating of the rectifier in a full-wave power supply?
A. One-quarter the normal output voltage of the power supply
B. Half the normal output voltage of the power supply
C. Double the normal peak output voltage of the power supply
D. Equal to the normal output voltage of the power supply

G7A04
What should be the approximate minimum peak-inverse-voltage rating of the rectifier in a half-wave power supply?
A. One-half the normal peak output voltage of the power supply
B. Half the normal output voltage of the power supply
C. Equal to the normal output voltage of the power supply
D. Two times the normal peak output voltage of the power supply

G7A05
What should be the impedance of a low-pass filter as compared to the impedance of the transmission line into which it is inserted?
A. Substantially higher
B. About the same
C. Substantially lower
D. Twice the transmission line impedance

G7A06
Which of the following might be used to process signals from the balanced modulator and send them to the mixer in a single-sideband phone transmitter?
A. Carrier oscillator
B. Filter
C. IF amplifier
D. RF amplifier

G7A01
(B)
Page 4-33

G7A02
(D)
Page 4-32

G7A03
(C)
Page 4-31

G7A04
(D)
Page 4-31

G7A05
(B)
Page 5-24

G7A06
(B)
Page 5-12

G7A07
(D)
Page 5-12

G7A07
Which circuit is used to combine signals from the carrier oscillator and speech amplifier and send the result to the filter in a typical single-sideband phone transmitter?
A. Mixer
B. Detector
C. IF amplifier
D. Balanced modulator

G7A08
(C)
Page 5-18

G7A08
What circuit is used to process signals from the RF amplifier and local oscillator and send the result to the IF filter in a superheterodyne receiver?
A. Balanced modulator
B. IF amplifier
C. Mixer
D. Detector

G7A09
(D)
Page 5-19

G7A09
What circuit is used to process signals from the IF amplifier and BFO and send the result to the AF amplifier in a single-sideband phone superheterodyne receiver?
A. RF oscillator
B. IF filter
C. Balanced modulator
D. Product detector

G7A10
(A)
Page 5-11

G7A10
What is an advantage of a crystal controlled transmitter?
A. Stable output frequency
B. Excellent modulation clarity
C. Ease of switching between bands
D. Ease of changing frequency

G7A11
(C)
Page 5-18

G7A11
What is the simplest combination of stages that can be combined to implement a superheterodyne receiver?
A. RF amplifier, detector, audio amplifier
B. RF amplifier, mixer, if amplifier
C. HF oscillator, mixer, detector
D. HF oscillator, product detector, audio amplifier

G7A12
(D)
Page 5-19

G7A12
What type of receiver is suitable for CW and SSB reception but does not require a mixer stage or an IF amplifier?
A. A super-regenerative receiver
B. A TRF receiver
C. A super-heterodyne receiver
D. A direct conversion receiver

G7A13
(D)
Page 5-19

G7A13
What type of circuit is used in many FM receivers to convert signals coming from the IF amplifier to audio?
A. Product detector
B. Phase inverter
C. Mixer
D. Discriminator

G7A14

Which of the following is a desirable characteristic for capacitors used to filter the DC output of a switching power supply?

A. Low equivalent series resistance
B. High equivalent series resistance
C. Low Temperature coefficient
D. High Temperature coefficient

G7A14
(A)
Page 4-34

G7A15

Which of the following is an advantage of a switched-mode power supply as compared to a linear power supply?

A. Faster switching time makes higher output voltage possible
B. Fewer circuit components are required
C. High frequency operation allows the use of smaller components
D. All of these choices are correct

G7A15
(C)
Page 4-34

G7A16

What portion of the AC cycle is converted to DC by a half-wave rectifier?

A. 90 degrees
B. 180 degrees
C. 270 degrees
D. 360 degrees

G7A16
(B)
Page 4-30

G7A17

What portion of the AC cycle is converted to DC by a full-wave rectifier?

A. 90 degrees
B. 180 degrees
C. 270 degrees
D. 360 degrees

G7A17
(D)
Page 4-30

G7A18

What is the output waveform of an unfiltered full-wave rectifier connected to a resistive load?

A. A series of DC pulses at twice the frequency of the AC input
B. A series of DC pulses at the same frequency as the AC input
C. A sine wave at half the frequency of the AC input
D. A steady DC voltage

G7A18
(A)
Page 4-30

Figure G7-1 — Refer to this figure for questions G7A19 through G7A24.

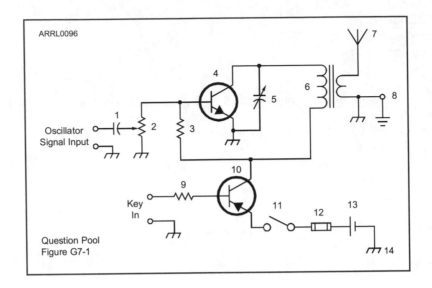

G7A19
(C)
Page 4-10

G7A19
Which symbol in figure G7-1 represents a fixed resistor?
A. Symbol 2
B. Symbol 6
C. Symbol 3
D. Symbol 12

G7A20
(D)
Page 4-35

G7A20
Which symbol in figure G7-1 represents a single cell battery?
A. Symbol 5
B. Symbol 12
C. Symbol 8
D. Symbol 13

G7A21
(B)
Page 4-23

G7A21
Which symbol in figure G7-1 represents a NPN transistor?
A. Symbol 2
B. Symbol 4
C. Symbol 10
D. Symbol 12

G7A22
(C)
Page 4-12

G7A22
Which symbol in figure G7-1 represents a variable capacitor?
A. Symbol 2
B. Symbol 11
C. Symbol 5
D. Symbol 12

G7A23
(A)
Page 4-16

G7A23
Which symbol in figure G7-1 represents a transformer?
A. Symbol 6
B. Symbol 4
C. Symbol 10
D. Symbol 2

G7A24
Which symbol in figure G7-1 represents a single pole switch?
A. Symbol 2
B. Symbol 3
C. Symbol 11
D. Symbol 12

G7A24
(C)
Page 4-30

G7B — Digital circuits (gates, flip-flops, shift registers); amplifiers and oscillators

G7B01
Which of the following describes a "flip-flop" circuit?
A. A transmit-receive circuit
B. A digital circuit with two stable states
C. An RF limiter
D. A voice-operated switch

G7B01
(B)
Page 4-25

G7B02
Why do digital circuits use the binary number system?
A. Binary "ones" and "zeros" are easy to represent with an "on" or "off" state
B. The binary number system is most accurate
C. Binary numbers are more compatible with analog circuitry
D. All of these answers are correct

G7B02
(A)
Page 4-25

G7B03
What is the output of a two-input NAND gate, given both inputs are "one"?
A. Two
B. One
C. Zero
D. Minus One

G7B03
(C)
Page 4-25

G7B04
What is the output of a NOR gate given that both inputs are "zero"?
A. Zero
B. One
C. Minus one
D. The opposite from the previous state

G7B04
(B)
Page 4-25

G7B05
How many states are there in a 3-bit binary counter?
A. 3
B. 6
C. 8
D. 16

G7B05
(C)
Page 4-27

G7B06
What is a shift register?
A. A clocked array of circuits that passes data in steps along the array
B. An array of operational amplifiers used for tri-state arithmetic operations
C. A digital mixer
D. An analog mixer

G7B06
(A)
Page 4-27

G7B07
(D)
Page 5-7

G7B07
What are the basic components of virtually all oscillators?
A. An amplifier and a divider
B. A frequency multiplier and a mixer
C. A circulator and a filter operating in a feed-forward loop
D. A filter and an amplifier operating in a feedback loop

G7B08
(C)
Page 5-7

G7B08
What determines the frequency of an RC oscillator?
A. The ratio of the capacitors in the feedback loop
B. The value of the inductor in the tank circuit
C. The phase shift of the RC feedback circuit
D. The gain of the amplifier

G7B09
(C)
Page 5-8

G7B09
What determines the frequency of an LC oscillator?
A. The number of stages in the counter
B. The number of stages in the divider
C. The inductance and capacitance in the tank circuit
D. The time delay of the lag circuit

G7B10
(D)
Page 5-16

G7B10
Which of the following is a characteristic of a Class A amplifier?
A. Low standby power
B. High Efficiency
C. No need for bias
D. Low distortion

G7B11
(B)
Page 5-16

G7B11
For which of the following modes is a Class C power stage appropriate for amplifying a modulated signal?
A. SSB
B. CW
C. AM
D. All of these answers are correct

G7B12
(A)
Page 5-16

G7B12
Which of the following is an advantage of a Class C amplifier?
A. High efficiency
B. Linear operation
C. No need for tuned circuits
D. All of these answers are correct

G7B13
(B)
Page 5-16

G7B13
How is the efficiency of an RF power amplifier determined?
A. Divide the DC input power by the DC output power
B. Divide the RF output power by the DC input power
C. Multiply the RF input power by the reciprocal of the RF output power
D. Add the RF input power to the DC output power

G7B14
(B)
Page 5-16

G7B14
Which of the following describes a linear amplifier?
A. Any RF power amplifier used in conjunction with an amateur transceiver
B. An amplifier whose output preserves the input waveform
C. A Class C high efficiency amplifier
D. An amplifier used as a frequency multiplier

SUBELEMENT G8
Signals and Emissions
2 exam questions – 2 groups

G8A — Carriers and modulation: AM; FM; single and double sideband; modulation envelope; deviation; overmodulation

G8A01
What is the name of the process that changes the envelope of an RF wave to convey information?
A. Phase modulation
B. Frequency modulation
C. Spread Spectrum modulation
D. Amplitude modulation

G8A01
(D)
Page 5-1

G8A02
What is the name of the process that changes the phase angle of an RF wave to convey information?
A. Phase convolution
B. Phase modulation
C. Angle convolution
D. Radian Inversion

G8A02
(B)
Page 5-2

G8A03
What is the name of the process which changes the frequency of an RF wave to convey information?
A. Frequency convolution
B. Frequency transformation
C. Frequency conversion
D. Frequency modulation

G8A03
(D)
Page 5-2

G8A04
What emission is produced by a reactance modulator connected to an RF power amplifier?
A. Multiplex modulation
B. Phase modulation
C. Amplitude modulation
D. Pulse modulation

G8A04
(B)
Page 5-10

G8A05
What type of transmission varies the instantaneous power level of the RF signal to convey information?
A. Frequency shift keying
B. Pulse modulation
C. Frequency modulation
D. Amplitude modulation

G8A05
(D)
Page 5-1

G8A06
What is one advantage of carrier suppression in a single-sideband phone transmission?
A. Audio fidelity is improved
B. Greater modulation percentage is obtainable with lower distortion
C. More transmitter power can be put into the remaining sideband
D. Simpler receiving equipment can be used

G8A06
(C)
Page 5-2

G8A07
(A)
Page 5-2

G8A07
Which of the following phone emissions uses the narrowest frequency bandwidth?
A. Single sideband
B. Double sideband
C. Phase modulation
D. Frequency modulation

G8A08
(D)
Page 5-13

G8A08
What happens to the signal of an over-modulated single-sideband phone transmitter?
A. It becomes louder with no other effects
B. It occupies less bandwidth with poor high frequency response
C. It has higher fidelity and improved signal to noise ratio
D. It becomes distorted and occupies more bandwidth

G8A09
(B)
Page 5-14

G8A09
What control is typically adjusted for proper ALC setting on an amateur single sideband transceiver?
A. The RF Clipping Level
B. Audio or microphone gain
C. Antenna inductance or capacitance
D. Attenuator Level

G8A10
(C)
Page 5-14

G8A10
What is meant by flat-topping of a single-sideband phone transmission?
A. Signal distortion caused by insufficient collector current
B. The transmitter's automatic level control is properly adjusted
C. Signal distortion caused by excessive drive
D. The transmitter's carrier is properly suppressed

G8A11
(A)
Page 5-2

G8A11
What happens to the RF carrier signal when a modulating audio signal is applied to an FM transmitter?
A. The carrier frequency changes proportionally to the instantaneous amplitude of the modulating signal
B. The carrier frequency changes proportionally to the amplitude and frequency of the modulating signal
C. The carrier amplitude changes proportionally to the instantaneous frequency of the modulating signal
D. The carrier phase changes proportionally to the instantaneous amplitude of the modulating signal

G8A12
(A)
Page 5-9

G8A12
What signal(s) would be found at the output of a properly adjusted balanced modulator?
A. Both upper and lower sidebands
B. Either upper or lower sideband, but not both
C. Both upper and lower sidebands and the carrier
D. The modulating signal and the unmodulated carrier

G8B — Frequency mixing; multiplication; HF data communications; bandwidths of various modes

G8B01
What receiver stage combines a 14.250 MHz input signal with a 13.795 MHz oscillator signal to produce a 455 kHz intermediate frequency (IF) signal?
A. Mixer
B. BFO
C. VFO
D. Multiplier

G8B01
(A)
Page 5-18

G8B02
If a receiver mixes a 13.800 MHz VFO with a 14.255 MHz received signal to produce a 455 kHz intermediate frequency (IF) signal, what type of interference will a 13.345 MHz signal produce in the receiver?
A. Local oscillator
B. Image response
C. Mixer interference
D. Intermediate interference

G8B02
(B)
Page 5-19

G8B03
What stage in a transmitter would change a 5.3 MHz input signal to 14.3 MHz?
A. A mixer
B. A beat frequency oscillator
C. A frequency multiplier
D. A linear translator

G8B03
(A)
Page 5-8

G8B04
What is the name of the stage in a VHF FM transmitter that selects a harmonic of an HF signal to reach the desired operating frequency?
A. Mixer
B. Reactance modulator
C. Pre-emphasis network
D. Multiplier

G8B04
(D)
Page 5-12

G8B05
Why isn't frequency modulated (FM) phone used below 29.5 MHz?
A. The transmitter efficiency for this mode is low
B. Harmonics could not be attenuated to practical levels
C. The bandwidth would exceed FCC limits
D. The frequency stability would not be adequate

G8B05
(C)
Page 5-13

G8B06
What is the total bandwidth of an FM-phone transmission having a 5 kHz deviation and a 3 kHz modulating frequency?
A. 3 kHz
B. 5 kHz
C. 8 kHz
D. 16 kHz

G8B06
(D)
Page 5-13

G8B07
What is the frequency deviation for a 12.21-MHz reactance-modulated oscillator in a 5-kHz deviation, 146.52-MHz FM-phone transmitter?
A. 101.75 Hz
B. 416.7 Hz
C. 5 kHz
D. 60 kHz

G8B07
(B)
Page 5-13

G8B08
(C)
Page 5-4

G8B08
How is frequency shift related to keying speed in an FSK signal?
A. The frequency shift in hertz must be at least four times the keying speed in WPM
B. The frequency shift must not exceed 15 Hz per WPM of keying speed
C. Greater keying speeds require greater frequency shifts
D. Greater keying speeds require smaller frequency shifts

G8B09
(B)
Page 5-3

G8B09
What do RTTY, Morse code, PSK31 and packet communications have in common?
A. They require the same bandwidth
B. They are digital modes
C. They use on/off keying
D. They use phase shift modulation

G8B10
(B)
Page 5-3

G8B10
When transmitting a data mode signal, why is it important to know the duty cycle of the mode you are using?
A. To aid in tuning your transmitter
B. To prevent damage to your transmitter's final output stage
C. To allow time for the other station to break in during a transmission
D. All of these choices are correct

G8B11
(D)
Page 2-14

G8B11
What part of the 20 meter band is most commonly used for PSK31 operation?
A. At the bottom of the slow-scan TV segment, near 14.230 MHz
B. At the top of the SSB phone segment, near 14.325 MHz
C. In the middle of the CW segment, near 14.100 MHz
D. Below the RTTY segment, near 14.070 MHz

G8B12
(A)
Page 5-8

G8B12
What is another term for the mixing of two RF signals?
A. Heterodyning
B. Synthesizing
C. Cancellation
D. Multiplying

SUBELEMENT G9
Antennas and Feedlines
4 exam questions – 4 groups

G9A — Antenna feedlines: characteristic impedance, and attenuation; SWR calculation, measurement and effects; matching networks

G9A01
Which of the following factors help determine the characteristic impedance of a parallel conductor antenna feedline?
A. The distance between the centers of the conductors and the radius of the conductors
B. The distance between the centers of the conductors and the length of the line
C. The radius of the conductors and the frequency of the signal
D. The frequency of the signal and the length of the line

G9A02
What is the typical characteristic impedance of coaxial cables used for antenna feedlines at amateur stations?
A. 25 and 30 ohms
B. 50 and 75 ohms
C. 80 and 100 ohms
D. 500 and 750 ohms

G9A03
What is the characteristic impedance of flat ribbon TV type twin lead?
A. 50 ohms
B. 75 ohms
C. 100 ohms
D. 300 ohms

G9A04
What is a common reason for the occurrence of reflected power at the point where a feedline connects to an antenna?
A. Operating an antenna at its resonant frequency
B. Using more transmitter power than the antenna can handle
C. A difference between feedline impedance and antenna feed point impedance
D. Feeding the antenna with unbalanced feedline

G9A05
What must be done to prevent standing waves on an antenna feedline?
A. The antenna feed point must be at DC ground potential
B. The feedline must be cut to an odd number of electrical quarter wavelengths long
C. The feedline must be cut to an even number of physical half wavelengths long
D. The antenna feed point impedance must be matched to the characteristic impedance of the feedline

G9A06
Which of the following is a reason for using an inductively coupled matching network between the transmitter and parallel conductor feed line feeding an antenna?
A. To increase the radiation resistance
B. To reduce spurious emissions
C. To match the unbalanced transmitter output to the balanced parallel conductor feedline
D. To reduce the feed-point impedance of the antenna

G9A01
(A)
Page 6-18

G9A02
(B)
Page 6-18

G9A03
(D)
Page 6-18

G9A04
(C)
Page 6-19

G9A05
(D)
Page 6-19

G9A06
(C)
Page 6-20

G9A07
(B)
Page 6-21

G9A07
How does the attenuation of coaxial cable change as the frequency of the signal it is carrying increases?
A. It is independent of frequency
B. It increases
C. It decreases
D. It reaches a maximum at approximately 18 MHz

G9A08
(D)
Page 6-21

G9A08
In what values are RF feed line losses usually expressed?
A. ohms per 1000 ft
B. dB per 1000 ft
C. ohms per 100 ft
D. dB per 100 ft

G9A09
(A)
Page 6-19

G9A09
What standing-wave-ratio will result from the connection of a 50-ohm feed line to a non-reactive load having a 200-ohm impedance?
A. 4:1
B. 1:4
C. 2:1
D. 1:2

G9A10
(D)
Page 6-19

G9A10
What standing-wave-ratio will result from the connection of a 50-ohm feed line to a non-reactive load having a 10-ohm impedance?
A. 2:1
B. 50:1
C. 1:5
D. 5:1

G9A11
(B)
Page 6-19

G9A11
What standing-wave-ratio will result from the connection of a 50-ohm feed line to a non-reactive load having a 50-ohm impedance?
A. 2:1
B. 1:1
C. 50:50
D. 0:0

G9A12
(A)
Page 6-19

G9A12
What would be the SWR if you feed a vertical antenna that has a 25-ohm feed-point impedance with 50-ohm coaxial cable?
A. 2:1
B. 2.5:1
C. 1.25:1
D. You cannot determine SWR from impedance values

G9A13
(C)
Page 6-19

G9A13
What would be the SWR if you feed a folded dipole antenna that has a 300-ohm feed-point impedance with 50-ohm coaxial cable?
A. 1.5:1
B. 3:1
C. 6:1
D. You cannot determine SWR from impedance values

G9A14
If the SWR on an antenna feedline is 5 to 1, and a matching network at the transmitter end of the feedline is adjusted to 1 to 1 SWR, what is the resulting SWR on the feedline?
A. 1 to 1
B. 5 to 1
C. Between 1 to 1 and 5 to 1 depending on the characteristic impedance of the line
D. Between 1 to 1 and 5 to 1 depending on the reflected power at the transmitter

G9A14
(B)
Page 6-20

G9B — Basic antennas

G9B01
What is one disadvantage of a directly fed random-wire antenna?
A. It must be longer than 1 wavelength
B. You may experience RF burns when touching metal objects in your station
C. It produces only vertically polarized radiation
D. It is not effective on the higher HF bands

G9B01
(B)
Page 6-6

G9B02
What is an advantage of downward sloping radials on a ground-plane antenna?
A. They lower the radiation angle
B. They bring the feed-point impedance closer to 300 ohms
C. They increase the radiation angle
D. They can be adjusted to bring the feed-point impedance closer to 50 ohms

G9B02
(D)
Page 6-4

G9B03
What happens to the feed-point impedance of a ground-plane antenna when its radials are changed from horizontal to downward-sloping?
A. It decreases
B. It increases
C. It stays the same
D. It reaches a maximum at an angle of 45 degrees

G9B03
(B)
Page 6-4

G9B04
What is the low angle azimuthal radiation pattern of an ideal half-wavelength dipole antenna installed ½ wavelength high and parallel to the earth?
A. It is a figure-eight at right angles to the antenna
B. It is a figure-eight off both ends of the antenna
C. It is a circle (equal radiation in all directions)
D. It has a pair of lobes on one side of the antenna and a single lobe on the other side

G9B04
(A)
Page 6-2

G9B05
How does antenna height affect the horizontal (azimuthal) radiation pattern of a horizontal dipole HF antenna?
A. If the antenna is too high, the pattern becomes unpredictable
B. Antenna height has no effect on the pattern
C. If the antenna is less than ½ wavelength high, the azimuthal pattern is almost omnidirectional
D. If the antenna is less than ½ wavelength high, radiation off the ends of the wire is eliminated

G9B05
(C)
Page 6-7

G9B06
Where should the radial wires of a ground-mounted vertical antenna system be placed?
A. As high as possible above the ground
B. Parallel to the antenna element
C. On the surface or buried a few inches below the ground
D. At the top of the antenna

G9B06
(C)
Page 6-4

G9B07
(B)
Page 6-6

G9B07
How does the feed-point impedance of a ½ wave dipole antenna change as the antenna is lowered from ¼ wave above ground?
A. It steadily increases
B. It steadily decreases
C. It peaks at about 1/8 wavelength above ground
D. It is unaffected by the height above ground

G9B08
(A)
Page 6-2

G9B08
How does the feed-point impedance of a ½ wave dipole change as the feed-point location is moved from the center toward the ends?
A. It steadily increases
B. It steadily decreases
C. It peaks at about 1/8 wavelength from the end
D. It is unaffected by the location of the feed-point

G9B09
(A)
Page 6-7

G9B09
Which of the following is an advantage of a horizontally polarized as compared to vertically polarized HF antenna?
A. Lower ground reflection losses
B. Lower feed-point impedance
C. Shorter Radials
D. Lower radiation resistance

G9B10
(D)
Page 6-3

G9B10
What is the approximate length for a ½-wave dipole antenna cut for 14.250 MHz?
A. 8.2 feet
B. 16.4 feet
C. 24.6 feet
D. 32.8 feet

G9B11
(C)
Page 6-3

G9B11
What is the approximate length for a ½-wave dipole antenna cut for 3.550 MHz?
A. 42.2 feet
B. 84.5 feet
C. 131.8 feet
D. 263.6 feet

G9B12
(A)
Page 6-4

G9B12
What is the approximate length for a ¼-wave vertical antenna cut for 28.5 MHz?
A. 8.2 feet
B. 10.5 feet
C. 16.4 feet
D. 21.0 feet

G9C — Directional antennas

G9C01
How can the SWR bandwidth of a Yagi antenna be increased?
A. Use larger diameter elements
B. Use closer element spacing
C. Use traps on the elements
D. Use tapered-diameter elements

G9C02
What is the approximate length of the driven element of a Yagi antenna?
A. ¼ wavelength
B. ½ wavelength
C. ¾ wavelength
D. 1 wavelength

G9C03
Which statement about a three-element single-band Yagi antenna is true?
A. The reflector is normally the shortest parasitic element
B. The director is normally the shortest parasitic element
C. The driven element is the longest parasitic element
D. Low feed-point impedance increases bandwidth

G9C04
Which statement about a Yagi antenna is true?
A. The reflector is normally the longest parasitic element
B. The director is normally the longest parasitic element
C. The reflector is normally the shortest parasitic element
D. All of the elements must be the same length

G9C05
What is one effect of increasing the boom length and adding directors to a Yagi antenna?
A. Gain increases
B. SWR increases
C. Weight decreases
D. Wind load decreases

G9C06
Which of the following is a reason why a Yagi antenna is often used for radio communications on the 20 meter band?
A. It provides excellent omnidirectional coverage in the horizontal plane
B. It is smaller, less expensive and easier to erect than a dipole or vertical antenna
C. It helps reduce interference from other stations to the side or behind the antenna
D. It provides the highest possible angle of radiation for the HF bands

G9C07
What does "front-to-back ratio" mean in reference to a Yagi antenna?
A. The number of directors versus the number of reflectors
B. The relative position of the driven element with respect to the reflectors and directors
C. The power radiated in the major radiation lobe compared to the power radiated in exactly the opposite direction
D. The ratio of forward gain to dipole gain

G9C01
(A)
Page 6-10

G9C02
(B)
Page 6-9

G9C03
(B)
Page 6-10

G9C04
(A)
Page 6-9

G9C05
(A)
Page 6-10

G9C06
(C)
Page 6-7

G9C07
(C)
Page 6-10

G9C08

What is meant by the "main lobe" of a directive antenna?

A.   The magnitude of the maximum vertical angle of radiation
B.   The point of maximum current in a radiating antenna element
C.   The maximum voltage standing wave point on a radiating element
D.   The direction of maximum radiated field strength from the antenna

G9C09

What is the approximate maximum theoretical forward gain of a 3 Element Yagi antenna?

A.   9.7 dBi
B.   7.3 dBd
C.   5.4 times the gain of a dipole
D.   All of these choices are correct

G9C10

Which of the following is a Yagi antenna design variable that could be adjusted to optimize forward gain, front-to-back ratio, or SWR bandwidth?

A.   The physical length of the boom
B.   The number of elements on the boom
C.   The spacing of each element along the boom
D.   All of these choices are correct

G9C11

What is the purpose of a "gamma match" used with Yagi antennas?

A.   To match the relatively low feed-point impedance to 50 ohms
B.   To match the relatively high feed-point impedance to 50 ohms
C.   To increase the front to back ratio
D.   To increase the main lobe gain

G9C12

Which of the following describes a common method for insulating the driven element of a Yagi antenna from the metal boom when using a gamma match?

A.   Support the driven element with ceramic standoff insulators
B.   Insert a high impedance transformer at the driven element
C.   Insert a high voltage balun at the driven element
D.   None of these answers are correct. No insulation is needed

G9C13

Approximately how long is each side of a cubical-quad antenna driven element?

A.   ¼ wavelength
B.   ½ wavelength
C.   ¾ wavelength
D.   1 wavelength

G9C14

How does the forward gain of a 2-element cubical-quad antenna compare to the forward gain of a 3 element Yagi antenna?

A.   2/3
B.   About the same
C.   3/2
D.   Twice

G9C15
Approximately how long is each side of a cubical-quad antenna reflector element?
A. Slightly less than ¼ wavelength
B. Slightly more than ¼ wavelength
C. Slightly less than ½ wavelength
D. Slightly more than ½ wavelength

G9C15
(B)
Page 6-13

G9C16
How does the gain of a two element delta-loop beam compare to the gain of a two element cubical quad antenna?
A. 3 dB higher
B. 3 dB lower
C. 2.54 dB higher
D. About the same

G9C16
(D)
Page 6-13

G9C17
Approximately how long is each leg of a symmetrical delta-loop antenna Driven element?
A. ¼ wavelengths
B. ⅓ wavelengths
C. ½ wavelengths
D. ⅔ wavelengths

G9C17
(B)
Page 6-12

G9C18
Which of the following antenna types consists of a driven element and some combination of parasitically excited reflector and/or director elements?
A. A collinear array
B. A rhombic antenna
C. A double-extended Zepp antenna
D. A Yagi antenna

G9C18
(D)
Page 6-8

G9C19
What type of directional antenna is typically constructed from 2 square loops of wire each having a circumference of approximately one wavelength at the operating frequency and separated by approximately 0.2 wavelength?
A. A stacked dipole array
B. A collinear array
C. A cubical quad antenna
D. An Adcock array

G9C19
(C)
Page 6-13

G9C20
What happens when the feed-point of a cubical quad antenna is changed from the center of the lowest horizontal wire to the center of one of the vertical wires?
A. The polarization of the radiated signal changes from horizontal to vertical
B. The polarization of the radiated signal changes from vertical to horizontal
C. The direction of the main lobe is reversed
D. The radiated signal changes to an omnidirectional pattern

G9C20
(A)
Page 6-13

G9C21
What configuration of the loops of a cubical-quad antenna must be used for the antenna to operate as a beam antenna, assuming one of the elements is used as a reflector?
A. The driven element must be fed with a balun transformer
B. The driven element must be open-circuited on the side opposite the feed-point
C. The reflector element must be approximately 5% shorter than the driven element
D. The reflector element must be approximately 5% longer than the driven element

G9C21
(D)
Page 6-13

G9D — Specialized antennas

G9D01
(D)
Page 6-14

G9D01
What does the term "NVIS" mean as related to antennas?
A. Nearly Vertical Inductance System
B. Non-Visible Installation Specification
C. Non-Varying Impedance Smoothing
D. Near Vertical Incidence Skywave

G9D02
(B)
Page 6-14

G9D02
Which of the following is an advantage of an NVIS antenna?
A. Low vertical angle radiation for DX work
B. High vertical angle radiation for short skip during the day
C. High forward gain
D. All of these choices are correct

G9D03
(D)
Page 6-14

G9D03
At what height above ground is an NVIS antenna typically installed?
A. As close to one-half wave as possible
B. As close to one wavelength as possible
C. Height is not critical as long as significantly more than ½ wavelength
D. Between ¹/₁₀ and ¼ wavelength

G9D04
(B)
Page 6-15

G9D04
How does the gain of two 3-element horizontally polarized Yagi antennas spaced vertically ½ wave apart from each other typically compare to the gain of a single 3-element Yagi?
A. Approximately 1.5 dB higher
B. Approximately 3 dB higher
C. Approximately 6 dB higher
D. Approximately 9 dB higher

G9D05
(D)
Page 6-14

G9D05
What is the advantage of vertical stacking of horizontally polarized Yagi antennas?
A. Allows quick selection of vertical or horizontal polarization
B. Allows simultaneous vertical and horizontal polarization
C. Narrows the main lobe in azimuth
D. Narrows the main lobe in elevation

G9D06
(A)
Page 6-15

G9D06
Which of the following is an advantage of a log periodic antenna?
A. Wide bandwidth
B. Higher gain per element than a Yagi antenna
C. Harmonic suppression
D. Polarization diversity

G9D07
(A)
Page 6-15

G9D07
Which of the following describes a log periodic antenna?
A. Length and spacing of the elements increases logarithmically from one end of the boom to the other
B. Impedance varies periodically as a function of frequency
C. Gain varies logarithmically as a function of frequency
D. SWR varies periodically as a function of boom length

G9D08
Why is a Beverage antenna generally not used for transmitting?
A. Its impedance is too low for effective matching
B. It has high losses compared to other types of antennas
C. It has poor directivity
D. All of these choices are correct

G9D09
Which of the following is an application for a Beverage antenna?
A. Directional transmitting for low HF bands
B. Directional receiving for low HF bands
C. Portable Direction finding at higher HF frequencies
D. Portable Direction finding at lower HF frequencies

G9D10
Which of the following describes a Beverage antenna?
A. A vertical antenna constructed from beverage cans
B. A broad-band mobile antenna
C. A helical antenna for space reception
D. A very long and low receiving antenna that is highly directional

G9D11
Which of the following is a disadvantage of multiband antennas?
A. They present low impedance on all design frequencies
B. They must be used with an antenna tuner
C. They must be fed with open wire line
D. They have poor harmonic rejection

G9D12
What is the primary purpose of traps installed in antennas?
A. To permit multiband operation
B. To notch spurious frequencies
C. To provide balanced feed-point impedance
D. To prevent out of band operation

G9D08
(B)
Page 6-16

G9D09
(B)
Page 6-16

G9D10
(D)
Page 6-16

G9D11
(D)
Page 6-17

G9D12
(A)
Page 6-17

SUBELEMENT G0
Electrical and RF Safety
2 exam questions – 2 groups

G0A — RF safety principles, rules and guidelines; routine station evaluation

G0A01
(A)
Page 8-7

G0A01
What is one way that RF energy can affect human body tissue?
A. It heats body tissue
B. It causes radiation poisoning
C. It causes the blood count to reach a dangerously low level
D. It cools body tissue

G0A02
(B)
Page 8-7

G0A02
Which property is NOT important in estimating if an RF signal exceeds the maximum permissible exposure (MPE)?
A. Its duty cycle
B. Its critical angle
C. Its power density
D. Its frequency

G0A03
(B)
Page 8-7

G0A03
Which of the following has the most direct effect on the permitted exposure level of RF radiation?
A. The age of the person exposed
B. The power level and frequency of the energy
C. The environment near the transmitter
D. The type of transmission line used

G0A04
(D)
Page 8-9

G0A04
What does "time averaging" mean in reference to RF radiation exposure?
A. The average time of day when the exposure occurs
B. The average time it takes RF radiation to have any long-term effect on the body
C. The total time of the exposure
D. The total RF exposure averaged over a certain time

G0A05
(A)
Page 8-11

G0A05
What must you do if an evaluation of your station shows RF energy radiated from your station exceeds permissible limits?
A. Take action to prevent human exposure to the excessive RF fields
B. File an Environmental Impact Statement (EIS-97) with the FCC
C. Secure written permission from your neighbors to operate above the controlled MPE limits
D. All of these answers are correct

G0A06
(C)
Page 8-11

G0A06
Which transmitter(s) at a multiple user site is/are responsible for RF safety compliance?
A. Only the most powerful transmitter on site
B. All transmitters on site, regardless of their power level or duty cycle
C. Any transmitter that contributes 5% or more of the MPE
D. Only those that operate at more than 50% duty cycle

G0A07

What effect does transmitter duty cycle have when evaluating RF exposure?

A. A lower transmitter duty cycle permits greater short-term exposure levels
B. A higher transmitter duty cycle permits greater short-term exposure levels
C. Low duty cycle transmitters are exempt from RF exposure evaluation requirements
D. Only those transmitters that operate at a 100% duty cycle must be evaluated

G0A07
(A)
Page 8-9

G0A08

Which of the following steps must an amateur operator take to ensure compliance with RF safety regulations?

A. Post a copy of FCC Part 97 in the station
B. Post a copy of OET Bulletin 65 in the station
C. Perform a routine RF exposure evaluation
D. All of these choices are correct

G0A08
(C)
Page 8-10

G0A09

What type of instrument can be used to accurately measure an RF field?

A. A receiver with an S meter
B. A calibrated field-strength meter with a calibrated antenna
C. A betascope with a dummy antenna calibrated at 50 ohms
D. An oscilloscope with a high-stability crystal marker generator

G0A09
(B)
Page 8-10

G0A10

What do the RF safety rules require when the maximum power output capability of an otherwise compliant station is reduced?

A. Filing of the changes with the FCC
B. Recording of the power level changes in the log or station records
C. Performance of a routine RF exposure evaluation
D. No further action is required

G0A10
(D)
Page 8 11

G0A11

What precaution should you take if you install an indoor transmitting antenna?

A. Locate the antenna close to your operating position to minimize feed line radiation
B. Position the antenna along the edge of a wall to reduce parasitic radiation
C. Make sure that MPE limits are not exceeded in occupied areas
D. No special precautions are necessary if SSB and CW are the only modes used

G0A11
(C)
Page 8-12

G0A12

What precaution should you take whenever you make adjustments or repairs to an antenna?

A. Ensure that you and the antenna structure are grounded
B. Turn off the transmitter and disconnect the feedline
C. Wear a radiation badge
D. All of these answers are correct

G0A12
(B)
Page 8-14

G0A13

What precaution should be taken when installing a ground-mounted antenna?

A. It should not be installed higher than you can reach
B. It should not be installed in a wet area
C. It should be painted so people or animals do not accidentally run into it
D. It should be installed so no one can be exposed to RF radiation in excess of maximum permissible limits

G0A13
(D)
Page 8-11

G0A14
(D)
Page 8-11

G0A14
What is one thing that can be done if evaluation shows that a neighbor might receive more than the allowable limit of RF exposure from the main lobe of a directional antenna?
A. Change from horizontal polarization to vertical polarization
B. Change from horizontal polarization to circular polarization
C. Use an antenna with a higher front-to-back ratio
D. Take precautions to ensure that the antenna cannot be pointed at their house

G0A15
(D)
[97.13(c)(1)]
Page 8-10

G0A15
How can you determine that your station complies with FCC RF exposure regulations?
A. By calculation based on FCC OET Bulletin 65
B. By calculation based on computer modeling
C. By measurement of field strength using calibrated equipment
D. All of these choices are correct

G0B — Safety in the ham shack: electrical shock and treatment, grounding, fusing, interlocks, wiring, antenna and tower safety

G0B01
(A)
Page 8-5

G0B01
Which wire(s) in a four-conductor line cord should be attached to fuses or circuit breakers in a device operated from a 240-VAC single-phase source?
A. Only the "hot" (black and red) wires
B. Only the "neutral" (white) wire
C. Only the ground (bare) wire
D. All wires

G0B02
(C)
Page 8-4

G0B02
What is the minimum wire size that may be safely used for a circuit that draws up to 20 amperes of continuous current?
A. AWG number 20
B. AWG number 16
C. AWG number 12
D. AWG number 8

G0B03
(D)
Page 8-4

G0B03
Which size of fuse or circuit breaker would be appropriate to use with a circuit that uses AWG number 14 wiring?
A. 100 amperes
B. 60 amperes
C. 30 amperes
D. 15 amperes

G0B04
(A)
Page 8-2

G0B04
What is the mechanism by which electrical shock can be lethal?
A. Current through the heart can cause the heart to stop pumping
B. A large voltage field can induce currents in the brain
C. Heating effects in major organs can cause organ failure
D. All of these choices are correct

G0B05

Which of the following conditions will cause a Ground Fault Circuit Interrupter (GFCI) to disconnect the 120 or 240 Volt AC line power to a device?

A. Current flowing from the hot wire to the neutral wire
B. Current flowing from the hot wire to ground
C. Over-voltage on the hot wire
D. All of these choices are correct

G0B05
(B)
Page 8-5

G0B06

Why must the metal chassis of every item of station equipment be grounded (assuming the item has such a chassis)?

A. It prevents blowing of fuses in case of an internal short circuit
B. It provides a ground reference for the internal circuitry
C. It ensures that the neutral wire is grounded
D. It ensures that hazardous voltages cannot appear on the chassis

G0B06
(D)
Page 8-4

G0B07

Which of the following should be observed for safety when climbing on a tower using a safety belt or harness?

A. Never lean back and rely on the belt alone to support your weight
B. Always attach the belt safety hook to the belt "D" ring with the hook opening away from the tower
C. Ensure that all heavy tools are securely fastened to the belt D ring
D. Make sure that your belt is grounded at all times

G0B07
(B)
Page 8-14

G0B08

What should be done by any person preparing to climb a tower that supports electrically powered devices?

A. Notify the electric company that a person will be working on the tower
B. Make sure all circuits that supply power to the tower are locked out and tagged
C. Ground the base of the tower
D. Disconnect the feed-line for every antenna at the station

G0B08
(B)
Page 8-14

G0B09

Why is it not safe to use soldered joints with the wires that connect the base of a tower to a system of ground rods?

A. The resistance of solder is too high
B. Solder flux will prevent a low conductivity connection
C. Solder has too high a dielectric constant to provide adequate lightning protection
D. A soldered joint will likely be destroyed by the heat of a lightning strike

G0B09
(D)
Page 8-7

G0B10

Which of the following is a danger from lead-tin solder?

A. Lead can contaminate food if hands are not washed carefully after handling
B. High voltages can cause lead-tin solder to disintegrate suddenly
C. Tin in the solder can "cold flow" causing shorts in the circuit
D. RF energy can convert the lead into a poisonous gas

G0B10
(A)
Page 8-2

G0B11

Which of the following is good engineering practice for lightning protection grounds?

A. They must be bonded to all buried water and gas lines
B. Bends in ground wires must be made as close as possible to a right angle
C. Lightning grounds must be connected to all ungrounded wiring
D. They must be bonded together with all other grounds

G0B11
(D)
Page 8-7

G0B12
(C)
Page 8-5

G0B12
What is the purpose of a transmitter power supply interlock?
A. To prevent unauthorized access to a transmitter
B. To guarantee that you cannot accidentally transmit out of band
C. To ensure that dangerous voltages are removed if the cabinet is opened
D. To shut off the transmitter if too much current is drawn

G0B13
(B)
Page 8-2

G0B13
Which of the following is the most hazardous type of electrical energy?
A. Direct Current
B. 60 cycle Alternating current
C. Radio Frequency
D. All of these choices are correct

G0B14
(B)
Page 8-2

G0B14
What is the maximum amount of electrical current flow through the human body that can be tolerated safely?
A. 5 microamperes
B. 50 microamperes
C. 500 milliamperes
D. 5 amperes

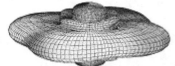

The Hottest Field Gear Anywhere!

HF/VHF/UHF Portable Operation Just Got a Lot More Powerful!
FT-897D
HF/50/144/430 MHz
100 W All Mode Transceiver
(144 MHz 50 W/430 MHz 20 W)

TCXO **DSP** **60 m Band**

HF/VHF/UHF Multimode Mobile Transceiver, now Including Built-in DSP
FT-857D
HF/50/144/430 MHz
100 W All Mode Transceiver
(144 MHz 50 W/430 MHz 20 W)

DSP **60 m Band**

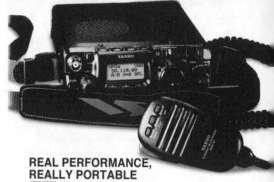

REAL PERFORMANCE, REALLY PORTABLE
FT-817ND
HF/50/144/430 MHz
5 W All Mode Transceiver (AM 1.5 W)

60 m Band

Automatic Matching for FT-897/857 Series Transceivers

FC-40
Automatic-Matching
200-Memory
Antenna Tuner
(160 m ~ 6 m Band)

WATERPROOF

Mobile Auto-Resonating 7~430 MHz for FT-897/857 Series Transceivers

ATAS-120A
Active Tuning Antenna System (no separate tuner required)

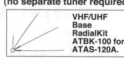
VHF/UHF Base RadialKit ATBK-100 for ATAS-120A.

ATAS-25
Manually-Tuned Portable Antenna

High-end HF/50 MHz Transceiver   6 meter Band included

HF/50 MHz Transceiver
FT DX 9000MP 400 W Special Order Version
Two Pairs of Meters, plus LCD Window; Data Management Unit and Flash Memory Slot Built In.
Main/Sub Receiver VRF, plus Full Dual Receive Capability,
External 50 V/24 A Switching Regulator Power Supply and Speaker with Audio Filters
Display color (Umber or Light Blue) may be selected at the time of purchase.
Modification from 400 to 200 W not possible.

HF/50 MHz Transceiver
FT DX 9000D 200 W Version
Large TFT, Data Management Unit and Flash Memory Slot Built In,
Main/Sub Receiver VRF, plus Full Dual Receive Capability,
Three µ-Tuning Modules for 160 - 20 M,
50 V/12 A Internal Switching Regulator Power Supply

Display color (Umber or Light Blue) may be selected at the time of purchase. Modification from 200- to 400-Watt version not available.

HF/50 MHz Transceiver
FT DX 9000 Contest
Custom-Configurable Version
Two Pairs of Meters, plus LCD Window, VRF Input
Preselector Filter, Three Key Jacks, and Dual Headphone Jacks,
50 V /12 A Internal Switching Regulator Power Supply

HF/50 MHz Transceiver
FT-2000D
200 W Version (External Power Supply)

HF/50 MHz Transceiver
FT-2000
100 W Version (Internal Power Supply)

YAESU
Choice of the World's top DX'ers℠

Vertex Standard
US Headquarters
10900 Walker Street
Cypress, CA 90630 (714)827-7600

For the latest Yaesu news, visit us on the Internet:
http://www.vertexstandard.com

Specifications subject to change without notice. Some accessories and/or options may be standard in certain areas. Frequency coverage may differ in some countries. Check with your local Yaesu Dealer for specific details.

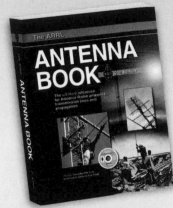

KENWOOD

Listen to the Future

KENWOOD SKYCOMMAND
TURN IT ON!

Kenwood SkyCommand has FCC approval.

Allows Global communication through remote operation on HF frequencies at home or in the field utilizing Kenwood's TS-2000 series transceivers.

Kenwood's TH-D7AG or TM-D700A required for remote use.

Perfect for use in hurricane or tornado zones, as well as Search and Rescue areas for Long Distance Communications when other normal modes of communications are out.

A great tool to monitor propagation while doing other things at home!

No cables or adaptors to fool with or buy!

No software or computer required!!

Step by step setup and programming taking only minutes.

Ease of use.

See your local dealer for details.

KENWOOD U.S.A. CORPORATION
Communications Sector Headquarters
3975 Johns Creek Court, Suite 300, Suwanee, GA 30024-1265
Customer Support/Distribution
P.O. Box 22745, 2201 East Dominguez St., Long Beach, CA 90801-5745
Customer Support: (310) 639-4200 Fax: (310) 537-8235

INTERNET
Kenwood News & Products
http://www.kenwoodusa.com
ADS#09207

ISO9001 Registered

HamTestOnline™

The software that knows you™

Web-based training for the ham radio exams

The fastest and easiest way to prepare for the exams

- 100% guaranteed — you pass the exams or get your money back.

- Better than random practice tests.

- Promotes learning, not memorizing.

- Includes the exam questions plus additional information.

- Presents concepts in logical order.

- Question drill keeps you engaged.

- Tracks your progress on each question.

- Focuses on your weak areas with *"intelligent repetition"*.

- Entirely web-based. No software to download or install. Access from anywhere.

- Includes all U.S. and Canadian exams.

- Quick, easy way to learn.

We GUARANTEE success!

When you have the right tools everything is easier

www.hamtestonline.com

INDEX

FEEDBACK

Please use this form to give us your comments on this book and what you'd like to see in future editions, or e-mail us at **pubsfdbk@arrl.org** (publications feedback). If you use e-mail, please include your name, call, e-mail address and the book title, edition and printing in the body of your message. Also indicate whether or not you are an ARRL member.

Where did you purchase this book?   ☐ From ARRL directly   ☐ From an ARRL dealer

Is there a dealer who carries ARRL publications within:

☐ 5 miles   ☐ 15 miles   ☐ 30 miles   of your location?   ☐ Not sure.

License class:

☐ Technician   ☐ General   ☐ Amateur Extra

Name _____   ARRL member?   ☐ Yes ☐ No

_____   Call Sign _____

Address _____

City, State/Province, ZIP/Postal Code _____

Daytime Phone   (   )   _____   Age _____

If licensed, how long? _____

Other hobbies _____   E-mail

_____

Occupation _____

For ARRL use only	GCLM
Edition	6 7 8 9 10 11 12
Printing	3 4 5 6 7 8 9 10 11 12